D1445722

UNITED STATES DEPARTMENT OF JUSTICE
FEDERAL BUREAU OF INVESTIGATION

WASHINGTON 25, D.C.

Airtel   5/1/72

TO: SACs, Denver   (Enclosures 5)
      Boston   (Enclosures 5)

FROM: Director Hoover, FBI

UNSUB:

Book of Unknown Origin

Author or authors credited as Umbra Arca Society

Rumored title: "Shadow Atlas"

Purported intent: uncertain

Enclosed herewith you'll find five photographs of a book sent
to the Los Angeles Field Office by a man named Dane Essa.

Essa claims to be an academic who came into possession of
this text through a chance encounter with a professor of
esoteric knowledge identified only as "D.S. of Harvard."

Essa maintains this book, which he calls a *Shadow Atlas*,
provides an alternate history of the Americas compiled by an
organization known either as the Umbra Arca Society or the
Umbra Arca Order. Mr. Essa claims D.S. offered to indoctrinate
him into Umbra Arca if he promised to swear allegiance to its
mission and vow total loyalty to its superiors. D.S. told him
the group had but one purpose and mission: to explore "hidden
realms" that apparently exist unseen all around us, and to
bear witness and record the "shocking truths" behind various
myths and legends.

Transcripts of multiple interviews Mr. Essa sat for with
two Los Angeles field agents will be forwarded to you by
priority air mail. Essa at first describes a global underground of adventurous historians who report their findings
to one of four international "scriptoriums" designated by
the cardinal points of the compass and founded along "dark
meridians" where different realities somehow intersect or
interact. (The "Western Scriptorium" is reputedly located in
Colorado; however, its exact location remains a mystery.) Essa
credits these "dark meridians" with the ancient origins of
much of the world's folklore, mythology, and superstitions,
and offers *Shadow Atlas* up as evidence. It is noteworthy that
he will not produce the book in any form other than photographs, though ████████████ said she was given a glimpse of
a very large text she could only describe as "appearing quite
ancient."

The first transcript provides most of the actual details Essa
puts forward about Umbra Arca. By his estimate, the organization currently numbers around thirty academics and approximately five financiers, but at some point in the 17th century
its membership exceeded several thousand, many of whom were
well-positioned in the upper echelons of various governments,
universities, banks, churches, and many more who remained
hidden amongst the trade classes, all but invisible to those
above. The organization maintained a central director and
four sub-directors who lived in and oversaw each scriptorium,
where rotating teams of at least one hundred scribes copied
details from far-ranging "field agents," whose reports arrived
at all hours of the day by land, sea, and air. It was not
uncommon, Essa says, for reports that began in ink to finish
in blood. "Umbra Arca field agents will give their last drop
bearing eyewitness to the truth, and they will sharpen their
own bones into quills and take their very skin for parchment
if no alternatives avail them." If we are to believe Essa's
account, his *Shadow Atlas* is both entirely unique and one of

many. He says there is one for each continent, and one for every ocean and sea. Because his copy was produced by the scribes of the Western Scriptorium, its contents are wholly focused on the exploration of the Americas.

While such lavish visions and paranormal claims deserve little credence, the possibility of secret societies cannot be over-looked. The efforts of such groups provide rich opportuni-ties for foreign actors. I am therefore tasking the Denver Field Office with a thorough investigation into this supposed "Western Scriptorium." You are directed to begin your search among the state's academic population which tends to be recep-tive to esoteric ideals.

The Department desires that Boston field agents conduct a similar interrogation of the academic elite in your state with the additional goal of identifying a possible candidate for "D.S." and conducting any interview you see fit.

                                        --Dir.

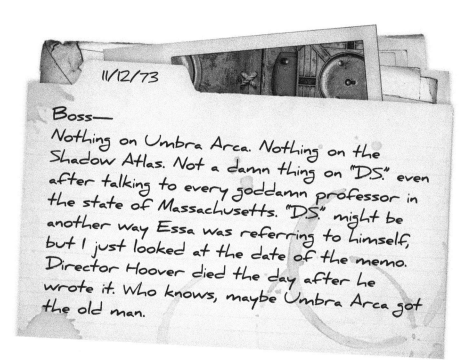

11/12/73

Boss—
Nothing on Umbra Arca. Nothing on the Shadow Atlas. Not a damn thing on "DS." even after talking to every goddamn professor in the state of Massachusetts. "DS." might be another way Essa was referring to himself, but I just looked at the date of the memo. Director Hoover died the day after he wrote it. Who knows, maybe Umbra Arca got the old man.

DR. DANE ESSA

700 Pennsylvania Avenue Northwest
Washington, D.C. 20408

June 27, 2021

Shadow Atlas Editorial Team
P.O. Box 298
Erie, CO 80516

Dear Editors:

Before publishing the pages I've included from the *Shadow Atlas*, it is imperative to know more about the book's origins, the Umbra Arca Society, and the man behind the hoax.

Few readers require an introduction to Professor Donald Sorensen. He researched and wrote in many fields—archaeology, history, and anthropology, of course; but also computer encryption, world finance, travel, numismatics, and equine sports. Sorensen had the good fortune of being that rarest of constructions, an academic embraced by popular culture. A precious few will argue his penchant for showmanship denigrated his scholarship. Many more offer it as final proof of his genius. He was Indiana Jones and Inigo Jones, P.T. Barnum and Barnum Brown, Andy Kaufman and Hans Kaufmann.

And I'm sorry to say, in the end, my dear mentor and colleague—my *friend*—Donald Sorensen was quite insane.

"Not content with the four corners of the world, I went looking for the fifth."

The quote is among Professor Sorensen's most famous, engraved even upon his cenotaph erected last year at Woodlawn Cemetery. Very few know its first recorded attribution comes from 1953, in an excised portion of Tenzing's famous memoir. If the redacted writing is to be believed (evidence exists that Professor Sorensen paid Tenzing a considerable sum to add the fictional encounter into his memoir, though if this is true, we can only hope he got his money back when the author failed to follow through on the prank), Sir Edmund Hillary and his Sherpa guide heard these words just as they reached the outcropping of rock near Everest's summit where a twenty-year-old Sorensen lounged like a man in a hammock. I bring up this anecdote not only as the perfect early example of the professor's mischievousness and flair, but perhaps as a dark foreshadowing of his desire to insert himself into history's great moments. Indeed, it may even give evidence of a troubling psychosis: if one cannot participate in history, then one must reinvent it, with one's own life rough-hewn into the preferred narrative.

If you do not comprehend the difficulty of the accusations I must make, then perhaps a brief self-introduction is in order. Professor Sorensen took me under his wing when he was forty years old and preparing for a sabbatical expedition into the Andes. At twenty-two, I was among seven graduate students who accompanied him as assistants. The other six are dead a long time now, but there are nights when I see their faces as I remember them best, revealed by a campfire in some cave or on some mountain crag, wide-eyed and hunched toward the man who favored us through the night with his voice. In those romantic climes, his mere presence turned the most unpromising of places into an ashram. We listened to strange tales of mythology and folklore, bits of incidental knowledge about geography and geology, little immoral parables regarding vanished tribes and fallen cities that brought forth the most delicious shiver. Call it *a little touch of Sorensen in the night.*

We'd forged our way high into the Andes and made camp for the night. Everyone had gone to bed when Sorensen's chanting woke us. We poked our heads from our tents in unison, looked at each other and then at our teacher. I might say *shaman,* for he had stripped himself almost naked and sat on the cold ground in the posture of a yogi, his spine rigid, his knees drawn tight against his chest, his palms sweeping the air above his head. My training being in archaeology, I had competence in Latin and Greek, but the chant was in neither language. I had a sense the words must be quite old, each syllable among the world's many dead things that found life again through Sorensen's benefaction.

To our great fortune, my colleague Samantha was a linguist, an expert in countless tongues. She stood to my left, and began whispering a fascinating translation—

—for kingdoms conserve
power, light, coins,
and the memory of ruin.
It is thin as paper,
as full as a coffin,
holds centuries
as if they are weightless.
And it will help you find
the way home,
even if it is not yours.

Samantha stopped translating. Her brow furrowed.

"What is it? What is he talking about?"

"Something called the *Shadow Atlas*," she said with a great deal of uncertainty in her tone.

We repeated the name amongst ourselves. Our supplies included any number of maps, many of dubious origin and quality. But we'd never heard of anything called a *Shadow Atlas*. Professor Sorensen went on chanting for another twenty minutes, but we found no elucidation there. Then he stopped and unfolded himself, noticed our attention, and smiled.

"I'm sorry if I disturbed your sleep," he said, and walked past us to enter his tent.

The next morning none of us spoke of what had happened, believing Sorensen would bring the matter up on his own time. But I was always the impatient and impetuous apostle, the professor's Peter, and two days later I took it upon myself to question him outright. Our band had found a mountain pool of crystal-clear water where we stopped to refresh ourselves. Sorensen knelt by himself, splashing his face and arms. He seemed oblivious to my approach as I crouched beside him. Staring down at my distorted reflection, I said, "What is the *Shadow Atlas*?"

Sorensen went on splashing and scrubbing his face. He continued for half a minute, and I feared he might not have heard me. Just before I dared repeat the question, however, he said, "Seek out Umbra Arca, and you will know."

The answer had an air of simplicity, as if I'd asked a dullard's question whose answer could be found in the index of *National Geographic*. He then stood and walked away, leaving me to mull the words.

Umbra Arca.

Shadow Cabinet?

Shadow Box?

A sense of shame stole over me. I'd been arrogant to ask the question, and he'd answered my vanity and presumption with a nonsensical response. I tell you no amount of water from the mountain pool could cool the heat from my cheeks that day.

I'll not demonstrate all the ways Donald could be cruel in his jests when directed at inferiors in need of a comeuppance. Doing so might make this entire letter seem nothing more than justification for a non-existent personal grudge. What I wish to bring to light is the difficulty in determining early evidence of mental illness in a man well-known for "playing the long game" when it comes to sowing the seeds of his pranks. This is, after all, the same person who began manufacturing and planting so-called Atlantean artifacts off the coast of Bimini in 1985, for the express purpose of fabricating the *discovery* of that ancient city in 2010. Who contemplates or proceeds with a hoax whose payoff won't happen for another twenty-five years? Is such a deed evidence of genius—or madness?

You'll remember his serious press conferences, and the fawning admiration of media around the world. You'll recall the experts shaking their heads in disbelief as radio carbon dating proved the authenticity of the pottery and the DNA testing on the skeletal remains demonstrated a Mediterranean origin. The sensationalism proved so great that the Penguin Classics edition of Plato's *Timaeus and Critias*, which contains the only ancient references to Atlantis, made it onto *The New York Times* Best Sellers list for one week.

Sorensen staggered his revelations in one amazement after another, building a fever pitch of astonishment over the course of two months. No professor, no archaeologist, no *expert* stood against him in the end. And once he had them all won over, once he had them all professing Atlantis must be true, Donald pivoted to laugh in their face.

> *What is this world's delight?*
> *Lightning that mocks the night,*
> *Brief even as bright.*

I must admit those exquisite lines from Shelley crossed my mind as I considered the short fire of the joke's payoff against the long time spent gathering its kindling. How could there not be some genuine mental illness at work, a creative monomania at the core of his being?

But it would be a few more years before I realized I, too, had fallen victim to it.

Twenty-five years is the mere blink of the eye compared to the decades he spent developing the Umbra Arca hoax that came to pepper every public reading, lecture, and interview he gave between 2011 and late 2019, in media appearances that ranged from CNN and CSPAN to obscure YouTube channels pushing biblical conspiracies. His many perplexing pronouncements during this period would cripple the reputation of any scholar but Sorensen. Rather than greeting him with scorn, however, it seemed the public abetted him. No doubt they believed he was joking again, and this time they wanted in on it from the start.

I'm afraid I alone have that particular privilege.

As time went on, my relationship with Donald changed. I went from student assistant to colleague and friend. Our adventures together were not without their improbable escapes, but more often than not we dwelt in the bowels of libraries rather than the Earth. "It will never cease to amaze me," he often said, looking up from some forgotten tome, "how preserving knowledge in books is the surest way to guarantee it will be lost."

In 1965, we went to Morocco, granted special access to the al-Qarawiyyin Library. So few scholars receive such an invite, but even then Donald's reputation opened the most imposing of doors. Though he claimed to be visiting for the first time, it soon became clear my cherished friend was lying. He navigated the labyrinth of rooms with too much certainty and had an uncanny knack for discovering hidden passages. I said nothing, however, too overcome by giddiness to be in the world's oldest library with its shelves of arcane wonder.

We were questing after a rumored but otherwise unknown work by Averroes, and I sat alone resting my eyes from exhaustion when Sorensen brought forth a massive book, bound in cracked leather and sealed with a peculiar iron clasp that resembled the first known compass dating back to the Han Dynasty. I didn't need Donald to draw my attention to it, but he did so anyway.

"Magnificent, isn't it? I don't know if you ever read the monograph I wrote on book clasps a few years back."

"I somehow missed it," I said.

"It's quite the topic. Clasps have a wonderful variation and history. Here you can see the prong's forked spacer implies a creation date of about 1360, which I'm sure is correct. The clasp's presence, however, makes the volume appear far younger than its contents. The book's design is comprised of various cultural techniques passed down through the ages. Each of its custodians applied their own methods for maintaining the tome."

"What is this book?"

"Come, Dane," he said. "You know all too well. I told you once."

Trying to recall our conversations over the years was difficult then, almost impossible now. Defeated, I could only shrug and ready myself for a serving of his disappointment.

Instead, he smiled and said, "Umbra Arca."

It was as if our time in the Andes happened the day before rather than years. "The *Shadow Atlas*," I said, rising.

"Few have ever seen one, my friend."

The leather was stamped with the imprint of an unspecified map, and there was no writing on the spine or cover.

"Do you mean there's more than one?"

"Four," Sorensen said. "One for each corner of the world. One for each of Umbra Arca's scriptoriums."

"You make it sound like an organization, Donald."

"Humanity's oldest, I should think. Perhaps you might call Umbra Arca humanity itself."

"I don't understand."

"Think of it this way," he said. "Adventure and exploration are the heart of Umbra Arca's mission. True humanity was invented the moment our first ancestor walked toward the horizon not in a search for food or shelter, but from a simple desire to see what waited. Umbra Arca came into existence on that day, too."

I smiled at the simple grandeur of his vision, though I didn't reflect on his word choice of *invented* rather than *born* until years later. He sketched for me some sense of how this secret society was organized. Those familiar with Sorensen's more recent and rich elaborations may be surprised at the paltry details he provided at the time. I suppose his imagination or his madness was only just hatching the concept of the scriptoriums, the directorship, the daring field agents, and the sober scribes who recorded their stories. I can only say that when he introduced Umbra Arca and its purported *Shadow Atlas* to me, the society seemed to consist of perhaps one hundred members. As the hoax or delusion grew in his mind, Umbra Arca became a clandestine organization with thousands of initiates ranging across the globe on an eternal mission into the world's twilight places. The details accreted like layers of ash from multiple eruptions of Sorensen's overheated mind. You may remember his last rambling lecture at Naropa University just over a year ago, mere months before his disappearance and presumed death. Not only did he declare the Naropa University library's basement to be the location of the Western Scriptorium, he went on to say:

> *The oath they take…it is a blood vow. Blood of all blood…You will know an adherent of Umbra Arca by the compass in their hands. The compass pointer is needle-sharp, its tip stained red with blood drawn from the initiate's own palm. It never points true North, but it always points in the direction of true desire. There is a song they sing, you see. I will reveal part of it now. I have never before done so.* **A book of pages blank and white, a yellow day, a purple night, and a road of flame before us.** *That is as much of the song as I dare give you, but perhaps it is enough to let you hear hints of its melody upon the wind.*

I could only shake my head when I heard this nonsense. I retained enough love for Donald that I almost wept at this insight into the ruined state of his mind. Then I heard the sustained applause of the crowd and the way they chanted *Umbra Arca* and *Shadow Atlas* like cheers at a football game. I wanted to believe it was the crowd going along with the delusions of a very old man, the way the citizens of San Francisco showed obeisance to their beloved Emperor Norton. But there was too much enthusiasm in their response, too much fervor. Even very intelligent people can be swayed by charisma. Innumerable cults demonstrate this fact. Hoaxes take root, turn into conspiracies and, if very pernicious, become religions.

This possibility remains my greatest fear regarding Umbra Arca:

watching some new belief system rise before me. I understand Umbra Arca's power to work upon the mind, being its first convert and for many years its most devout—and perhaps only—follower.

I take you back to that moment in the al-Qarawiyyin Library, as I stood over the iron-clasped book my dear friend, colleague, and mentor Donald Sorensen called the *Shadow Atlas*. My imagination was aflame even without the embellishing details that came so much later. I was enchanted by the idea of underground societies and secret knowledge, and how could I doubt the veracity of the great Professor Sorensen? Above all else, did I not have my right palm resting upon the *Shadow Atlas* itself? Some of my life's great leaps of faith seem naive in hindsight, but any empiricist would have given the ancient book and Sorensen's explanation credence.

"Let me open it."

"What do you expect to find?"

"Lost maps?"

"Ah," he said. "Maps can take many forms and shapes, my friend. The *Shadow Atlas* charts a different geography. We members of Umbra Arca are cartographers of *truth*."

Whether or not I stifled a gasp at this revelation is irrelevant. "You mean to say that *you* belong to Umbra Arca?"

"I do, and I have long sought to bring in another initiate. I considered you long ago, Dane. That morning by the water, when you asked your question. Every question is a footstep, and I know you to be a fond traveler."

I moved to undo the clasp, but Donald grabbed my wrist. "Open the book before it's time, and you will find only heartbreak."

"In what sense?"

"In the sense that you've been judged unworthy of its secrets."

"But how can I possibly know when I'm ready? Will *you* tell me?"

Smiling, he said, "I may be quite dead before that date. The *Shadow Atlas* itself will tell you."

I laughed at the notion. "Oh? Will a little voice speak to me from within?"

"No," he said, pressing his lips together tight.

"Then *how*?"

"One day, you will find the clasp has fallen away on its own. When that moment comes, you may open the book. Not a moment before."

I vowed it would be so. My intrigue outweighed common sense and reason. I did not even question how Donald took the book from the library. Doing so only reinforced the notion that the library doubled as a secret *scriptorium*, and since my friend belonged to Umbra Arca's hierarchy, he did as he pleased. Now, of course, I conceive of a very different reason the librarians never opposed the book's removal. Why would they care about a volume that never belonged to their collection in the first place?

I'll not detail how our relationship soured in the ensuing years. The tensions between aging men are seldom interesting to uninvolved parties. For the longest time I kept true to my word. I put the *Shadow Atlas* on a table under glass in my library. How foolish I must have looked, checking on it at odd hours of the day and night, perpetually hopeful the clasp would be open.

I saw Donald less with each passing year. He kept to his adventures and increasing notoriety, while I became a prized guest lecturer at several universities. No matter how many honorary chairs I held, however, my true self-worth rested on being a member of Umbra Arca. Was anyone ever so self-deluded? Sorensen never introduced me to another member of Umbra Arca, nor did I ever attend a single meeting of this secret society. I was given no tasks which I might fulfill in order to prove my worthiness. As far as I knew, being a part of Umbra Arca just meant waking up and going to bed. I lacked even something as juvenile as a secret handshake.

But I had the *Shadow Atlas*, and I continued to check every day through the 1960s, the 70s, the 80s, the 90s. The century changed, but I did not. Day after day, year after year, I never failed to check the clasp of the *Shadow Atlas*.

It was always locked.

Until the day it wasn't.

It happened almost at the same time Donald began talking about Umbra Arca to the public. I rushed to the desk, removed the glass lid, and almost hyperventilated. To say I opened the book is accurate, but it diminishes the reality of at least ten false starts, the pulling back of the hand to touch my chest, the spasm of muscles in the forearms, the growing tremor that palsied the fingers. Yes, I opened the book and beheld an interior composed like a Mayan codex, a concertina of hu'un sheets stitched to the leather cover with a weave reminiscent of something from the Middle Ages.

The first page was blank. It was crinkly, almost brittle, and foxing everywhere.

The next page was identical. So, too, the third and fourth.

I began to treat each empty page with less care as I turned them, shouting, "It can't be!"

Had I failed Umbra Arca at the last minute? What else explained how the pages were bled of their precious, impossible contents? This secret society was such a *concrete* concept in my mind that I couldn't conceive it was never real, and that the *Shadow Atlas* was a clever invention built around some ancient book Donald found whose pages happened to be blank. No doubt he'd designed the clasp with a hidden spring meant to trigger according to some internal clock.

No, my self-excoriation did not allow me to entertain such thoughts at all. It would in fact be a full year before I allowed myself to consider alternative notions about the book and the organization supposedly behind it.

One night, I sat at my computer listening to a podcast. Donald was supposed to be addressing the finer points of stamp collecting, but he kept interrupting himself and his interviewer with long ramblings about Umbra Arca and details he'd never told me about the *Shadow Atlas*. He suggested that the Umbra Arca compass becomes one with its holder. That they can *feel* where they must go, and their very bones guide them to their destinations. He even suggested that the book's pages themselves are a compass, and the kineograph at the top of each page points to the story's corresponding region depending on where the reader is standing. But most interesting, he blathered on about a force or mysticism at play, linking all of the tomes together. When a new entry is added to a volume, it mysteriously appears in the others.

For just a moment, I shook my head, angered that he'd withheld the information from me all these years. Then I realized the grave possibility it was a terrible hoax concocted by a man who'd never been in his right mind. The more I listened, the more convinced I became. A fit of pique made me determined to destroy the *Shadow Atlas*. I resolved to burn the book's pages one at a time. I tore out the first and brought it to a candle. Before the paper caught, however, the flame's heat revealed words composed in invisible ink.

It was a table of contents.

Rushing but careful, I warmed every page and discovered what seemed to be a collection of stories. Tales of horror and adventure, folklore and myth. I read through the night, remembering those youthful nights hearing him at a campfire, holding court. Some of the entries were very old, but others were dated more recently. Had Sorensen gone so far as to orchestrate the addition of new, modern pages for me to find, decades after he'd gifted me the book, to fulfill this notion that the book updates itself with each new entry? Had he hired someone to break into my home to accomplish this task?

Of that, I have no doubt.

I now offer these stories and field guide pages in the exact order I uncovered them, including Sorensen's own notes, journal entries, and drawings he attached to various pages without a detail added or subtracted. I cannot say if sharing Sorensen's *Shadow Atlas* with the world is an act of love or an ode to hatred for the man I once esteemed my friend and mentor. It is, at the very least, an offer of lies for the sake of a truth that must be told.

Respectfully,

Dr. Dane Essa

EDITORIAL EMAIL

From: Josh Viola
Sent: Tuesday, July 13, 2021 7:46 PM
To: Hillary Dodge; Carina Bissett
Subject: Letter from Dane Essa

Carina/Hillary,

Has anyone actually heard of this guy? Just like that old FBI report we found, there's nothing on him. Nothing noteworthy on Google. Testimonies concerning his age vary by a decade earlier or later depending on the source. Even the letter's address makes no sense. It's from the National Archives. I called and they said they've never heard of a Dane Essa. I asked if the *Shadow Atlas* pages we received might be theirs, perhaps stolen, but that's not the case either (though they did ask to see them). Even the Sorensen Estate denies knowing anything about Essa. When asked about the *Shadow Atlas*, they hung up and haven't answered my other calls.

This is getting weird.

Best,
Josh

From: Hillary Dodge
Sent: Tuesday, July 20, 2021 9:23 PM
To: Josh Viola; Carina Bissett
Subject: Re: Letter from Dane Essa

As a librarian, I get really into the hunt for stuff like this and, of course, I've got contacts. So, I asked one of my old grad school friends who works at the Library of Congress to look into it—deep—and they found something (!)—well, sorta.

Although no digital records exist in the ILS, she did find an old catalog card that could be related. It indicated that the library housed a copy of a dissertation by Essa, D. entitled "Cartography of Early America: Native American Wayfinding in Oral Tradition." The call number was listed as Microform Reading Room GA201.H5339 1959, but when my friend tried to locate a copy, the microfiche file was missing—and no amount of shelf-reading could locate it.

I tried to cross reference this dissertation in *Dissertation Abstracts International* as well as ProQuest and Theses Global, two online databases that should at least have a listing if not the full text. But nothing anywhere. So, while I couldn't scrounge up anything, we have one mysterious catalog card that hints that something might have existed once. Weird thing is that the card didn't list a university or a location of publication which are both usually included.

What do you think? Could this be legit?

Hillary

From: Carina Bissett
Sent: Friday, July 23, 2021 11:21 AM
To: Hillary Dodge
Cc: Josh Viola
Subject: Re: Re: Letter from Dane Essa

Hey guys. I've been trying a narrower approach.

I wondered if I could trace Dane Essa as a contributor to specialty maps, as I suspect he would have collected and contributed to the field of cartography to support his academic agenda. However, all references connected to his personal pursuits lead to paper towns, phantom settlements, and a few scattered nihilartikel. The more I dig for information, the more subversion I encounter. That being said, I did find a reply in a thread on post-colonial maps at the Library of Congress that appeared to be a response to a D. Essa, but the original comment no longer exists. It appears D. Essa has a thin skin. Go figure.

—Carina

SHADOW ATLAS

Dark Landscapes

of the

Americas

Edited by

Carina Bissett

Hillary Dodge

and

Joshua Viola

Hex Publishers, 2021

TABLE OF CONTENTS

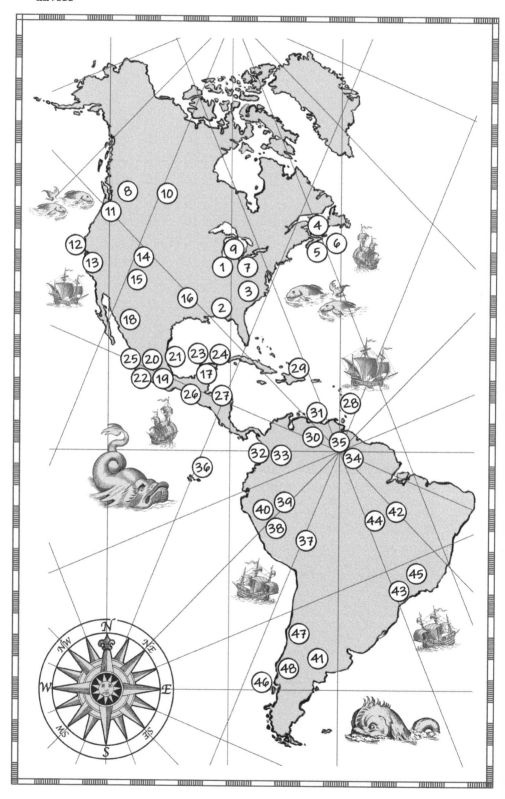

MAP OF OCCURRENCES

OATH OF THE UMBRA ARCA

A book of pages blank and white,
A yellow day, a purple night,
And a road of flame before us.

Fellow traveler, set your feet.
Together we'll go forth and greet
Whatever is in store for us.

I have a compass in my hand
To guide us over sea and land,
We joyous, venturing chorus.

Hear our song reclaiming stories
Of dark deeds and brighter glories.
Restore them, for they restore us.

The book becomes an atlas soon,
We'll map the sun, we'll map the moon,
Lands triumphant and lands dolorous.

Friendships struck, new hopes anointed,
These are cardinal points appointed
To the bearer of this compass.

I now invite you to behold
The atlas, compass, and the road.
Onward, onward, they implore us.

NEW GROWTH

Dr. Sara Cleto and Dr. Brittany Warman

The stories come up through the ground.
Grasses whisper, a crow laughs;
We push our nails into the dirt,
And listen.

Listen.

Legends dwell, retell in raindrops,
Lightning sears their afterimage
As pale ghosts,
Chromatic gossip.

Sing fragments, remnants
Of beginnings.
Sing the quiet rebellion
Of new growth on pensive soil.

The land is old,
The land is new,
Its tales distressed, dressed in
Clothes to match the occasion.

Replant, rewire, inspire.
Pull out the dead, water,
Reach through memory.
The stories are growing.

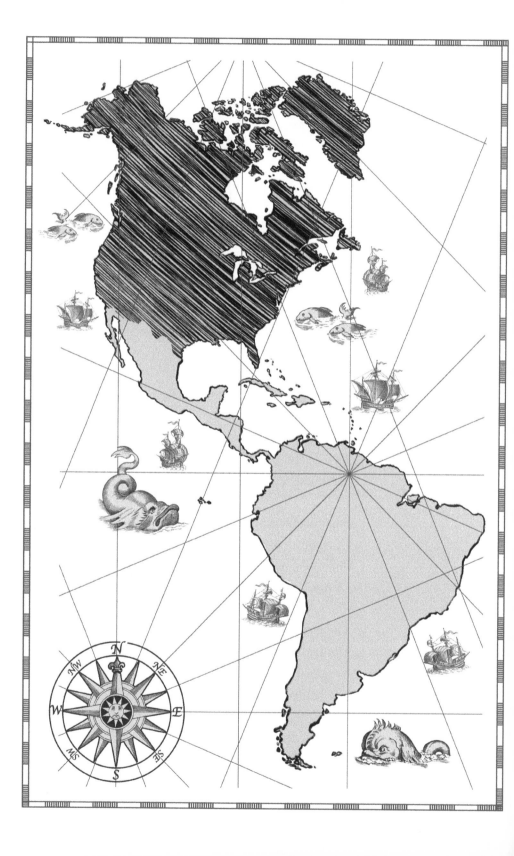

NORTH AMERICA

THE SHADOW ATLAS

is kept in a box
that looks as if it holds candies,
but it does not.
There is nothing sweet
about it, for countries
are not sweet
though they are often edible.
It is not real,
but it is true.
It leans to the right,
for kingdoms conserve
power, light, coins,
and the memory of ruin.
It is thin as paper,
as full as a coffin,
holds centuries
as if they are weightless.
And it will help you find
the way home,
even if it is not yours.

—Jane Yolen

DAUGHTERS OF THE BEAR

Lee Murray

Iowa, USA

ONLY THREE WARRIORS ACCOMPANY YOU when you leave your mountain home and descend the valley to the wetland realm of the Snakes. With the Wolves howling at the Bears' eastern flanks, your father cannot spare more. It does not do to turn your back on the Wolves. Your father had already made that mistake, his ruined leg a near-fatal blow to the Bear clan. Dragged from the battlefield by his loyal guard, they say he had thrashed and screamed nearly as much as his dying horse. Now, even his own warriors look away when he lumbers up the mountainside to join your mother and her sisters to tell you the good news.

You will go in his stead to broker an accord with the Snakes. The chief's own daughter in a show of good faith. Of *trust*.

Your mother bellows her protest. You're just seventeen. Too young for such a dangerous mission, she says.

You stifle your annoyance. You're *not* a baby.

"But that's just the point. The girl poses no threat," your father says.

In the end, your mother is forced to relent. You all know there is no other way. To protect your mountain homeland, the Bears need allies. Besides, who else is there? Your brother is still just a cub.

"I'll send my best warriors," your father promises.

"Better her loyal friend," your mother insists.

"The Eagle, then."

Your mother nods. "And she'll wear her grandmother's bearskin."

And so, it is agreed: your mother and her sisters will lead their cubs north through the pines to where the hills blend with the sky, while your father and his Bear warriors will travel east to hold the Wolves at bay. Meanwhile, with your grandmother's spirit draped across your shoulders, you will seek the aid of the Snakes.

pine needles / scattered / on a howling wind

You descend swiftly, speaking rarely. Your childhood friend, Tocha, an Eagle, takes the lead, flying through the trees ahead of you, while Oto, your father's advisor, brings up the rear, his old bones creaking as you run. When twilight falls, a handful of Wolves have caught your scent, the monsters stalking you from the shadows. It is Liwanu, huge even for a Bear, who spies their eye-gleam in the trails of mist. You might have doubted him, were it not for the graze of air on your neck and the prick of their death-musk in your nostrils. You pull your grandmother's bearskin around your shoulders, while your escort pull their weapons and draw close.

By morning, steadfast Liwanu is dead, and the Wolves have fled, their ululations carrying on the wind even as the blood of your clan brother seeps into the earth. Worried that the Wolves will return in force, you do not spare the time to bury him; instead, you leave him there, a great bear mound among the grasses.

You hurry on, the three of you crouching low, scanning the trees, the ditches, the sway of the grass, until your eyes ache with the strain. You don't stop to rest, reaching the Snake settlement on the morn of the next day, just as the sun's pink-gold rays touch the plains.

The Snake warriors surround you in moments, their knives at your throats.

"Chaska," Oto calls, addressing the Snake chief. "The Bears call for your aid."

"Lies! They've come to scout and to spy," screams a withered Snake.

Tocha scoffs. He pushes against the blade and blood trickles down his chest. "If we were spies, would we have walked into your camp?"

"A ruse," the Withered One says.

Another Snake, his skin slick with grease, thrusts his face close to Tocha's. "I say we kill them," he hisses.

But, reaching out a sinuous limb, the Snake chief intervenes. "There'll be time enough to kill them after we've heard what they have to say." He gestures to the longhouse.

Pushing aside the blade with your palm, you follow him.

a hatchling / unfurls / a milk tooth

You sit cross-legged in the longhouse, encircled by Snakes: Oto, Tocha, and you. Shivering in the smoky haze, you huddle closer to your father's advisor.

Oto opens the dialogue: "Brother Snakes, the Wolves are getting bolder. They lurk at our borders, darting in to attack our villages at night, targeting the vulnerable. While our warriors are occupied elsewhere, they steal children from their sleeping mothers, dragging them into the shadows. At dawn, we find their shredded carcasses strewn across the mountainside."

"The Wolves have always been cunning strategists," the Snake chief says. "So you've lost a few cubs and the women's keening is keeping you awake; I don't see how this concerns us."

Trembling, you bite your tongue to silence. Cruel or no, the Bears need help. You are the sole envoys, the Snakes your only option, so you straighten your back and say, "It's time to put old hurts aside." Your voice is thin and hollow in the gloom. "My father calls for an alliance between Snake and Bear."

The Withered One snorts. "Why risk our necks? The Wolves are far away."

"Not so far," Tocha says. "Our brother Liwanu was slaughtered not a day's journey from here."

This time, it is the slick-skinned Snake who snorts.

Beside you, Tocha leans forward, his body tight with tension. "Liwanu's corpse lies there still, a sorrowful bear mound amid the flies. Go see for yourself. His tendons have been stripped to the bone."

The memory almost overwhelms you; still, you lift your chin to the chief. "Tell me this, if the Bears fall, who will stop the Wolves invading the valley? What of your own young? Are they not the future of your clan?"

The chief considers your statement, the moments spooling outwards like curls of smoke. "It's true that a clan does not survive without its young," he says at last, the gleam in his eye causing you to shiver. "Our warriors love a skirmish, so we will join the Bears' crusade against the Wolves. But an alliance works both ways: should the Wolves descend the mountain to the wetlands, I would have your father's word that the Bears will come to our aid."

Your blood singing with hope, you get to your feet. "You have my word," you say.

The Withered One spits, as if what you say counts for nothing.

"Enough!" the chief says.

And so, it is done. The negotiations concluded, you set to feasting with your new allies, although the mood is not festive. On the eve of battle with the Wolves, no one has the heart for it.

That night, as you lay beneath the stars, wrapped in the bearskin your mother insisted you carry, your grandmother steps into your dreams.

when night falls / ancestors' fires / flicker in the sky

A healer, they'd called her. Among other things. One of their own, still the Bears had feared her, yet she'd saved them more than once. One bitter winter, when even the pines shrunk from the cold and the Bears were too weak to hunt, your grandmother dared to leave her body, sending her spirit soaring across the Mississippi to bewitch the Elk chieftain. He led his clan into the mountains, where the starving Bears fell on them. They say she dragged your grandfather from the brink of death too, and with nothing more than cedar bark tea and a whiff of smoke. You wonder, if she were still alive, would she have healed your father's withered leg.

"If I'd mended the bone, do you think he would have descended the valley to parley with the Snakes?" your grandmother asks.

"He swore he never would. Said the wetlands would have to crust over first."

Grandmother's spirit-self gestures for you to shuffle over, then slips in beside you under the bearskin, her corpse cold against yours. "It is you who gave your word. The hardest tasks always fall to the clan's daughters."

You frown. "But the warriors risk their lives," you say.

She sniffs. "Always with the grand gestures. Dying is easy. Who protected the cubs, who fed them and kept them safe all this time, while your father made war with the Wolves?"

An ache flares under your ribs. That task has always been your mother's.

"Do you trust them? The Snakes?" you ask.

Your spirit-grandmother clucks her tongue. "About as much as I trust the Wolves," she says.

under desolate skies / two white pines / entangled

Tocha wakes you before dawn, like he did when you were children, when you would steal away to climb trees and swim in the river before the clan stirred. Today, his eyes are wide with terror. "Oto is dead," he whispers. "Strangled. This is a mistake. The Snakes can't be trusted. We need to leave now."

Your heart pounding, you throw on the bearskin and follow him, creeping through the mass of sleeping Snakes.

"Don't look," Tocha warns as you pass the heaped mound. But even as a child you always peeked, and you can't help yourself.

Oto lies face-down in the mud.

You break free of Tocha's grasp and run to Oto's side. Perhaps Tocha had been wrong. Maybe Oto is simply sleeping off the effects of too much jimson weed. He always loved a celebration. But as soon as you touch him, you know; the old one's spirit has fled, leaving his body stiff and cold.

"We have to go," Tocha urges, his hand on your arm.

But already it is too late. Behind you, the Withered One laughs. "Looks like the old Bear was scared to death."

You turn, your blood freezing as the crowd of Snake warriors coils around you.

"Tocha," you murmur. "Go. Leave me. Warn the Bears."

He hesitates, only a split-second, but it is enough for the Snakes to claim the advantage. Grasping him on either side, they pin him to the ground. Agile, he twists sideways and wrenches free, leaping into the air, his feathered cloak flashing.

The Snake chief springs forward, flashing his curved fangs, and sinks them deep into Tocha's neck.

Your friend crumples, his chest still heaving. But treachery travels quickly, and the venom surges through his body until his face and limbs swell, his skin close to bursting.

"What are you doing? We have a treaty!" you shriek, flying at the Snake chief.

You have barely travelled two steps before the Slick-skinned One seizes you. He clenches his fingers around your neck and squeezes. You claw at his fingers. You kick. Thrash. Gasp. Your eyes swim, and darkness threatens.

"Enough! We still need her."

You slump to the ground, gulping.

Tocha.

Scrambling forward on your hands and knees, you throw your arms around your friend. While you'd fought for breath, the Snakes staked him spreadeagle in the mud alongside Oto, blood oozing from the wounds. His eyes are swollen shut. "Tocha!"

He can only croak.

"Please," you beg, twisting to face the chief. "Don't let him suffer."

He smiles. "Tie her up. We leave at sunrise."

plucked from the river / a salmon flails

As the pink-gold rays touch the valley, you leave the village as the Snakes' captive. You glance backwards at the two mounds—eagle and bear—and you wish their spirits well on their journey to the afterlife. You hope by now Tocha has caught up to Liwanu and Oto. He was always the swift one. You blink back tears.

"Faster!" the Withered One screeches. Beating your back with a stick, he forces you forward at a run.

The Snakes waste no time, their ascent into the mountains swifter than your descent, Liwanu and Tocha hampered by Oto's old bones and your young ones. You've already passed by the mound of your brother, when the Snake chief calls a halt for the night.

Trembling with fatigue and fear, you lie in the dark, in the coil of Snake warriors, and will the Wolves to come. If only the brutes would attack, you might slip away in the turmoil. You scan the trees but see no eye-gleam in the

mist. There is no graze of air on your neck, or prick of death-musk in your nostrils. Even the Wolves have betrayed you. Exhausted, you fall asleep.

dreaming of turkey / the sleeping dog runs

Grandmother-spirit joins you under the bearskin, her death-chill jerking you awake. "What do you think they're planning?" she asks.

You've been too heartsore to think about it.

"And why bother to bring you?" she insists. "Why not just kill you with the others?"

She has a point. You watch the stars while you ponder it. "They'll arrive as allies," you decide, "—my presence will be sufficient proof—and while my father is rejoicing at the reinforcements, they'll perform some treachery."

"Some treachery..." Your grandmother nods. "Perhaps your arrangement is not their only alliance," she suggests.

Your pulse thrums, loud in the darkness. Was that why the Wolves stayed away? Sitting up, you twist to face her. "Grandmother, we need to warn the Bears," you whisper. "The Snakes will kill me before I make it out of the camp, but you could go, send your spirit-self and warn my father."

She grimaces. "That old story. You're letting in the cold air." You wince, the welts on your back cracking as she pulls you back.

"It's just a story then? You never sent your spirit soaring over the river to bewitch the elk?"

Grandmother draws the air over her teeth. "Used to be, I could send my spirit anywhere—into the trees, the birds, rocks; I even swam with the salmon once." She cackles. "Almost got eaten by my uncle."

"You could go then," you say, hope budding like prairie flowers. Already, you imagine your father striding to free you.

But Grandmother shakes her head. "I wish I could. When I still lived, my body anchored my spirit and led it back. Now I'm dead, my spirit is bound to this bearskin." She pulls the hide up to her chin. When she sighs, her ghost-breath makes you shiver.

morning trail / the quail run before you

The Slick-skinned One is even more brutal with the stick. Desperate to avoid its sting, you stumble forward, your legs burning with effort. Wait. Your heart flutters. You recognise this trail. But something isn't right. The Snakes are no longer heading east. They've veered north to where the hills blend with the sky... Your blood freezes as you recall the chief's words. *A clan does not survive without its young.*

No! You stop running. Suck in a breath. Then you open your mouth and scream. The Slick-skinned One thrashes you and you trip, rocks gouging your knees, but still you scream. You pray your mother has heard you, that she will lead the cubs to higher ground.

"Shut her up," the chief hisses. "It's too soon."

You keep screaming.

The Withered One yanks your head back by your hair and stuffs your mouth with grass. You struggle, and he shoves you sideways, your head bouncing on stone...

a blur in the darkness / eel

Grandmother shakes you with her frozen ghost fingers. "Wake up! We have to do something. The Snakes will slaughter everyone."

You spit out the grass and sit up. "What? What can we do? You already said you can't leave the bearskin."

"That's because I'm dead. But you're still alive."

"I could send my spirit? Leave my body?"

"I'll show you."

There is no other way. Besides, who else is there? Just you, your dead grandmother, and a dusty bearskin. You stand up, steadying yourself against a gnarly pine.

"Close your eyes," Grandmother says, taking your hands.

You squeeze your eyes tight and feel her death-cold creep like water through your limbs, forcing your spirit out of your body and into the trees. You flood

the sap, feeding a million branches, a thousand trunks, and burrow your toes into the earth, sending out roots that extend for miles.

"Hurry," Grandmother urges.

You fly to the canopy, where you see them—the Snake warriors—closing in on your mother and her sisters. *On the cubs.* But to the east, you see something else: your father's warriors at war with the Wolves.

The wisdom of the pines surging in your veins and your mother's voice in your heart, you throw up a line of mighty tree trunks to block the Snakes' passage. While they search for another route, you thrust your roots outwards, shifting rocks and forging a new trail to force them downhill. You chase after them with branches that whip and roots that trip, turning and whirling them so they run farther and farther east. Finally, you topple an ancient tree and bring down a cliff, separating the Snakes from your father's warriors.

Your allies, the Snakes, dash headlong into the Wolves.

Yellow eyes gleam.

The battle is fierce. Skin is punctured, ruptured. Tendons stripped to the bone.

You allow a handful of survivors to limp away. The Withered One is among them. As he slithers past, you raise a root, opening a trench, and shove him in, closing it afterwards.

pine needles / scattered / on a howling wind

You follow the destruction back, recreating the path to lead the Bears home, before you look for your body. You find it where you left it, where the Withered One shoved you to the ground, your mouth still tastes like grass. You touch it with a craggy branch. It is stiff like Oto's. Your heart clenches. You know now you can never go back. Your spirit is trapped, bound to the pines, just as your grandmother's was bound to the bearskin.

"Grandmother," you say wistfully. There is no reply.

You gaze at the horizon. Barely moving in the distance, your mother and her sisters are returning from the sky, a line of marching Bears, heading home.

You spiral to the treetops.

"Mother," you call, and she looks up.

UMBRA ARCA
CASE NOTE

AGENT No. _____

Pascagoula

Scales?

UMBRA ARCA CASE FILE

Mississippi Mermaids
Pascagoula River, Mississippi, USA

Transcript prepared on 22 September 1924
by clerk 279, Western Scriptorium Archive.

Description: Document is a piece of formal correspondence
written by agent M. Lambert and addressed to the West
Director, Umbra Arca 1920-1929. Composed on one sheet of
personal letter paper, accompanied by original envelope with
stamp, postmark originating in Pascagoula, Mississippi, dated
23 August 1924. Extensive water stains and crumpling noted
upon arrival. Original destroyed after a noxious black mold
developed and spread onto nearby surfaces. Transcript follows.
Accompanied by one yellow-green and slightly translucent fish
scale, about one inch in length. Agent compass originally
included was returned to West Vault.

Ma'am,

Please accept my apologies for the manner in which the
following missive has come to your attention. Should you find
this letter in your possession, know that I left it sealed
in my room on the 18th of August 1924 at the Magnolia Motor
Hotel with instructions that it be posted were I not able to
return.

Agent C. Appenworth and I arrived in Pascagoula six days ago

to begin our investigation, and he has been missing fully
half that time, the circumstances of which I will endeavor to
relate here as succinctly as possible.

Pascagoula is a small seaside town currently entrenched in
a political campaign to gather funds to raise a seawall on
the south side of town which abuts the sometimes tempestuous
Gulf. The northern reaches of the town intertwine and disappear into the swamplands that spread over this part of the
state. The river, which is the focus of our interest, weaves
sinuously through these swamps for miles before draining out
into the Gulf proper.

A series of classified ads taken out in the *Biloxi Sun
Herald* one month prior drew our attention to the region and
the aforementioned river. In the ads, a Mrs. Helen Holsom
was pleading for information about the disappearance of her
husband and son, whose vanishing she blamed on "the fish
people" and "that blasted singing river."

It is our assumption that she was referring to the tale of
the Mississippi River mermaids who have been rumored to dwell
in that region. There are several disparate yet intersecting
legends relating to the mermaids, the truth of which we were
determined to unfurl. Some stories say that the mermaids
were made when the Pascagoula people went peacefully into
the river rather than lose their lives and lands to an enemy
tribe. Another legend asserts that the mermaids have always
lived in the river, long before the Pascagoula and, ultimately,
lured them and others to watery deaths with their hypnotic
song. For the river itself is said to sing, the strange
humming of which has been documented repeatedly over the past
one hundred years.

Upon our arrival, we located Mrs. Holsom at South Winds
Asylum, locked in a small, padded cell, humming madly with

her thumbs pressing her ears closed. Although she was heavily
medicated, we were able to obtain some information about the
location of the disappearances, a disused fishing dock about
twenty miles upriver from the town.

The following morning, we drove out to the dock, located in a
sweltering mass of overgrown swampland (30.663613, -88.636566).
We found a fishing rod and bucket sunk into the silt beside
the dock and a handful of large iridescent scales floating in
a pool not far beyond. You will find one enclosed with this
letter, for the rest have disappeared, presumably taken by C.
Appenworth. We cased the location all day, separating for a
short time to explore upriver and down. When C. Appenworth
did not report back at the agreed upon time, I went to search
for him and ultimately found him on his knees at the edge of
a particularly deep riverside pool staring into the waters. He
claimed to hear the water humming, not unlike when you run a
wet finger around the edge of a wineglass, although I could
hear nothing.

All that evening and into the next day, when we interviewed
the local librarian, C. Appenworth appeared distracted and
unfocused. I noticed he refused all food but consumed water
like a man dying in the desert. And the next morning he was
gone.

He left everything in his room, except the clothes he was
wearing, and he took the car. After some time waiting without
his return, I asked the hotel receptionist to bring me out to
the dock. There I found the car, C. Appenworth's shoes, and

his compass which I have also enclosed with this letter.

I've spent the past two days searching for him, in bars,
along the waterfront, in other hotels and lodges - anywhere
that I can think he might have gone. But as he left his
compass behind, I can only assume he did not mean to be
found. With all other sensible leads followed to no result,
I am going to the deep river country, to interview some of
the families that have long made their homes in the midst of
the swamps fed by the Pascagoula River. It is my intention to
follow up on a few leads provided by the librarian in regard
to some land agreements by the old families dating back a
century ago.

And, as I have begun to suspect that I am being followed, I
am taking the precaution of writing this letter.

Respectfully,

Agent M. Lambert

UMBRA ARCA
CASE NOTE

AGENT No. _____

MOON-EYED WOMEN

Kay Chronister

Blue Ridge Mountains, North Carolina, USA

T HERE ARE RUMORS that the Widow Nell procures wives for all the lonely Welshmen in the backcountry. And not just wives but true pure women, Welsh-bred though Appalachian-born. Moon-eyed people, the Cherokee used to call them. Descendants of the ancient Welsh prince Madoc, who crossed the Atlantic and laid claim to the Blue Ridge Mountains a hundred years before Columbus ever dreamt of sailing. "The kind of ancient bloodline a man like you deserves," Roderick's father says to him from their cramped bunks in the belly of a schooner sailing westward. Telling and not asking him what he will do when they arrive ashore.

After weeks at sea, they make landfall at Mobile Harbor, where a statue of Madoc with his foot propped on the prow of an invisible ship points the way. Then it's north through the Appalachian towns that cling like ticks to the spines of the mountains. In the valley town of Amantha, they meet up with Roderick's father's distant cousin, whose arm twines around the waist of a pale, unsmiling woman. "You fixin' to settle down at last, big fellow? Had enough of the rake's life?" the cousin says to Roderick.

Roderick's shoulders cringe inward; he manages belatedly a soft huff of laughter. He is almost twenty-four, young for marriage still, and he has never been nor ever will be the kind of man that women are interested in.

"He's been in some trouble back home," his father says, voice lowered as if Roderick won't hear. "I'm hopeful that a good woman will set him straight."

"Oh, she will at that," says his father's cousin. "My Mari brooks no nonsense, and I've never known a moon-eyed girl who would." He chucks his wife's chin. She does not smile. She says nothing for the whole duration of their visit. At the end, she leads them silently across town to the Widow Nell's cabin.

The cunning woman's cabin stands with its back to Amantha. When she comes to the door, her eyes reflect the glow of twilight like something nocturnal. She is ninety if she is a day, and slight as a child. "No shortage of men wanting to be married into the land," she tells them. "But I hope you know what you're getting."

"'Course he does. A moon-eyed woman and a good salt-of-the-earth Welsh man," Roderick's father replies, hand on his son's broad shoulder. "It can't be but a perfect match. They're very near kin."

The Widow Nell makes a sound of amusement. "There'll be a storm tomorrow night," she says, once she's been paid. "That's the right time for it. Soon as the sun goes down, come back here."

As twilight falls and lightning cracks the dog-days heat, the Widow Nell leads Roderick and his father away from town and deep into the forest. At last, they emerge onto a bald marked by a half-circle of dark stones. On a low flat boulder, the Widow Nell assembles an effigy. Rhododendron bloom eyes; cornhusk limbs; ribcage of aspen branches. Tucked inside like a heart, a lock of Roderick's hair. Earlier, he'd resisted when the cunning woman approached him with her sewing scissors. "No choice," she said. "Possession don't go in only one direction." And seeing his father's eyes on him, Roderick bent his head, assented.

At the end of the working, they bury the effigy. "To call the moon-eyed woman inside the body," the Widow Nell says. Roderick has never witnessed magic before but he knows too well already how this part is done: a deep and narrow pit dug, a prone form crumpled in his arms for only a moment, a face staring open-eyed ponderously up at him until it is concealed by shovelfuls of earth. As he digs, he thinks on the old Welsh fairytale of Blodeuwedd, who was created out of flowers for a man cursed never to marry a human woman.

Far from the bald and from the forest, on a finger of land sliding slowly down into a bog, Roderick and his father raise a cabin. They clear undergrowth and hammer down fence posts. His father goes one day to Amantha and spends his son's inheritance on a dairy cow and two piglets, sacks of salt and flour and coffee, a featureless cotton dress that hangs on the cabin wall like a skin

waiting to be filled. And once they have carved something like a home out of the wilderness, he says goodbye to Roderick.

"You cannot come back to the old country," he says. "Not ever. Understood? They'll have found you out by now, after that last one. They'll be looking for you. And if I see you back there, I'll knot the noose myself."

Roderick does not protest, he does not say yes, he does not say anything; his hands, curled at his sides, do not become fists before his father has vanished over the hillside.

That night, a woman walks barefoot into the homestead. Small but fully formed, she is just the height of Roderick's hammering heart. Her hair and her skin and her eyes are all the same milky white. When Roderick carries her across the threshold of the cabin, her body feels as insubstantial as the wind. He is certain that he loves her. No vulgar sensuous farmer's daughter, no snobbish overscrupulous gentleman's lastborn, not this one. He is now certain he has never before laid eyes upon a true Welsh maid.

"What's your name?" he asks in the dark.

Her answer is incomprehensible to him. She speaks not in Welsh or the King's English but in a dialect that he does not recognize and only half-understands.

"I'll call you Blodeuwedd," he says, and she does not protest, she does not say yes, she does not say anything.

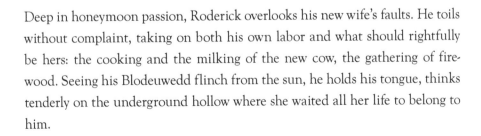

Deep in honeymoon passion, Roderick overlooks his new wife's faults. He toils without complaint, taking on both his own labor and what should rightfully be hers: the cooking and the milking of the new cow, the gathering of firewood. Seeing his Blodeuwedd flinch from the sun, he holds his tongue, thinks tenderly on the underground hollow where she waited all her life to belong to him.

When a hunting expedition becomes a necessity, he is sorry to leave her, although another part of him is relieved to escape the permanent twilight of their housebound love. "A few hours," he assures her. By now he knows that she can speak his language when she wishes, in tones halting and low, but she does not answer him. As he goes, her eyes follow him from the shade of the threshold; she holds her breath until he has gone.

When he comes home, Roderick finds her sitting across the table from a traveling minister in a white shirt and suspenders, a treacherous-looking Virginian with an easy lilt to his voice and a knowing curl on his lips. Roderick orders him out, but he can feel the lingering stain of the man on his home and worse on his wife.

"You can't be letting strangers in," he says to her.

"He wasn't selling anything," she replies, not as contrite as he would wish, not as fearful. Her pale eyes linger on nothing; he can feel her retreating from him.

"No one sets foot in or out of this cabin without my say," he says.

"Sometime it will get dark," she says a moment later, almost vengefully. He doesn't know what she means, not then, but at twilight as he's mucking the pigsty she slips out of the cabin. When he finds her gone, Roderick kindles a lantern and goes hunting, his rifle propped on his shoulder only in case he should encounter a bear or a wildcat, something deadly, something that leaves him with no other options.

After an hour, he finds her. A pale shadow in a dark mountain holler, she lies on her back with her strange glowing eyes fixed on the stars. He eases himself down beside her, his gun hitched awkwardly up at his shoulder like a third body in a marriage bed.

"You gotta come back," he says.

She rolls over and faces him, bending her knees and tucking her chin so that she appears even smaller than she is. "Don't I know it," she whispers.

"I wish I had met you in the old country," he says. "I would've courted you proper. Brought you flowers. Met you at the well, as if by accident, but really by design. Had our wedding in the village church with the selfsame reverend who'd baptized us."

She says, "We would never have met, in your old country."

He feels the words like a slap: in Wales, she would have been like all the rest. She would have laughed at him, darted her eyes away from his, whispered

some venomous remark about him into her friend's ear as he passed her. She would have discovered French fashions and Italian poetry and German prayers and lost all her purity. But here in the New World, she is perfectly pure; she will follow him home when he tires of lying in the holler; she has no friend in whose ear she can whisper.

Roderick does not raise his voice when he finds grease-crusted pans left overnight or the rafters of the cabin accumulating cobwebs. He does not complain when his wife refuses to tend the livestock or the struggling vegetable garden. He does not even punish her when he finds her abed in the middle of the afternoon, her body curled and the covers over her head. He holds his tongue until the day he comes home and finds the traveling preacher in his house again.

At the sight of the slick-mouthed man, Roderick aims his gun and nearly fires, then thinks better of it. Someone will be looking for the traveling preacher, sooner or later, he reasons; besides, the preacher is not the real problem here.

Once the notion enters his head, the rest of the world goes blurry and he is half-absent from every room he enters. That's always how it has been. A walking dream that collapses only when the blood awakens him. In the end, he thinks, his Blodeuwedd is like all other women, never mind her ancient heritage. The only difference is that there will be no trouble with her kin sniffing after her, because all the moon-eyed men are oblivious underground; although his father would never say so, Roderick knows that's why he had to come to the New World. He was always going to indulge himself again. But no man on the surface of the Earth will go looking for the murderer of a moon-eyed woman.

Afterwards, he mourns in the half-abashed way of a child who wanted to see a plaything broken but not taken away from him. He remembers that in the fairytale, Blodeuwedd took a lover and tried to have her husband murdered, but did not succeed. For her perfidy, she was turned into an owl, or a wolf, or something else despised and nocturnal.

The first time his wife comes back, Roderick is half-certain he is dreaming. She opens the door and crosses the room in a series of long, careful steps, then climbs in bed, notches her head into his chest, tangles her legs with his. She does not seem to remember any of the unpleasantness between them – she spits mud onto the cabin floor, draws an entire horsetail stalk from her throat, but says nothing of her strangulation, of her sojourn back into the soil.

The pity is that if she won't hold a grudge, she also won't learn her lesson. For two days, Roderick is enraptured. Then he sees that again she neglects her chores, again she refuses to step across the threshold if the sun is high. No possibility of the traveling minister coming again to the house, not after the scare Roderick's given him, but still Roderick can't trust her on her own. He fears, even if no one came, what treacherous things she might think or say or feel in the never-ending twilight by herself.

"You scarce even speak or eat," he says to her one night over bowls of burnt cornmeal.

She fidgets with her spoon. "You ever been homesick?" she says to him. "Ever long for the taste of your favorite dish, the smell of the earth, the sounds of the voices of your kin?"

His mother's sweet and fresh-made bara brith, the rich and generous scent of black Welsh soil upon tilling, the laughter like swallows' song from his small cousins as they tussle in the yard. "You are home," Roderick says, forcefully.

The next time he murders her, he drops her body into the depths of the bog. He has heard stories of thousand-year-old women preserved in the peat bogs of the old country, their skin and hair unblemished but their insides collapsed into nothing. His Blodeuwedd is empty like that, he has already concluded. There is nothing beneath the pale eyes, the translucent flesh, the blue veins deceptively pulsing away although nothing undead still has a heartbeat. After he discards her, he does not dare look back. He does not want to see if or when she rises. In the fairytale, Blodeuwedd-as-owl was hated by all the other birds. She was chased from tree branch to tree branch. She never could find home.

His wife returns trailing milkweed stalks, raspberry vines, pine branches, strands of algae. Vomiting mud, silty water, a stream of tadpoles, once a glistening black rat snake. Resembling more and more closely every time the effigy that the cunning woman made her from. When her ribcage cracks, the scent of aspen wafts out from her clothes. When Roderick carries her body through the rain, her limbs flop haplessly like cornhusks. When he lays her in graves, her white eyelashes fold like petals.

After her half-dozenth resurrection, Roderick goes to the Widow Nell. Enough is enough, he says to himself as he stands in front of the cunning woman's cabin. "My wife won't die," he tells her when she opens the door, and the admission is like letting go of a long-held inhalation. Now he has said it: he wishes that she would stay dead, or at least have the decency to become an owl.

"It needn't startle you any," says the Widow Nell. "You knew what you were marrying."

But he didn't: he has begun to suspect, with a creeping dread, that his moon-eyed woman is not a pure living descendent of Prince Madoc. That she is not a Welshwoman at all. *We would never have met, in your old country,* she'd said. "Isn't there any way I can be rid of her?" he says.

"As I *said,* possession never goes in only one direction. You are hers as much as she is yours." The Widow Nell hesitates. She squints at the altar in the corner, inclines her head as if listening. "But if she's too troublesome to you, there is a working we could do."

"Like what?" says Roderick.

"To tear you asunder. To cut the tie that binds you to each other. It'll hurt a mite, but it'll finish things surer than you can do yourself. Next storm, you come find me."

The sky withholds thunder for fourteen days. By then, Roderick has buried his wife three more times and endured three more silent reunions. When at last he sees clouds on the horizon darken, feels the wind rise, he is overcome by relief. At the first lightning bolt, Roderick follows the Widow Nell out to the bald and the moon-eyed woman follows Roderick.

"Lie on the stone," says the Widow Nell, and Roderick obeys.

The Widow Nell lays rhododendron blossoms on his eyelids, heaps dirt on his ribs. After a moment, Roderick feels his Blodeuwedd's hands on him, gentle and sweet, and he thinks tenderly that she has never before held his wrists like this. His eyes closed, blossom-weighted, he does not see the wives of every lonely Welshman in the backcountry emerging from between the trees and onto the bald. He does not see their just-alike pale eyes spitting back the moonlight, their diminutive fingers curled around the hatchets and cleavers and kitchen knives of their lonely wifehoods as the moon-eyed women come to avenge their kin.

3 February 1959

"Moon-eyed people, the Cherokee used to call them."

Collected reports of Cherokee oral traditions support original documentation of the "moon-eyed" people in the Appalachians as late as the 18th century. However, recent evidence suggests they were not driven off as previously believed. Welsh-gold bracelets stamped with the image of an owl have been discovered in a buried Civil War-era strongbox, which only strengthens the connection of this ancient race with the 12th-century voyage undertaken by Madoc ab Owain Gwynedd. Similar artefacts in Wales from the Iron Age are on display in the National Museum Wales.

I came across one back in '38, while perusing the wares of an antiques dealer in Boston. The dealer almost wouldn't part with it, so entranced was he by the story I told of its probable background. While persuading him to sell me the trinket, I noticed a man standing in the shadows at the back of the shop. He watched the transaction with keen interest. Later that day, I could have sworn I spotted the man again, clearly following me. I spotted him several times over the next few weeks before he finally arranged to speak with me—this marked the beginning of everything—the beginning of my association with the Umbra Arca and its terrible secrets.

4 February 1959

"After her half-dozenth resurrection, Roderick goes to the Widow Nell."

Also of note, according to the last of the four branches in the Mabinogion, Blodeuwedd is purported to be the wife of Lleu Llaw Gyffes, who was cursed by his mother to never have a human wife. To counter the curse, the magicians Math and Gwydion created a woman from broom, meadowsweet, and oak. In the language of flowers, these three sources ensured that Blodeuwedd was blessed with abundance, beauty, and strength. Following this pattern, the moon-eyed women in Appalachia are reputedly constructed from rhododendron (caution), cornhusk (prosperity), and aspen (resurrection). It remains to be determined if the moon-eyed women purposefully change their composition when they reemerge from each new burial. I have plans to investigate this when I'm next in Appalachia country.

Sorensen

UMBRA  ARCA
CASE   NOTE

AGENT No. _____

THE KEEPER

Angie Hodapp

Île de la Crinière, Acadia, Canada

T HE FUNERAL DIRECTOR TOLD ME the cost of cremating my mother included two hours in the chapel for a service, and ten to noon on Tuesday was available. I took it. There was no one to invite, so at ten on Tuesday, I walked into that empty chapel, opened one folding chair, and set it before the cloth-draped table that held my mother's ashes. I sat. I listened to the chapel's airy silence. I looked everywhere but at the urn. Until I could no longer ignore it.

When I saw it, I was confused. Then upset. The funeral director had made a mistake. This wasn't the sensible urn I'd picked from the budget-friendly section of his catalog. This urn was ornate, enameled in blue and green and wrapped in silver filigree as fine as a spider's web. I leaned forward in my chair and saw figures hidden in the design. A lighthouse on a cliff. A whale's fluke. A seagull. A fishing boat. A horse galloping along a beach, hooves pounding the waves into seafoam.

The urn was from Île de la Crinière, the island of my mother's youth. I knew it without a doubt. Her sketchbooks were full of those same images, rendered in pastel and watercolor. But how had the urn gotten here?

"It is a gift. I hope you don't mind."

Startled, I spun in my seat. The man who had spoken sat in a folding chair behind mine. How had I not heard him come in? Walk across the room? Set out his chair?

How had I not felt his breath on my neck?

Gooseflesh crawled along my arms. "Who are you?"

He rose, and I was surprised to find he was barely three feet tall. "Little Travers." He gave a bow. "A distant cousin of your mother's."

The room began to tilt. "My mother had no family."

"She did. Does. So do you."

I stared at him. He wore a felt beret the color of poppies, but the rest of his ensemble, from his turquoise bolo tie and plaid button-down to his belted jeans and cowboy boots, was straight out of a Western. This was Arizona, sure, but he looked absurd in those clothes. He was difficult to take seriously. But I was grieving, and I was now wholly alone in this world. I had no friends, not even among my coworkers at the supermarket. I had never been on a date, had never been interested in going on one. At twenty-two, I had only just begun to realize how odd my mother and I must have seemed to others. Each of us orbited the other. To discover I had family was bewildering.

Presently, I decided to be gracious. The urn was a lovely gift, and I didn't want to be rude.

"How did you hear that my mother died?" I asked Little Travers.

"Oh, she and I kept in touch over the years."

"That doesn't answer my question."

"Let's just say I've been keeping an eye on you two. Your mother meant a lot to us. I wanted to make sure she was safe. You, too. But she wanted to be left alone, so I did my best to keep a respectable distance."

"How respectable?"

"I move around a lot. Always have. Last few months, though, after I learned your mother was sick, I took a job on a ranch up near Flagstaff."

"Flagstaff," I said.

He nodded. "Have you been to Île de la Crinière?"

"Never." I was a desert girl, born with sand in my hair and a big, hot southwestern sun in my soul. I'd never seen an ocean, let alone visited my mother's island, which I understood to be a tiny speck of rock somewhere in the north Atlantic.

"Well, you have a reason to go now."

His R's and vowels took turns pooling at the back of his throat and pushing at his lips—that same Acadian mix of clipped French and Canadian English my mother sometimes slipped into whenever she forgot herself.

"What reason?" I asked.

"To take your mother's ashes home, of course."

"If she'd wanted me to do that, she'd have told me. Besides, she made me swear I'd never go there."

His eyes narrowed. "Tricky."

"Excuse me?"

He huffed, dragging his chair beside mine and climbing up onto it like a child. "What did you swear? What were the exact words you used?"

I thought back to the conversation. It had occurred maybe six or seven years ago, when I was in the thorniest of my teenage years and had threatened to run away. *It's a big world,* my mother said matter-of-factly. *Go anywhere you want. Just don't go to Île de la Crinière.* When I said that maybe I *would* go to Île de la Crinière, she grew serious. *Swear to me you won't, Sophie. Swear it.*

What had I said then? Nothing. I had rolled my eyes and stomped off to my bedroom and slammed my door. We'd never spoken of it again.

"I guess I didn't swear. She asked me to, but I didn't."

"Ah! Well, then!" His tone was suddenly bright, as though all was right with the world.

I stared at the urn, my thoughts rolling and crashing like waves inside my skull. I felt a bit ill and wondered if this was what seasickness was like. *I had family.* Why had my mother never told me? Was she ashamed of them? If they were all as absurd as Little Travers, then perhaps she was.

Or was it *me* she was ashamed of? Was it me she was hiding away from *them?*

This was a possibility I didn't wish to contemplate in the company of Little Travers. I tucked it away for later and said, "What do you do on the ranch?"

"I break horses."

That was unexpected. I struggled to picture him working with any horses, let alone ones that needed breaking.

"One sprint with me on their backs," he said, "and the wild drains out of them like whiskey from a gun-shot barrel. They walk home to the stables just as biddable as you please. The secret is to braid their manes and tails first. Hard to act wild when someone's got you gussied up."

His old-timey vernacular sounded odd, gilded as it was by his Acadian lilt.

I said, "How do you get close enough to a wild horse to braid its mane and tail?"

"Didn't I just say that's the secret? Now stop knocking me off track. When are you taking your mother's ashes back to the island?"

"I told you. She didn't want that."

He clicked his tongue. "The thing about our family, Sophie, is that we travel. We need to see the world. But there's nothing more important than going home. Even after we're dead. *Especially* after we're dead. We have an obligation to each other to make that happen. Do you understand?"

"Not even a little."

"Let me say it another way. Your mother didn't want her ashes taken back to the island. But I do. And I'm your family. If I were to die—hypothetically speaking, of course—would you swear to take me there?"

The thoughts I'd tucked away broke free and started rolling and crashing again. Either my mother was keeping the island from me, or she was keeping me from the island. I had a right to know why. Finding answers meant I must, sooner or later, travel to Île de la Crinière.

After all, I'd never sworn I wouldn't.

That was what I was thinking when I replied, absentmindedly, "Sure, Little Travers. If you die, I'll take you to the island."

"Do you swear?"

"I swear."

Three days later, I got a call from Flagstaff. Little Travers had been thrown from a horse. He died quick. A handwritten will found among his personals named me his next of kin and specified that I should lay eyes on his body prior to his cremation.

As for what was to be done with his cremains, the will said *Sophie will know what to do.*

I flew to Quebec and from there to New Brunswick. In Moncton I rented a car. I threw my overnight bag in the trunk—I didn't intend to stay on the island more than one night—and placed Little Travers's boxed-up ashes on the seat beside me.

I'd thought long and hard about whether to bring my mother's ashes as

well, but in the end, I left the urn on the floor of my closet. Unreasonable as it seemed, I worried that if I took her ashes to the island, she'd know I defied or disappointed her. And though I never swore to her that I wouldn't go, I did swear to Little Travers that I would.

From Moncton, I drove east toward the coast, then crossed the Confederation Bridge to Prince Edward Island. The bridge was so long that at the middle you could see land neither before nor behind you. The effect of being flanked by wide, gray water under a wide, gray sky was, for a desert girl like me, unsettling. I gripped the wheel and sat low in my seat. I'd never thought of gravity as a variable thing, but it felt upside down here. The heavy clouds exerted a force of their own, one that felt as though it might draw the car right up off the bridge and into the heavens.

On Prince Edward Island, it rained. I drove northeast, crossing the island on narrow roads that traversed low hills. I was not expecting farmland, but that was much of what I saw: white clapboard houses and red barns dotting newly harvested fields, rusty metal roofs on ramshackle sheds, and crooked mailboxes marking dirt roads that disappeared into distant groves of maples and pines.

Despite the rain, when I neared the northern coast, I lowered the window. I breathed in the scent of salt and fish and windblown beachgrass. I ached for something here to feel familiar, but nothing did. Everything here was foreign to me. I was a stranger.

My destination was a small harbor town called Naufrage. There, I was to catch the ferry to Île de la Crinière.

The ferry turned out to be a trawler captained by a bearded man named Seb, hired by the proprietress of Île de la Crinière's sole inn to collect me. Seb told me *naufrage* was French for *shipwreck* and laughed heartily at my reaction. I was sure I went quite pale, but that was because the boat had cleared the harbor and was being tossed high and low by open water. I was immediately sick.

After an hour of wishing for death and cursing the box of ashes on my lap, I saw, for the first time, my mother's island. I was not prepared. Striated cliffs stood high above the waves, monuments to eons of oceanic cause and geological effect. Atop the cliffs, a lighthouse rose from salt-scrubbed pines. Twilight had fallen, and its beam turned slow and sure, cutting through the gloom to the purple-black water below.

Seb left me standing on the pier. I called out to him through the rain. "Tomorrow! What time will you be back for me?"

Though I was certain he heard me, he wordlessly crossed himself and motored away.

Still seasick, I shambled along the pier to the beach, only to find that the beach rocked beneath me as well. I hoped the effect would wear off soon. "Here you are, Little Travers," I said to the sodden box beneath my arm. "Happy now?"

A path led through the beachgrass to a road that wound around the foot of the cliff. I wondered how far the inn was. I hefted my overnight bag higher on my shoulder and glanced up at the lighthouse.

There, white as the moon and galloping through the rain along the edge of the cliff, was a horse. It was no majestic stallion, no fairy-tale steed, but it was sure of foot and racing with dangerous speed toward the point.

I gasped. It was going too fast. It needed to stop. But its rider, small as a child and wearing a red hat, gripped the ribbons braided into its mane and kicked booted heels into its sides.

With one mighty leap, the horse vaulted into the void.

Horrified, I watched as horse and rider fell. And fell. And fell. Until at last they hit the water and disappeared beneath the waves.

A scream tore at my throat, but when I opened my mouth to release it, it stuck there. I couldn't breathe. It was as if it were me under the waves, as if it were my lungs filling with seawater, as if it were my bones broken against hidden rocks.

"Quite a shock the first time you see it, no?"

I turned. An old woman holding a red umbrella stood just behind me. She was tall and thin, and she wore yellow rain boots. A matching yellow slicker hung open, revealing overalls and a cabled sweater. Like Little Travers in the chapel, she seemed to have appeared from nowhere.

"What...what was...?" This was all I could manage. The image of the horse

and rider throwing themselves over the cliff burned bright behind my eyes.

The old woman smiled. "You'll get used to it. Sometimes they're lucky and make it off the island. Sometimes not."

I stared at her. How could such a harrowing spectacle be something anyone could get used to? "Are you the innkeeper?"

"When it comes to this island, I'm the keeper of everything. Now. Who have you got there?"

Numb with shock and cold, I stared at the box that lay at my feet. I hadn't realized I'd dropped it. "Little Travers," I said.

"Did you bring your mother, too?"

"No."

The old woman's expression fell. She stared out across the water I had just crossed, and the great sadness in her eyes was the first thing that felt familiar since I left Arizona. It was the same sadness I saw in my mother's eyes whenever I caught her watching the sun rise over the desert.

"What a shame," said the old woman. Then all at once, she seemed to recover. She closed her umbrella and jabbed it upright into the sand. Paying no mind to the rain, she reached into her slicker and withdrew a pocketknife. This she opened with one expert flick of her wrist as she stalked toward me.

I stumbled back in sudden fear for my life. No one knew where I was or would come looking for me. Fate didn't care. Here is where I would die, stabbed by a murderous crone on Île de la Crinière, the one place in the world my mother told me never to go.

But the old woman dropped to her knees and buried the blade into the top of the box. One quick slash, and both the cardboard and the plastic within it were split. She stood and shook the ashes out onto the ground. The rain beat what was left of Little Travers into the sand.

"That's done." She tossed the empty box aside and wiped the blade clean on her thigh.

Once more, I was speechless. For all Little Travers's talk of being returned to the island, this was not the ceremony I expected. This was no ceremony at all.

Slipping the knife back into her pocket, the old woman said, "Let's go up to the house and get you dry."

"Don't you mean the inn?"

"There is no inn."

I felt seasick again. I had been deceived—by my mother, by Little Travers, and, I was quite sure, by this woman as well. But to what end?

Blinking rain from my eyes, I watched the old woman open her red umbrella. "Who are you?" I asked.

"Georgette Laroche," she replied. "Your grandmother."

We sat at her kitchen table and drank verveine tea, the water for which she boiled in a kettle on an old woodstove. The house—small, rustic, held up by rough-hewn beams but charming in an old-world way—was decorated with a profusion of folksy handicrafts: embroidered curtains, wood carvings of animals both real and imagined, patchwork quilts, and ceramic vases, some of which, I noted, were enameled like my mother's urn. Several items looked quite old. Others were newer. Who had made so many beautiful things?

Over the mantelpiece hung a framed watercolor painting of the island's lighthouse. Though it was clearly the work of a child, I recognized my mother's style. Tears sprang to my eyes. I dashed them away with the back of my hand.

"Besides the lighthouse," Georgette said, "this home is the only manmade structure on the island."

"What does that mean?" I set my teacup down with a hard clink. "Assuming I'm awake and not insane, what does any of this mean?"

Footsteps sounded on the porch. There was a knock. The door opened, and in walked Little Travers.

My heart skittered against my ribs. I clutched the edge of the table to keep from toppling out of my chair. "It can't be!" I stared at Georgette, then at Little Travers. "Is it really you?"

Little Travers, in his red beret and ridiculous cowboy clothes, gave a bow. "In the flesh."

"Welcome home, Little Travers," said Georgette. "It's been a long time.

Welcome home to you, too, Sophie."

"This isn't my home."

"It is now." Her voice held something of an apology.

"It's *not*. I'm leaving tomorrow." I whirled on Little Travers, my tone rising along with the panic in my chest. "I did what you asked. I brought you back."

"No, Sophie. I brought you back. The only way I knew how."

The walls of the house suddenly seemed impossibly close, the heat from the woodstove stifling. "I saw your body. You were dead."

"And now I am not."

"You tricked me."

"Trickery is our specialty."

Georgette, perhaps sensing I was at the end of my tether, said, "We are keepers of the island, you and me, and the caretakers of its inhabitants."

"What inhabitants?"

"The lutins. The little people."

She watched my face, which must have betrayed the fear and disbelief warring inside me. I was beginning to grasp why my mother left. She didn't want to be the keeper of this island, and she didn't want me to be the keeper either. I looked at my grandmother's wrinkled skin, her tired eyes, the iron-gray hair that stuck out from her scalp in wiry patches. She needed a successor, and with my mother dead, I was the end of the line. That was why Little Travers had gone to such grim lengths to get me here.

Georgette sipped her tea, then set down her cup and began to speak. "When the French settled Acadia four-hundred years ago, they unwittingly brought the lutins with them across the sea. Little troublemakers. That's their nature. So the settlers rounded them up and banished them to Île de la Crin-ière. Lots were cast, and our line was chosen. Since 1608, from mother to daughter to granddaughter and so on, our ancestors have kept this island."

"Kept it from what?"

"From the outside world. From itself." She shrugged. "It is the nature of the lutins to attempt escape. That's what you witnessed on the cliff. It's also their nature to return and be reborn. We must always be here to keep the lighthouse burning so they can find their way back."

"And if we're not?"

Little Travers cleared his throat. His expression somber, he said, "Without a home to return to, we lutins would cease to be."

I stared at him, this little man who, if I understood correctly, had just been resurrected by the island. What deep magic made such a thing possible? Did I want to know?

"The cliff..." I shook my head. The terrible image of the white horse and its tiny rider falling into the ocean still plagued me. "That was suicide."

"Far from it." Georgette closed her eyes and recited: "*You are invisible when you like. You rise without wings. You fall into the abyss of the sea without drowning. You enter, though windows and doors are closed. And when you decide to, you let yourself be seen.*" She opened her eyes. "Marie-Catherine d'Aulnoy wrote that about the lutins in 1697, and it's as true now as it was then. They charm their horses with enchanted ribbons and ride them across the sea. But the journey is treacherous. Only the lucky ones make it to foreign shores. The others—well, some of them—wash up back here with their horses and start over again. That's its own kind of luck, isn't it?"

A terrible thought occurred to me. The heat that moments ago had threatened to suffocate me rushed from the room, leaving ice under my skin. "My mother. If I had brought her ashes here, would she be alive now?"

Her eyes grew sad again. "It's possible. As you can imagine, our line crossed with theirs once or twice over the centuries. Most of our ancestors were born of shipwrecked fishermen, ill-fated explorers, downed pilots—men brought to us by thalassic magic. Even so, we all ended up with some measure of lutin blood in our veins. I always suspected that's why your mother, like them, so desperately wanted to escape."

"I'll go back," I blurted. "I'll get the urn and bring her ashes here, and we can try—"

"No, dear. If you leave now, you'll never find your way back. But if you stay..."

She trailed off, but her meaning was clear. She was asking me to take her place. To be the next keeper of this island. To lie with whichever man the ocean brought to me and to bear a daughter.

I remembered the knife in my grandmother's hand and the moment when I was sure she intended to kill me. My first thought was that no one knew where I was. That I wouldn't be missed, not even at the supermarket where I worked. There, I'd be just another clerk who stopped showing up for her shifts, replaced within a day. I thought of the funeral home's chapel, empty because there was no one to invite. We'd kept to ourselves, my mother and I, and I was happy with that. Why did it take so long to see such a thing as strange? Why had I never wanted friends or lovers? Perhaps because I wasn't meant for the modern world. My mother had done all she could to give me a good life. The only thing she hadn't given me was a choice.

I met my grandmother's eyes. "Tell me what to do."

She smiled, stood, and motioned for me to follow her to the door. I did. So did Little Travers. She opened it, and the three of us peered out into the night.

"Do you see them?" she asked.

At first, I saw nothing but the rain and the great eye of the lighthouse turning in the dark. Then I saw little spots of red among the shrubs and boulders at the edges of the clearing on which the house had been built. The longer I looked, the more I saw. There were dozens of them.

"Hats," I said. Every one of them was red. Berets like the one Little Travers wore. Fedoras and fezzes, beanies and ballcaps, tams and turbans, cloches, fascinators, newsboys, deerstalkers, sombreros, bowlers, and more. In the dark, those bright spots were all I could see, but I knew every one of them sat on the head of a lutin.

"They need a red hat to be seen," my grandmother said. "For centuries, they've been bringing hats back from their travels. A bit of a competition, I think."

"Why be dull?" said Little Travers.

"They want you to see them," Grandmother continued. "They're saying hello."

"How am I supposed to...*keep* them?"

"Keep the lighthouse burning so they can find their way home. Not all of them do, and they are the last of their kind." She clapped once and rubbed her hands together. "Now, Little Travers, I believe my time has come."

Little Travers pinched two fingers between his lips and gave a sharp whistle. A white horse trotted out of the dark and stopped at the porch steps. Red ribbons streamed from the braids in its mane and tail. My grandmother stepped toward it and with surprising agility swung herself onto its back.

A sudden dread coursed through me. "Where are you going?"

"I've been on this island all my life. It's time for a little adventure of my own."

"But what if—?" What if she didn't have enough lutin blood to make it off the island? Enough lutin blood to bring her back?

"Bah! What if, what if." She waved her hand, dismissing my worry. Then the familiar sadness returned to her eyes. "I would have liked to have known you, Sophie. Perhaps someday I will."

With that, she clutched the horse's mane and kicked its sides. It bolted toward the path that led up to the lighthouse. The path that led to the cliff.

I drew an anguished breath to shout *Wait! Come back!* The words never left my lips. Little Travers reached up to pat my shoulder, and his friendly touch instantly comforted me.

"She was tired. She devoted her entire life to our care, and it was well past her time to rest," he said. "You're going to be a great keeper."

I didn't know if he was right, but I knew I wanted to try. Out at the edges of the clearing, the spots of red disappeared, blinking out one by one like Christmas lights as the lutins removed their hats.

"Where are they going?" I asked.

"To the places they go."

"There's so much I don't know. Will you help me?"

"For a time. Until I go adventuring again."

That, I knew, would have to be good enough. I closed my eyes and discovered that the desert sun in my soul had set. In its place, I saw beachgrass blowing under cold, gray skies. Salt and rock and a gull soaring low over a savage sea. A lighthouse high on a cliff.

In its place, I found Île de la Crinière.

IGNIS FATUUS
(Giddy Flame)

Sinister "Ghost Light" only seen at night. Known to lead travelers astray. Thought to be mischievous fairies or elemental spirits.

WILL-O'-THE-WISP

Tiffany Morris

Kejimkujik, Nova Scotia, Canada

Te's qalqwasiet
On each sunset
their silhouettes rise
from the Still Brook
marshland:
stretching horizon to
darkening water,
ghostbright women
singing luminous death.

Puntalatl,
they cast a spell:
words slide from
their many teeth,
weaving gold
strands into a
web of burning.

Walk closer: your
hope and flesh
blister into stars
melting skyward
becoming the grey
hovering heavy
clouds slung
above.

THE MAN WHO WASN'T THERE

Betty Rocksteady

Antigonish, Nova Scotia, Canada

*M*Y HEAD IS A HAUNTED HOUSE.

Into the phone, I say, "Yeah Dad, everything is fine. I just think I could get more done up here."

He hesitates, and all the words he is not saying stream through my mind. I almost wish he would just say them. I'm sure it wouldn't take too much prying before I burst open like a dam, but he doesn't, so I keep talking. "Honestly, I guess I am a little stressed but it's just that these exams are like, huge, and I really need to use this Spring Break as an actual study break. Clinical starts soon and I need to be ready."

"The apartment is nice and quiet, huh? Easier to study there? Worth the money?"

"So much better than the Living Learner's residence. I think I'm just meant to be an introvert—I'm so grateful you set me up here. Second year nursing is intense; I never would have survived it in residence." I've always been good at telling him what he wants to hear, even when the ghosts in my head are muttering so loud I can barely think.

"Well, you're still seeing that friend, Mary, right? Getting out and exploring the town a little? You could use the fresh air. Your mother and I spent some beautiful days in Antigonish when we were taking nursing." He sighs. "I sure miss her."

"Me too."

"What about the therapist? Has she given you anything useful to work on?"

Well, she said my dreams about hurting people are normal, but I haven't told her about the thoughts, the compulsions, the way each lesson seems to open up a brand-new door in my head and behind each door, a torture chamber designed especially for my future patients. Oh, and she's just an email therapist, so it's not like she can tell when I'm lying. "Yeah, she's helped with sleep a lot, actually. She has me doing this whole relaxation thing, you'd love it, very woo-woo. Relax from the tips of your toes to the top of your head, then slowly visualize counting down from ten as you walk down a flight of stairs, deeper into sleep, deeper into your subconscious. Sort of self-hypnotism, I guess."

Dad laughs, and I choke down tears. "And that helps?" he asks.

"Weirdly enough, it helps a lot."

Any relief of getting away with my lie fades and is replaced with a sudden gush of shame. I say my goodbyes quickly, abruptly, so I can let the tears come, so I can sink to my knees on the floor and cry.

It's okay. I got what I wanted. A week to myself, in my apartment, with just my own thoughts to keep me company—and already I know it was a mistake. I should have gone home. I should have told him everything. I should have told him everything *last* Spring Break, instead of letting him believe it was something he could fix. I tried. I told him I couldn't handle school, I told him I wasn't happy, but I couldn't tell him why. And how could I, when he was so *proud* of me, following in his and Mom's footsteps? The breakdown he saw was nothing compared to the possibility of what slithers inside me.

I backed down last year, and this year I hide, and maybe next year it will be too late.

Leaving the Living Learner's residence has only made it worse, but how could I tell him that? The quiet of the apartment only makes my thoughts louder. The walls and ceiling inch closer, the ghosts cackle in my brain. Sure, I get away from St. FX University for a few hours, but it's not far enough to quell the thoughts.

I have hours to fill, days to fill, and I'm doomed to spend them pacing, climbing the walls, eating too much and trying to drown myself out with the TV up loud. I think about going for a drive, but instead I dive deeper into myself, and when I finally lay down in bed, eyes bleeding from the screen, it takes me hundreds of flights of stairs to fall asleep, and when I do, I dream all night of suffocating pediatric patients in their beds.

I look at my phone the second I wake up, and again and again over the ensuing hours as I toss and turn and try to drift back into the comforting emptiness of sleep. Instead, I see innocent smiles, trusting faces, and the grim possibilities I hold in my pale hands. The dread sits high in my stomach, and the guilt spills over me like a blanket, and eventually I have to get up.

My email therapist said when I feel like this, the best thing to do is *anything*, distract myself, move into the next moment of the day, but I just move into the living room, and the pile of books on the table and the dishes in the sink cause an actual physical pain in my chest.

Especially the books, with their secret recipes for death.

I have to get out of here.

Arisaig Park is about thirty minutes from my apartment and absolutely beautiful, or so I've been told by Dad a thousand times. I've never cared enough to check it out myself, but maybe today is the day, because I have to go, I have to drive somewhere before I go crazy. Before I hurt myself. Because more and more that's seeming like the only possible option, either hurt myself or hurt someone else.

I put on the college radio station as I drive and end up turning it off immediately. It makes the nostalgia for when I thought I was normal too thick.

I arrive at Arisaig as the afternoon sun creeps out from behind a cloud, melting the last remnants of dirty snow. White spruce reach into the sky, branches moving with eager squirrels and birds, or maybe just the breeze. I wonder if it's possible to walk so far into these woods that I can't find my way out again. Walk until I am too tired to walk anymore and stretch myself out on the grass and let the moss and mud and leaves cover me, let my flesh and bone melt away and make sure that I never have the chance to cause anyone pain.

But, instead, I stick to the trail and as I walk its circling path, something slowly seems to open up inside me, and maybe a little of the poison drains out. I feel my breath in my chest and I feel my lungs working and there is a slight dizziness. The cold spring air feels like *something*, reminds me there is life inside me, rips me away from the tunnel of my thoughts into the present. I should be studying but I am walking, and I am just a little bit more free than I thought I was.

There are multiple paths and even as part of me fears getting lost, another part of me still welcomes the idea and so I take them intuitively.

I hear the ocean before I see it. A salty breeze plasters my hair to my face. I find a set of wooden stairs leading down to the rocky beach. The sky above is pale blue, almost white, and the water is indigo waves.

As I walk down the crumbling wooden steps, my breathing slows and I find myself counting down from ten, as if I am falling asleep, as if the ocean is a dream. As if instead of walking down this path, I am spiralling deeper into myself.

Cliffs of ancient swirling rock bracket the beach. Dad told me about this—Silurian rock, some of the oldest in the world. Mom and Dad used to come here to find fossils when they were first dating. I press my hand against the stone and wonder if once my mother pressed her own hand here.

I wonder if she ever felt how I feel.

I walk through the muck where the waves crash, let my old sneakers sink in a few inches. What does it matter? The vastness of the ocean overwhelms me and tears creep from my eyes again, blasted away by the wind, leaving my cheeks chapped.

I take a step into the water, and instantly my jeans are soaked. I think about taking another step, and another, and I think about letting the ocean swallow me whole. What would my father think had happened? Maybe this is the best way. Maybe I will never be found and he can imagine someone took me, can always imagine me in the prime of my life, ready to succeed.

The water is cold, and I am a coward. Instead, I ask the ocean, *please, please, take this from me* but the wind makes my eyes leak. Tears spill. For a moment, the waves go silent and I feel like something has heard me, but the moment passes and I don't feel powerful. I feel ridiculous.

Nothing can wash this away.

It's not just the thoughts about hurting people that scare me. It's how *good* they feel. It's the certainty that I will take the knowledge I've worked so hard for and use it to *kill*, and I will be able to make it look so natural that I will get away with it and it will be so easy there will be no reason not to do it again and I am so *tired* of the way these thoughts run incessantly through the stupid meat

of my brain. I am so tired of fighting all the time.

Maybe tomorrow I will send my therapist an email and tell her a little more of the truth.

The wooden stairs splinter beneath my feet and as I climb them, twilight gently turns to night, and my stomach turns over. I don't understand how I could have lost track of time so easily. I push down the panic. No sense in freaking out. It won't take long to be out of here, soon I'll be back in my apartment wanting to die, and this excursion can be a distant memory.

It's nearly an hour before I have to admit I'm walking in circles. Everything looks the same in the dark, and I swear I'm following the path but I keep coming back to the same stump of a log, the same scattering of rock. I check my phone repeatedly but there's no service, and I start to wonder if I really could die here in the woods.

The ocean roars in my ears.

The moon is huge and pink and throbbing in the sky, and it illuminates something between the trees that is not quite a path.

The moon's light moves behind a cloud and I lose myself again, find myself tangled in branches, pushing through bushes, and I see something between the trees, silhouetted in darkness, a jutting of rock that arcs into the sky and swirls toward the moon. I step closer and realize it is another staircase, and the world grows hazy around me, and I wonder again if I'm dreaming.

The burnt-out foundation of a house surrounds the stairs, implying that someone lived here once, but the steps are massive slabs of stone that spiral hundreds of feet into a sky that couldn't possibly be contained by four walls and a roof. My feet move towards the steps. I am close enough to touch them before I see the ancient fossils that swirl up the rock.

I see myself walking to the top and tumbling off the other side.

I take the first step.

My phone moves in my hand, and I drop it down the stairs and realize I've climbed more than I thought because somehow I am halfway up, somehow I can see the tops of the trees. I recognize the blare of the ring. At the top of the stairs there is a void I can climb into, and at the bottom of the stairs is my father's familiar voice.

I walk down the stairs and pick up my phone, but I don't answer it.

I see the way out of the trees, and finally, hours later, I make it home.

I fall into bed exhausted, and the second I close my eyes, reality blurs and bleeds around me, something lifts off my chest and something drains away and the stairs descend, and I am taking them one by one. Moss squishes beneath my feet, obscuring strange fossils.

I take the steps, one per breath, as they spiral deeper and deeper into darkness. Stars dance in the distant sky. The sky is somehow wet, dripping with the reek of bile.

I hear footsteps behind me but when I turn, no one is there. Filthy skeletal impressions quiver beneath my feet and deep in my gut, something turns over.

Wake up.

I open my eyes so wide they feel like they are bleeding, but wherever my body is, it doesn't stir. I am still here.

There is a presence and it is coming closer and I know I can't let it catch me so I keep walking down the stairs, deeper into sleep, and the night sky seems to breathe around me.

It is more dangerous down here.

He is gaining on me, he is getting closer, and from the corner of my eye I see him, I try not to look but he is looking at me and I turn, and above me on the stair, something undulates, and my limbs turn to jelly.

I think I am falling.

A sliver of muscle and fat. A crooked slice of smile. Something bursts inside my brain, nerve endings tremble and spill down the stone, veins drip over the stairs, and over the fossilized remains of something ancient, blood spills.

I am tumbling, gripping at rock, shattering fingernails. Pain spikes in my kneecap, and I wonder if when I land I will even be able to walk, or will I crumple and bend and break, but eventually my fingers grip and I gasp for breath. My ass slides down a few more steps, but finally I stop.

He is not there, but something inside me still sees him.

His eyes spin with stars.

He opens his mouth and he speaks and the words that come out are familiar, but the sound is guttural, the language is wrong. The dark current of his voice makes me weep. I can't understand a word he is saying but I can feel each syllable diving into the grey wet meat of my brain and making a home there.

Maybe it's not me dreaming. Maybe it's him.

He smiles. He lets me go.

I am falling through the stars.

When I finally wake up it's to rush to the toilet. My anxious stomach erupts in an endless stream of bile, and when it's finally all out I stand over the sink, sipping water, looking out the window, trying not to think.

The snow has all melted, revealing dead grass and the stray garbage blown through the city over the winter, stained and faded logos that make things look even sadder than they should.

I think about emailing my therapist. I think about texting my dad. But the faded paint in here is getting to me and it's too hard to breathe and I'm tired of not sleeping and I can feel the panic welling up so I think *do anything* and I step outside.

Everything is too sharp. The streets are quiet, but color and movement are extra bright. Even the chip bags that blow by seem alive with meaning. Air moves through my lungs, and I try to convince myself I feel better. A little bit.

The bushes in the front yard are too green. Between the houses, something is moving.

He's here.

I wonder if maybe I am going completely insane.

A gust of wind shakes the trees in my front yard, blowing stray leaves and bits of paper past me. I close my eyes, remind myself to breathe, and something wet plasters itself to my cheek. My pulse pounds through my ears, and I feel that welling sense of panic again. I pull the object from my face, and it's a piece of paper. Wet. Dripping. I am floating far away from my body as I read the words that bleed across the page.

Yesterday, upon the stair,

I met a man who wasn't there!

He wasn't there again today,

Oh how I wish he'd go away!

As I read the last word of the last line, I am suddenly, violently ill on the sidewalk. The sickness pours through me, black bubbling stuff that runs in rivulets down the drains and I hear someone scream and it just keeps coming and the words repeat again and again, they wind and spiral deeper into the deepest part of my brain *oh how I wish he'd go away!*

Black muck is still spilling from my lips, bitter as vinegar. I lurch to my feet. The paper tears, melts away, was never there at all. Across the street I can feel someone staring at me, their face a blur of concern, but I don't meet their eyes as I run back inside.

▬▬▬▬▬▬

I am reading my nursing book. I am reading the same words again and again and trying to force myself to commit them to memory. I imagine myself writing them on a chalkboard, looping letters that sink deep into my mind but when they get in there they wiggle about and they transform.

Yesterday, upon the stair,

Dad has texted me three times today. First to ask how I was doing, then to say he really wishes I'd reconsider coming home for the rest of break, and then just a thumbs up, something to prompt me to reply. I don't. I read instead, the same pages, over and over...

I met a man who wasn't there!

...and outside the twilight turns to darkness.

I am studying and I am getting better and I am not thinking about hurting people.

My therapist said it was normal to have intense dreams in times of stress.

He wasn't there again today,

I read the next paragraph and think about how many of my patients will be completely helpless and how much they will trust me...

Oh how I wish he'd go away!

...and I decide maybe I'll take a break after all. I don't have to think about school all the time. I don't have to think all the time. If I didn't think all the time everything would be fine.

Intrusive thoughts are just that. Intruders. Just because I've let them in doesn't mean I have to let them stay.

My phone vibrates with another text message, and I decide that if it is Dad I will tell him the truth, I'll tell him I'm not cut out to be a nurse, I'll tell him I can't help other people yet because I need to help myself, but it's an invite to a party from Mary, my one friend from the dorm last year who didn't quite give up on me.

Heard you were sticking around for break. Party at Aiden's if you're interested in getting away from the books for a bit! Love to see ya!!

I look like shit and I feel like shit...

Yesterday, upon the stair,

...and I think that maybe I will go after all. Surprise Mary. Surprise myself. Aiden lives close enough to walk, and just getting out for a bit is bound to do me some good.

I wash my face and zip up a hoodie. I'm not trying to impress anyone. I'm just trying to get out for a bit, clear my head, socialize. I'm not really a pariah. The girls all liked me last year, it was just me being stuck in my head, and staying here on my own all the time just made it worse.

I met a man who wasn't there!

I cut through Cairn Park across from St. FX, passing the monuments to Scottish families. The wet grass sucks at my sneakers and I feel suddenly, bone-achingly tired, and I let myself sink to the concrete base of one of the monuments, hold my head in my hands for a few minutes. I think probably I will turn around and go back home. There is nothing out here for me.

And when I take my head from my hands, everything has changed, the cairn has expanded, exploded, reaching up through the trees, concrete and dirt and stone and a spiral of stairs, huge and hulking and impossible. They don't belong here.

Neither do I.

He wasn't there again today,

I hear slow footsteps, taking their time, making their way down the stairs.

I think, probably, that I have gone insane. Or maybe I am still dreaming, right now.

Oh how I wish he'd go away!

My phone buzzes. Dad again, just a thumbs up, just letting me know he's there, and when I look up, the stairs are gone and everything is as it should be. It starts to rain, a wet drizzle. I turn my back on the park. I make it to the party after all.

———

It's pretty lame. A lot of *older* people, like older, like people who live in this town and aren't just college students. Men who think they know how to show young girls a good time. Aiden's friends. I can't find Mary anywhere. She's probably upstairs, in one of the bedrooms.

I sit on the stained couch, turned away from the dudes playing video games. I can see some girls I know in the kitchen mixing drinks, and I think about grabbing one but instead I retreat further into myself. The rain pounds against the windows. I am so tired. When one of the video game guys leaves, I stretch out on the couch and wonder if I could sleep here, listening to the party in the background, voices and words that have nothing to do with me, a strangely comforting white noise that drowns out other thoughts.

Yesterday, upon the stair,

My phone is nearly dead, eleven percent, and I should save the battery. Instead, I find myself typing into Google the words that won't leave. Someone retches in the backyard as the first result comes up on Wikipedia. Antigonish (poem). With trembling fingers, I click through to the brief entry—*inspired by reports of the ghost of a man roaming the stairs of a haunted house, in Antigonish, Canada.*

Nausea pulses through my throat again. Sound dies. All I can hear is the blood rushing through my ears. I don't want to know more but I need to, I need to know where the house was, exactly where it was, but no matter what phrases I Google there is no more information, there is nothing, just this fragment of a thought, this fragment of a poem.

My head is a haunted house and in that house there is a stairway and on that stairway—

Oh how I wish he'd go away!

I stand up so abruptly I nearly bang into Mary, who has come back downstairs finally, looking dishevelled, looking happy to see me but this is over, I'm gone, I'm going home. I won't sleep until I'm miles away from whatever the fuck is happening here.

Not too much later, I pull into a gas station on the way out of town. I'm ready to tell Dad everything. I'm ready to give up. I just want to go home. I want to crack my head open in front of him and let the ghosts burst free.

I don't have to be a nurse. I can be anything. He'll understand.

I get gas, grab some energy drinks and before I leave I should piss, so I take the huge key from the attendant and make my way to the side entrance.

And behind the dumpster out back, behind last year's untrimmed weeds, a staircase juts up, towering above the gas station, joining the stars somewhere above. The swirls of stone trace out intricate patterns, and the fossils look like words that I could read if I just got a little closer.

My cheeks are wet, and in the distance, I hear a voice. I am turning around, I am running back to my car, I'm sure that I am escaping but then my foot hits the first step and somewhere he is counting and I drop to my hands and knees to crawl and I claw my way up bit by bit and he counts to ten again and again and finally when I reach the top of the stairs, Antigonish is tiny and warped in the distance, and he is there. Beside me.

The wetness of the internal. The sharpness of bone. The leak of fluid. The dim light of life. His empty face—on its blank canvas, an indigo pit yawns open and from its wet depths sprays a dark mist. I kneel, press my knees into stone and press my forehead to the stair directly between his feet. A scuttling of spiders as his fingers twist through my hair and yank. The tearing of skin and a gush of fluid as my scalp is peeled back and a trapdoor in the crown of my head opens and the mist enters me. He enters me.

He locks the trapdoor and he walks down the stairs *one, two, three, four, five, six, seven, eight, nine, ten* and I am getting so, so tired. And with each step he takes, I fall deeper into sleep, and with each step he takes, he sinks deeper into me.

Have you hurt anyone?

Not yet.

Then, for a long time, we fall.

We pick ourselves up off the concrete and think about how much there is to learn.

We start the car, and drive back to the apartment, and we study all night, and all day, and all night, and we find so many new corners where we can keep our nasty little secrets; in the attic, in the basement, in the walls, in the deep, dark meat of my brain where no one else can ever find them, at least not until it's too late.

UMBRA ARCA
C A S E   N O T E

_____

_____

_____

_____

_____

_____

_____

_____

_____

_____

_____

_____

_____

_____

_____

_____

_____

_____

_____

AGENT No. _____

GOD SPELLED BACKWARD

Tim Waggoner

Ohio, USA

MOVEMENT IN THE DARK, shadows shifting among shadows, forms emerging, taking shape, solidifying. A half dozen figures, maybe more, crammed into your small bedroom, shoulder to shoulder, front to back. You feel heat radiating from their bodies, smell the nauseating tang of their rank scent, hear their deep growling. They tower over you—seven, eight feet tall—and as they gather around your bed, foot claws *tkk-tkk-tkking* on your hardwood floor, you sit up, press yourself back against the headboard, heart pounding so hard your head thrums in response to each rapid beat.

"Go away. You—you're not *real*."

Terrified as you are, you feel ridiculous saying this. If they're not real, why ask them to leave? Why speak to them at all?

There's a small lamp on the nightstand next to your bed. You stretch your right hand toward it, fingers trembling so hard that, at first, they can't grip the plastic switch. When they finally do, you hesitate. If you can't see them, maybe they can't see you. A child's logic, desperate, pathetic.

You turn on the light.

You see eight of them, three standing at the left side of your bed, three at the right, two at the foot. They're human-shaped, fur-covered, with canine heads—eyes blazing feral yellow, mouths open wide to reveal sharp white teeth and lolling pink tongues. Their colors vary, jet black, brown, a mix, muzzles and chests matted with blood that's still wet. They have hands instead of paws, clawed fingers coated crimson. They reach up, place these hands on the sides of their heads and lift.

You scream.

———

Malcolm Hudson is driving down State Route 32, roughly ten miles outside Hadleigh, Ohio, when a woman steps into the road in front of his car, turns to face him, and—illuminated in the bright wash of his headlights—raises her arms to get his attention. As if stepping in front of a moving car isn't enough of an attention-getter in itself. Malcolm grips the steering wheel tight, slams his foot down on the brake pedal, and his white Toyota Prius skids to a halt, bumper only a couple feet from the woman. He was going forty-five miles an hour, and if he'd been going any faster—a lot of people go sixty, even seventy on back country roads like this one—he wouldn't have been able to stop in time. She hurries to the driver's side door and motions for him to lower his window. He does, but only a couple inches. He doesn't know this woman, and he has no reason to trust her. Better safe than sorry.

She leans close, as if afraid he won't be able to hear her otherwise.

"Thank God you stopped!"

She's in her forties, not much older than him, with short brown hair and glasses. There's a gash on her forehead, a line of blood running down the left side of her nose. Some of the blood has dripped onto her white blouse, the splotches a bright, startling red in the glow of his headlights. He looks to the right, sees a blue Ford Explorer in the ditch, headlights off, engine not running, its front end pressed against a wooden telephone pole. The pole lists to the side somewhat, as if the vehicle's impact knocked it askew—assuming there *was* an impact. The Explorer doesn't look damaged from what he can see, and the "blood" on the woman's face could easily have been faked.

"They forced me off the road," she says, voice strained, eyes darting back and forth, a frightened animal alert for danger. "They came out of the fields and rushed toward me. I swerved and…" She frowns, reaches up to touch the wound on her forehead, winces, pulls her fingers away, examines the blood on them, a bemused expression on her face. "I must've hit my head on the windshield."

Malcolm looks at the field beyond the Explorer. It's fenced in, the ground flat, grass low, pastureland for cows or sheep, maybe, or land for horses to run on and graze. The field on the other side of the road is the same. Both are empty. Whoever or whatever *they* are, there's no sign of them…if there ever was a *they* in the first place.

"Let me in your car. *Please*. They could be back any moment!"

Malcolm isn't about to let a stranger into his Prius, not without asking a few questions first.

"What ran you off the road?"

"I'm not sure. They were like dogs, except they were bigger—a *lot* bigger—and they...they..."

He knows what she'll say next. He hopes he's wrong, but he isn't.

"...walked on their hind legs, like a human."

"Dogmen." He barely whispers the word.

His eyes dart back and forth, but he sees no sign of the creatures. Why would they drive this woman off the road and then not attack her? Are they playing games, tormenting the woman? Or—he fears this is most likely—were they waiting for him to arrive?

He then looks deeply into the woman's eyes, searching for any hint of deception. It would be an easy thing to pull your vehicle into a ditch to make it seem it had been in an accident. Maybe a prank played on a hapless driver, to be recorded and uploaded to the Internet or a ploy to get people to stop so the woman's friends can rush out from wherever they're hiding and rob the driver. In other words, a *trap*, of one kind or another. Malcolm's too smart to fall for it, though. He intends to raise his window, drive off, and let the woman wait for the next potential victim to come along—while he calls 911, of course—but before he can do this, shadowy figures rise from the ditch around the Explorer and start moving toward his car.

He knows these figures, has felt the baleful intensity of their yellow eyes, inhaled their thick, musky-sour scent, heard the low threatening rumble of their growls.

He takes his foot off the brake, jams it onto the gas. The Prius lurches forward, the woman jumps back, afraid she might get knocked down, and the dark figures start running, clawed hands outstretched. As Malcolm roars away from the scene of the "accident," he keeps his gaze focused on the road in front of him, refuses to look up at the rearview mirror, doesn't want to witness the scene spotlighted in the red glow of his departing taillights. He hears the woman scream, the dogmen howl with savage delight, and he turns on the radio, cranks the volume as high as it will go, drives on.

He shouldn't have left the woman alone with the dogmen. If it had been a trap, why would they have attacked her as he left, why would she have screamed? No, she'd been telling him the truth. He should've let her get in his car and driven her away from those things. He doesn't question whether the creatures are real. He learned a long time ago not to trust anything, and that includes what most people think of as reality. He should go back, try to help her. He turns off the radio, and the resulting silence seems as loud as the music was.

"She's probably dead," he says.

But how could they kill her? Their teeth and claws are plastic, and not particularly sharp.

"They could've taken off their costumes. Whatever is underneath could've killed her."

They're your dogmen. You dream them. That makes you responsible for them.

He doesn't buy that logic, but he turns around in the next farmer's driveway he comes to and heads back, driving fast, the scars where Bear bit him burning like acid.

Malcolm is six. He's sitting on the floor of his family's living room, playing a video game—*Mega Man 4*—his back against the couch, legs crossed, tongue sticking partway out of his mouth, brow furrowed in concentration as he works the controller. Bear, the family dog, is lying on the couch behind him. Bear isn't supposed to be on the couch. He's a big dog, an Airedale, and Mom doesn't want him scratching the fabric. Bear is Malcolm's buddy, though, so when no one else is around, he lets him sneak onto the couch where Bear always stretches out with a contented sigh.

On the TV screen, a Gachappon appears and attacks Mega Man, but Malcolm isn't worried. He knows a Drill Bomb will stop it easily. But before

he can use the weapon, he senses sudden movement behind him, hears Bear snarl—a sound he's never heard the dog make before—then feels points of pressure on both the front and back of his head. Pressure becomes fire as Bear bites down, teeth piercing thin, tender flesh, and Malcolm releases a high-pitched shriek that is as much a cry of surprise and betrayal as it is pain.

Thirty-seven stitches in all.

Boy's lucky, the doctor tells Malcolm's parents. *His hair will hide the worst of the scarring.*

Malcolm doesn't feel lucky, but he says nothing. On the ride home from the hospital, Mom and Dad debate what to do about Bear.

"Thank God he's had his rabies shots," Mom says.

"Malcolm must've done something," Dad says. "Bear's a gentle dog. He'd never do something like that unless he was provoked."

"Are you saying Malcolm *made* Bear bite him?"

Mom and Dad continue arguing once they're home. Mom thinks they should rehome Bear, but Dad thinks she's overreacting. There's something about that word—*overreacting*—that sends Mom into a fury, and the two of them go to their bedroom so Malcolm won't have to hear them yell at each other, but of course he still can. Malcolm's alone in the living room. Bear's tied to a stake in the backyard, and Malcolm's glad. He wouldn't feel safe with Bear in the house, especially when Mom and Dad aren't around. He's scared of Bear now, sure, but it's more than that. He doesn't *trust* Bear anymore.

One good thing about his parents fighting: There's no one around to tell him what he can and can't watch on cable. He sits on the floor—he doesn't want to sit on the couch, not yet, maybe not ever—grabs the remote and turns on the television. If he was a teenager, he might have gone looking for R-rated movies in hope of seeing naked breasts, but he's six, so he scrolls through the on-screen menu until he comes to a movie called *Night Scream*. He loves horror movies, the scarier, the better. Who cares if they give him nightmares? They're totally worth it.

He selects the movie, which has already started, but he hasn't missed much, maybe five minutes or so. He didn't pay attention to the description on the menu, so when one of the characters—a hunter walking around in the woods at night with a shotgun—is attacked by a hairy monster with a canine face, Malcolm's shocked. *It's a dog,* he thinks. *A monster dog. Just like Bear.* He can't take his eyes off the screen as the creature rakes the hunter's face with its claws, and then sinks its teeth into the man's neck and tears out his throat. At least, that's what Malcolm thinks is supposed to happen. But the monster dog costume is so cheap that none of its features move. Its face is clearly a plastic mask—eyes that don't blink, mouth that remains frozen open—so the actor inside can only pretend to bite the other actor's throat. The effect isn't any more convincing than the creature costume, but despite that—okay, for some weird reason because of that—the scene is scary, *really* scary, like something out of a nightmare. Malcolm continues watching, transfixed, not realizing that he's trembling.

As the movie progresses, Malcolm learns the monster is called a dogman, and that this story takes place in Ohio, which is extra creepy because that's where Malcolm lives. He doesn't pay attention to the movie's plot much, but in his defense, the script isn't that great and the story's hard to follow. At first, it seems like there's only one dogman, but then it turns out there's a pack of them. The dogmen aren't shown much throughout most of the movie, which makes sense given their truly awful costumes, but at the film's climax, when the hero of the movie—a local veterinarian—teams up with a retired sheriff to battle the monsters, all the dogmen are clearly visible. Malcolm scoots close to the screen so he can examine their suits. He can easily see the lines where the masks, gloves, and boots end, and there are easy-to-spot zippers running down their backs.

After the battle, the sheriff is dead, as are all the dogmen. The vet's badly injured, and on the way to the hospital, he turns into a dogman—complete with a terrible mask covering his head—in the back of the paramedic van. The medics scream as he attacks, and that's The End. Roll credits.

As names scroll by on the screen, Malcolm sits silently, trying to process what he's watched. He doesn't hear his parents yelling anymore, but they're still

in their bedroom. Maybe they've stopped fighting and are having what Mom calls *Mommy-Daddy Time.* He thinks about something the sheriff said in the movie.

No one knows where dogmen come from. Maybe they were human once, like you and me. Maybe they were dogs or wolves. Maybe they are dogs most of the time, living with us until they're ready to kill...and when that happens, they change.

—

He finds blood-slick bones with only a few meager scraps of flesh left on them scattered across the road.

He frowns then. The closest bone to him is a femur—at least, that's what he thinks it is. It's been a long time since he took anatomy in college. Something about it doesn't look right, but he's not sure what. He nudges it with his foot. He expects it to make a clattering sound on the asphalt, but it's softer, almost like...

He crouches, reaches out to touch the bone.

It's plastic.

There's blood on his fingers now, and he raises them to his face, sniffs, licks.

Corn syrup and red food coloring.

He hears laughter then, made by multiple voices. Eight of them, he guesses. He stands, looks around, sees no one. The laughter continues, grows louder.

—

"Malcolm, do you know where Bear is?"

Malcolm is sitting on the floor, playing *Mega Man 4.* He doesn't look up as he answers Mom's question.

"He's in the back yard."

"No, he's not. Someone untied the rope around his neck and let him loose. That same someone left the fence door open."

Better safe than sorry, he thinks.

Malcolm looks at his mother, concern in his voice as he asks, "He'll come back, won't he?"

But inside, he smiles.

Bear never returns.

He dreams of the dogmen that night. It's the first of many such dreams throughout the course of his life, and they're always the same—except for their ending. The first time when they remove their masks, they're all real dogmen underneath. The second time they have Bear's head. The third time they have Malcolm's. The fourth time there's only empty space beneath their masks. Those four endings cycle over and over, in no specific sequence, and Malcolm never knows which he's going to get. It doesn't matter. He hates them all.

The scars on his head—which *are* hidden by his hair, the doctor was right—itch sometimes, and when they do, he scratches them without thinking. Some of the kids tease him about having dandruff when that happens. He doesn't care. He doesn't have friends, doesn't want them. People only pretend to be your friend until they decide they want to hurt you, just like Bear.

Fuck 'em.

He's thirty-six now, and he works as a health inspector. Too many businesses don't give a shit about regulations, try to cut corners to save a buck. He's happy to expose the bastards. He's never been married, never had a serious relationship. He's been told by more than one person that he has *trust issues.*

Fuck 'em.

He realizes that he's made a mistake. He trusted *himself*–his perceptions, his intuition. If he'd just kept driving and gone home, he would've been fine. He could've continued to live his life as an untrusting sonofabitch and died a bitter old man. But now...

The woman's Ford Explorer is still there, and for the first time since returning, he notices there's something on the hood. Scared but compelled, he climbs down into the ditch, walks to the front of the vehicle, and finds a mask waiting for him. Like the dogmen's, this mask is cheaply made. Unlike the others, it was made to resemble a specific breed of dog. An Airedale, in fact. He gazes at it for a long time, and then he realizes the laughter has stopped. There's a hush in the air, a tense atmosphere of anticipation.

"Everything's fake," he says to the mask, "isn't it? Including me."

The mask doesn't reply, but does Malcolm see an approving glint in its plastic eyes? Maybe.

He slips the mask over his head, and his brothers step out of the shadows to congratulate him.

11 March 1996

"'Dogmen'. He barely whispers the word."

The typical range of the dogman was mostly confined to Michigan in the late 19th-century. However, reports such as this one suggest that these werewolf-like creatures had successfully established new packs and were well-established in the adjoining state of Ohio by the early 1990s. The shift in sightings aligns with a southward migration that started in the 1930s with the earliest documented instance in Ohio occurring in 1972. This report places a dogman in Defiance, three hundred miles south of the 1967 sighting in Cross Village, Michigan. In response to finding this memoir, I spent the better part of June 1995 scouring the backwoods of Michigan and Ohio for signs of the dogmen alongside one other agent.

The dogman is only seen at night and has been known to walk bipedally or on all fours. Delayed transformation linked to puncture wounds by infected animals. Using this information, we set up in deer stands in areas where animal attacks had been reported and kept vigil for a total of seventeen nights before we saw anything of import. My old bones were aching, and I was almost ready to give it up and return to the motel when I heard a scuffling sound not far from where I was hidden among the trees. Not two minutes after, one of them stepped from the bushes and stood as plain as day beneath the moon. Although my glimpse was brief, I was certain these creatures were no myth. Also certain was I, that if I moved in the slightest, or if the wind turned, I would be detected and that would be the end of it. The dogman was terrifying—from the

serrated edges of his claws to the burning fury seated deep within his eyes—I made the decision to terminate the investigation until better prepared. Level 7 classification, aggressive when provoked, inhabits border of populated areas.

Sorensen

Ogopogo
Lake Monster

Lake
Okanagan

UMBRA ARCA CASE FILE

Ogopogo Lake Monster

Lake Okanagan, British Columbia, Canada

Eyewitness Report #NW50:186-31:24996

Latitude: 49° 50' 1.86'' N
Longitude: 1119° 31' 24.996'' W

This report follows up the claim by Tom and Bobby Chambers.
The brothers spotted the Ogopogo monster from their canoe in
the 135-kilometre-long Lake Okanagan. The sighting occurred
at approximately 7:45 a.m. on Tuesday, May 6, 1986. The
serpentine creature surfaced in the middle of the lake just
south of Rattlesnake Island (a.k.a. Monster Island).

"The wind whipped up early that morning. The water was
choppy, so we decided to head back. We rounded Squally Point,
and the lake went calm. Right then, we both saw it - four
humps in a row," says Bobby Chambers. "It must've noticed us
'cause it took off fast and went underwater."

"It's true. I saw it too. Left our canoe bobbing in a wake
a half-metre high," says Tom Chambers. "Maybe higher."

This eyewitness account confirms evidence recorded near
Squally Point for more than a century. Today, the creature
is called the Ogopogo monster, but the Syilx natives call it
by a different name - "N'ha-a-itk" ("Water Demon").

Sonar confirms that Lake Okanagan reaches a maximum depth of 232 metres, a habitat that could easily support this monster, which purportedly reaches up to 25 metres in length. Chambers' descriptions of this sea serpent align with other reports. The Ogopogo monster has been known to whip up the lake surface with its long tail, and many people have been drowned by these sudden squalls. Tom and Bobby Chambers can consider themselves lucky that they weren't sucked to the bottom of the lake like so many others who have seen this creature.

July 18, 1986
Archivist N. Anderos

UMBRA  ARCA
CASE   NOTE

AGENT No. _____

THE TIME THAT IS LEFT
Sarah Read
Lake Michigan, USA

THE SKY STRETCHED LARGE OVER THE LAKE. Maddie found it difficult to tell how far away the storm was. It was close enough that the air smelled electric, but too far off for her to hear its rumble. She eyed the dark horizon, disoriented. It made the morning feel like evening, like time had warped, to see darkness in the east. But there was still a long day ahead.

"Mads, do you have our waters?" Allie asked.

Maddie took her eyes from the horizon and checked the bag in her kayak's cargo. "Yeah, I've got them. Do you have Dad?"

Allie held up a nylon sack that bulged in the shape of their father's urn.

"It's going to be weird going there without him." Maddie couldn't look at the urn. It unnerved her to think of someone as big and real as her father so diminished.

"We're not," Allie said, waving the bag in the air between them.

"You know what I mean."

"I think it will help, to see a familiar place. To see the island hasn't changed, that some things never change." Allie tucked the bag carefully into her own kayak.

"Well, I hope you brought a change of socks this time."

Maddie triple-checked her bags and hauled her kayak through the reed-studded sand toward the water.

"Only freaks wear socks to the beach." Allie dragged her craft behind her sister's.

They'd had to leave a lot of gear back at the cabin. And the third kayak.

Their father would have carried their tent and bedding, all the food. Now they carried him. They'd divided the load as best they could, but there were no extras, no comforts. *It's only a short trip,* Maddie reminded herself. Just long enough to scatter their father's ashes in the place he loved best—at the fishing dock on St. Martin Island in the heart of northern Lake Michigan.

A gale warning hovered in Maddie's notifications, but it wasn't set to go into effect until the afternoon. They could beat it if they rowed hard.

More concerning were the rip currents that threaded like ribbons past the break, promising hard work and strained shoulders.

"We're going to get rained on," Allie said, finally noticing the ominous sky.

"If we hurry, we can get the tent pitched first."

They waded their boats into the shallows, climbed in, and aimed their bows toward open water.

Waves kicked up and caught the sun, arcing aqua and falling back to a darker blue, laced with foam. The scent of wind and stone and algae, of gulls and fish and driftwood, washed away the scent of exhaust and human industry. Maddie filled her lungs for what felt like the first time in years.

"That's coming in quick," Allie said, breaking her rowing rhythm as she stared at the sky instead of the rough water.

The wind had already knocked Maddie's hair loose from its tie, and the spray off the wave caps was so thick it might as well be raining already.

They had rowed against the current for three hours and should be over halfway to their landing, but Maddie felt, deep in her internal compass, that something was off. That the current had carried them too far off course.

Allie must have felt the same unease, as she pulled her boat in close to Maddie's.

"Hold onto me; I'm going to check."

Maddie stowed her oar, grateful for a break from rowing, and gripped Allie's kayak while she fumbled in her vest for her phone.

Allie held her phone in one hand and pulled at her rowing glove with her teeth. She leaned over the side of her kayak and spit into the water.

"What's wrong?" Maddie asked.

Allie stared at her glove, then touched her fingers with the tip of her tongue before shuddering. "It's salty."

"What?"

"Salt water."

Maddie shook her head. "You must be really sweaty. Gross."

"No, look." Allie pushed her hand toward Maddie's face. Maddie let go of Allie's boat to get away from her sister's hand, just as a wave hit them broadside.

Allie shrieked. Maddie steadied her own boat, then reached for Allie's, but Allie was bent over, arms tucked down by her feet. "Dammit, Maddie!"

"What?"

"I dropped my phone in the hull." She pulled the dripping phone up from between her feet. She shook it and blew in the ports, pressed the button to try and bring it to life. The screen flickered grey and then blackened. "Fuck."

Allie tossed the phone back into the hull.

"Wait, get it back out, we might be able to save it." Maddie pulled her sister's boat closer.

"No point. I was going to trash it soon, anyway. But you should check yours. See where we are and where this storm is."

"But what if your doctor calls?"

Allie tensed, her lips pursed shut.

"Fine. Whatever. They can call me if they need to reach you." Maddie patted her vest pockets, trying to remember which one held her phone.

Allie held on to Maddie's boat. "They're not going to call. I already talked to them."

Maddie's hands lost their grip on her pocket zipper. "And?"

Allie shook her head. "Can we talk about it later? When we're not lost and drifting into a storm?"

Maddie nodded, a knot rising in her throat. She pulled her phone free and opened her map. Nothing loaded. The pink dot that should mark her location flickered, surrounded by a screen of grey that warped like static. None of the islands appeared, not even Washington Island, which should have loomed behind them.

The knot in Maddie's throat unraveled into tendrils of panic.

"No reception," Maddie said, her voice coarse. Her eyes stung. She licked her lips and tasted salt.

Allie looked to the sky. The thick layer of clouds had moved in, blocking the sun and creating a milky ambient light that cast no shadows. "What are we going to do?"

"Keep rowing. This part of the lake is full of islands. Even if we miss St. Martin, we're bound to find another."

Maddie caught her breath when the kayak dipped between swells, then held it as she crested each wave, and the roar of wind knocked into her, blasting spray across her face like stinging buckshot. Allie clung to the end of the rope tied to Maddie's kayak, her own boat distant enough that they wouldn't impact, close enough that they wouldn't lose each other in the erratic currents. Maddie paddled as if she could beat the waves down, using the storm's surge to try and regain her sense of direction. The storm had come in from the southeast. She kept the waves at an angle to her right, hoping that would keep her in line with her northeast destination, knowing still that they were blown far off course.

A wall of water rose in front of her, bottle-green in the storm-light. A dark shape moved through the arched wave, massive, twisting, and it lunged for Maddie just as her boat skirted the break and the water fell away beneath her, taking the dark mass with it. She shook stinging water from her eyes and searched for any sign of the shape. She scanned for a fin, a tail, a wake. Allie's kayak still trailed behind Maddie; her paddling weak and half-hearted.

A rugged shape jutted out of the water to her left. A scream rose in Maddie's throat, but she choked it down. The shape didn't move with the water. The waves crashed against it. It was some kind of land or platform—something they could hold onto till the storm passed.

Maddie rowed toward it with renewed energy, her eyes scanning for the shape in the waves. Twice something nudged the bottom of her kayak, a sharp bump that she couldn't attribute to rough water. She pulled harder, moving herself and her sister closer to the rocky outcrop.

It was all jagged limestone and gnarled trees. Maddie waited for another swell to push her close to the rocks and the ropey tree root she hoped to grab. Her shoulders burned with the effort, and she was sure she'd torn muscles

with endless hours of rowing through waves. Allie had given up, exhausted, and slouched in her kayak, holding on to the rope that tied their boats together. Their father had done the same for them when they were younger. They'd always arrived at St. Martin with their kayaks tied like train cars, their father, the engine, pulling them to the station. Allie had been the first to row the whole way herself, and had even helped to pull Maddie once. But illness sapped her strength. The lump in Maddie's throat returned, and she wanted to wake her sister up and ask her what the doctor had said.

Maddie shook her head free of worries and salt water and focused on the tree root. She grasped it as the waves lifted her, and she summoned all the strength left in her shoulders to pull herself up onto the rocks. She jumped free of the cockpit and grabbed the rope tied to her boat before the swell of waves dropped away. She anchored herself against the stones and pulled, hauling Allie's kayak close to the shore.

"Allie! Grab the root, and I'll help pull you up."

Allie lifted her head and slowly made sense of the plan. Maddie's heart ached at the sight of her sister's weary face. Only a few years ago, she'd have surfed her boat through those waves like they were a playground.

Allie grabbed the tree root, and Maddie hauled the weight of the boat while Allie pulled herself, and soon they were both lying, tumbled out on a jutting sheet of limestone.

Maddie caught her breath and pushed herself to sit. "Well, it's not St. Martin."

Allie sat up beside her, scanning the rocky shoreline and the tall pole trees that crowded up to where stone met water. "What if it's private property? I don't want to piss off some rich Yooper on their private island."

Maddie half smiled, but she couldn't peel her eyes from the vegetation. The shrubs weren't the wispy brush she was used to, but lush broad-leafed ferns that arced tall over spreading vines. The tall poles of trees were not the wind-blown spruce she was used to camping under but scaled palms with jagged canopies.

"Wherever we are, we should get out of the wind," Maddie said. She flexed her stiff legs and pushed herself to stand, pulling Allie up beside her. They grabbed their kayaks and dragged them over the stones to the tree line. Maddie saw her own confusion reflected in Allie's face as the strange vegetation came into focus.

"Okay, this is definitely some rich bastard's island retreat. Like some kind of botanical garden." Allie pushed a broad frond out of the way so Maddie could pull their gear through.

"Yeah, well, let's hope he's got piña coladas."

They found a level break in the brush, the ground padded with moss and mushrooms and more flowering vines.

Maddie's arms shook, as she bent their tent poles into the sockets.

The rain had slowed to a soft shower, but the tent nylon was soaked. Their sleeping bags were soaked. Their shoes and clothes and even the bag containing their father had been drenched by blowing water. But it was a blessedly warm night, and Maddie didn't think any amount of damp would keep her from sleeping.

████████

Dawn came filtered through steaming air and with a symphony of countless insects. Maddie woke to swollen shoulders that seared with pain as she tried to sit.

Allie was already awake, sitting next to her, pale and drawn.

Maddie lifted a shaking arm to her pack in the corner of the tent and pulled out two water bags, handing one to Allie.

"Did you get any rest?" Maddie asked.

"I couldn't sleep. Did you see it out there? I have no idea where the hell we are."

"These islands will be crawling with tourists all weekend. And now the storm has passed, we'll be able to navigate back on course." Maddie felt sure she could figure out their location, get them back on track. She felt less sure she could endure another day of rowing.

"No, Maddie. Those palm trees, the salt water. I saw the biggest fucking black cockroaches I've ever seen when I went out to pee. We're not on the lake."

"Allie, there's no way we're not still somewhere on Lake Michigan. I admit I don't know where. But we never left the lake."

"Listen."

"No, you listen, Allie—"

"No, not to me, just listen." She put a finger to her lips.

Insects chirped a cacophony. Waves hit the rocks. "So? What?"

"No birds. No animals. Just big-ass bugs."

Maddie sighed, reached for her vest and pulled her phone out of the pocket again. The screen glowed to life, but the map still wouldn't load. Neither would her email, or any social media apps.

Allie lunged for the tent entrance and threw herself outside, rushing to the bushes to vomit.

Maddie followed her, bringing more water. "What's wrong? Is it nerves? We'll be okay..."

"No, it's not nerves." Allie took the water bag and drank deeply.

"Is it because of what your doctor told you that you won't tell me?"

Allie nodded.

Maddie's stomach twisted. "Should you even be out here? Allie, you should have said something. This could have waited."

"No. It couldn't have waited. We needed to do this for Dad. And later this summer, you can do it again. For me."

Maddie shook her head, eyes stinging as if they were back in the heart of the storm. She was too exhausted to hold back the sob that fought its way up her throat.

"I'm going to go pack our camp. Why don't you walk around? See if you can find any clue about where the fuck we are." Allie turned back toward the path they'd worked through the vegetation.

Maddie stumbled through the vines and ferns to the rocky shore, choking on the sobs she didn't want Allie to overhear.

The lake had calmed, but waves lapped the rocks that formed the edge of the beach. She stared out across the water. The sun was behind her, casting her shadow toward the swells, so she should be facing Washington Island. There was a definite shadow to the west. Some darkening to the horizon that must be more land. Her arms ached to think of it, but she knew if they rowed straight for it, they could reach it before dark. They could go home, and Allie could rest. They could bring Dad back out next summer, when things were better.

Maddie calmed her ragged breaths and turned back to camp, faced again with the strangeness of the trees and greenery. Enormous insects scurried away from her steps through the undergrowth. She shuddered.

Allie had their bags packed and stowed, the kayaks roped together and ready to set out.

"I see land to the west. It's probably Washington Island. We'll head that direction and figure things out from there."

"What about Dad?"

"Allie, now's not the time—"

"Now is literally the only time I've got, Maddie."

"It's not worth risking—"

"Risking what? What's left to lose?"

Maddie's tight throat cut off her voice.

"If we're going to Washington Island, we'll pass right by St. Martin. We can stop there on the way. Just for an hour or so."

Maddie took a deep breath and nodded once. "If we pass it. If we see it."

Allie dragged their boats through the vines and out onto the rocks. "Gonna be a soggy drop into the water."

Maddie stared over the edge of the rocks to the waves. It wasn't a long drop—just five feet—but enough to make a splash. Everything would be soaked again. "Better get started."

They weren't fifty yards from shore when Maddie felt the first bump against the bottom of her kayak. She turned to Allie. "Did you feel..."

"What?" Allie asked.

"Something bumped my boat. I felt it last night, too."

They peered over the sides of their kayaks, but the morning sun reflected off the choppy water in a thousand points of light, and it was impossible to see through the glare.

Allie shrieked. Her kayak splashed as it reconnected with the water. The waves around them darkened and then lightened again.

"It's a sturgeon, right? It's got to be a sturgeon," Maddie said.

"I'd agree. If we were on the lake."

Maddie shot Allie a glare. "Stop it. We cast out on the lake. We never left the lake. We're still on the lake."

Allie reached into the water and scooped a big splash right into Maddie's face.

Maddie choked and spluttered. Her lips and eyes burned. "Dammit, Allie!"

"Salt water. This is the ocean."

"Look, I know I paddled pretty fucking hard last night while you took a nap in your kayak, but I don't think I dragged us all the way to the goddamn ocean."

Allie pointed to the sky then. "Still no birds. The sky should be full of gulls so close to the islands. Pelicans, too. Herons, plovers...nothing."

"Let's just move, Allie. We'll feel better once we get somewhere familiar."

"Maddie, I don't think we're lost some*where*. I think we're lost some*when*."

The sun was getting hot, and Maddie's face heated in frustration. She turned away from Allie and rowed hard, feeling the tug of the tow rope to her sister's boat.

"A salt sea in the Michigan basin? Big-ass bugs and no birds or mammals? Giant fucking fish?" Allie joined in the rowing, punctuating each point with the splash of a paddle.

"You're sick," Maddie said. "You're confused and not feeling well. I'm taking you home if I have to drag you the whole way."

The shadow darkened the water beneath them again.

"Ever seen a one-ton sturgeon? Because I'm pretty sure even the big ones are a tenth that size."

Maddie ignored her and rowed harder, her shoulders burning, her teeth gritted. She locked her eyes on the horizon and its faint promise of land.

Their father had plastered his study walls with posters of the prehistoric lake. He collected the crinoids and trilobites, the Petoskey stones lining his bookshelves full of the geologic history of how the Devonian sea had become a glacial freshwater lake.

She's having a breakdown, Maddie thought. Grief and stress and anxiety. Who wouldn't? Maddie felt her irritation melt away, replaced with a determination to take care of her sister, to get her safely home.

Her kayak lurched and spun. Hard water shocked her frame as her boat flipped. She gripped her paddle and slipped from the cockpit, reaching up to spin her boat so she could climb back in before whatever had flipped her could snatch at her exposed legs. Her hands waved in the water, but she couldn't feel her kayak. She pried her eyes open. There—its bright red hull floating just above her, out of reach. And below her, a thirty-foot body, gnarled and grey, coated in segmented plates with a jaw like a sabered beak. Razor fins lined its thick body, whipping the creature around to lunge at her again.

Maddie screamed a curtain of bubbles and hauled herself back into her boat. She choked on air that turned seawater to spray in her throat. "*Row*," she rasped at Allie.

They paddled faster, but soon Allie's boat jumped again.

Instead of screaming, she laughed.

"Allie!"

Allie steadied her boat. "Dad would think this was so cool," she said.

Maddie shook, staring at her sister. She began to wonder if she was the one having the breakdown—if this was a nightmare and she was lying feverish in a tent on St. Martin, still waiting to wake up.

Allie bent and dug through the cargo in her cockpit. She pulled out the nylon bag and lifted Dad out of it.

"Allie, what are you doing? Row!" Maddie paddled faster but couldn't look away from her sister.

Allie unscrewed the top of the urn.

"Stop it, Allie!"

"This is even better than fishing crappies off the end of a dock." She tossed the urn lid into the water.

Where it splashed, enormous, armored jaws emerged, snapping at the air.

Maddie screamed and finally tore her gaze from Allie. She turned and rowed, rowed as if her shoulders weren't breaking, as if she could outlast this nightmare. The tow rope stretched tight, as she dragged Allie behind her.

The soft sound of powder dropping into the water came from behind.

Maddie chanced a glance back, and saw Allie pouring their father's remains into the dark water. A sob caught in her throat. *At least we can skip the layover on St. Martin.*

Her kayak lurched again, and this time she felt it lifted and carried forward on the back of the creature before it dove below again.

Maddie gritted her teeth and rowed harder. The splash of the urn hitting the water sounded behind her, and again the creature breached and snapped at the offering.

"Amazing," Allie said.

Maddie rowed harder.

"You can't row faster than a Dunkleosteus can swim, Maddie. It won't stop hunting till it's fed."

Maddie's throat burned, as she panted in the sea spray, her arms burned as she pushed them past their limits, pulling at the tow rope, determined.

Then she shot forward, the weight of the rope released. Her kayak skimmed the water with the momentum she'd built up. She stopped rowing and spun, panic turning her face numb.

Allie grinned at her from her kayak, the cut end of the rope still in her hands. Her paddle floated on the water out of reach. "Row, dummy," Allie said. "I don't know if you can row all the way to the twenty-first century again, but if anyone can, it's you." She stood up in the cockpit, arms outstretched to the sky.

"Allie, no!"

"Come back fishing next summer, okay? Bring a big goddamn net."

Maddie's scream stuck in her throat as Allie leapt out of her boat. She hit the waves with a graceful splash that set the water rippling, set Maddie's boat to rocking gently, until the Devonian jaws emerged again, sluicing sheets of red water over its armored plates. It breached and splashed, and the wave it cast set Maddie's kayak shooting forward.

She sobbed, and turned, and rowed, and sobbed and rowed, her eyes on the horizon and her back to the past, praying for the future, for any future at all.

UMBRA   ARCA
CASE   NOTE

AGENT No. _____

Louis Ghost Train
(aka St. Louis Ghost Light)

UMBRA ARCA CASE FILE

St. Louis Ghost Light
Prince Albert, Saskatchewan, Canada

Centennial Survey #NW54-48:5999

Latitude: 52° 54' 59.99" N
Longitude: -105° 48' 59.99" W

Paranormal sightings of the Louis Ghost Train (St. Louis Ghost Light) persist in the Canadian village of St. Louis, a rural community located south of Prince Albert in the province of Saskatchewan. Reports place the location of the ghost light along the site of abandoned railroad tracks. Although the rails have long since been removed, historical markers placed during the initial investigation confirm the route.

Night mission records are enclosed. As shown therein, the Louis Ghost Train made an appearance every night for the duration of one full moon to the next. Time stamps of the sightings remain consistently within the time frame of an hour before and an hour after the strike of midnight. No differences observed at the sighting during the autumn equinox.

The white light appears without warning. Luminous flux remains static across multiple sightings. The smaller, red light was present during 87 percent of the observations. Findings confirm the potential match of the white light as

consistent with train engines of the time period. The white
light stays fixed in place according to the preferred align-
ment of a 4-8-2 steam locomotive. In contrast, the red light
bobs in an erratic fashion between ground level and 1.5
metres, which correlates with the legend of the conductor
searching for his head with the aid of a kerosene lantern.
Evidence suggests he has yet to find it.

Identity of the conductor reputed to have been beheaded while
examining the tracks remains a mystery. The railway's files
on the incident have been lost or destroyed. Resident and
tourist reports align with agency recordings (see attached
documentation).

EVP recorder did not register sounds related to the appearance of the phenomenon. EMF meter findings are promising, but
inconclusive. Thermal images attached. Diffraction from nearby
roadway ruled out. Further study required.

Agent C. Morrison
31 October 2020

UMBRA ARCA
CASE NOTE

AGENT No _____

FAN TAN ALLEY

Once a popular gambling district.

CINNABAR

Colleen Anderson

Victoria, British Columbia, Canada

The bricks of Fan Tan Alley hold their history dear—
gambling halls, opium dens press close together
their acrid and somnolent smoke wafts through
busy brothels—oh the stories they can tell of Gold
Rush years and the Chinese men who came
to build the great Canadian Pacific Railway

This lane, so narrow one can reach from doorways
to touch the other side, embraces merchant shops
steamy kitchens feeding hungry laborers
as do the captive sing-song girls—so the rumor goes

A sloe-eyed dove leans out the window showing off
her trade, a vermillion comb adorns her splendid hair
with carved red lacquer bangles about her birdlike wrists
the men who come to admire her feed her more than money
upon their adulation she thrives, soaking up their spirits

She may once have had another name besides
that of a hundred men's wife, this flower girl
they've named Cinnabar as much for her ornaments
as her sharp and acid wit, and men exiting befuddled—
depleted after being ministered a certain exquisite death

Cinnabar has not yet been poxed from the plying
of her wares, her startling scarlet, and lustrous ebon hair
draw every man's attention, even Chung a young cook
who cleans, chops and cooks the meals every day he watches
this caged bird he hopes to spring, and imagines her still pure

One day Cinnabar gazes at each man strolling by her perch
time to time she pats a head, giggles when they turn to look
Chung, carrying a chicken, navigates the narrow lane
she winks at him and smiles but does the same to several men
he stops as sunshine polishes her hair—she is his eternal light

He will have her, knots a ribbon as a poor man's tie—it's all he can do
Cinnabar, he cries, and clasps her hand, you are all
that I desire...marry me, I love you, I need you as my wife
Cinnabar hesitates, then she laughs, pulling back her hand
you can't afford me, Chung, nor the jewelry that I crave
be on your way, I'm needed here, and here is where I'll stay

Chung falls against rough hewn bricks as workers wander by
spurned, he storms back to butchering hapless pigs and chickens
he hacks and slams the cleaver so it sticks in bone and wood
no matter how hard he works he hears Cinnabar's contempt
her voice lilts down the alley as she calls to other patrons

Cleaver in hand, Chung shoulders people walking single file
he squeezes in between, the walls framing his focused sight
on that singing bird—Cinnabar, oblivious, flutters eyes and flirts
Chung grabs her by that glossy hair, the crimson comb tumbling
she shrieks—his blade hacks her neck, fury spent in his blows
as he stands with Cinnabar's head, eyes shocked and staring

Chung wakes to what he's done, drops her head to hide
careening off red brick, he pushes cringing passers-by
the bloody deed revealed, splattered garnet, cleaver dripping
in another part of town he's caught and loops a final necktie

She needs no footnote in history as just a soiled dove
whose name is lost, but Chung will always flee the accusations
tourists feel that frantic thrust as something invisible rushes past
he cannot escape his dreadful act nor her poisonous vapors

Each day Cinnabar hunts Chung whose spirit doesn't dissipate
her rage saturates Fan Tan's russet bricks but she's never seen
and men who come to hear the tale may experience double vision
they feel fatigue and are drained as if their life were leeched

She loves her rich blood jewelry, content to stay in Fan Tan Alley
Cinnabar selects her visitors and filches tiny keepsakes
from their smoky souls to relive her former glories

THINGS TO DO IN PLAYLAND WHEN YOU'RE DEAD

Gwendolyn Kiste

San Francisco, California, USA

1. YUK IT UP WITH LAFFING SAL AT THE FUN HOUSE

It's dusk when you materialize on the amusement park midway. You don't know how you got here—you don't even know who you are—but you're used to that by now. The delirium of being dead.

But even though you can't remember who you are, you know this place. Playland at the Beach. They used to call it the West Coast's answer to Coney Island, the former pride of the Bay City, but these days, nobody calls it much of anything at all. Though the place is still open—for one more night anyhow—half the old rides are already boarded up, the splintered wood bowing over broken windows, the yellowed paint peeling away like rotted flesh.

Still, if you're already here, then the Fun House is always a perfect place to start. It's the star attraction of the amusement park. What's left of it anyhow.

At the front window, you meet Laffing Sal, who always lives up to her name. She's the giant animatronic clown that never stops smiling, her wide eyes staring out through the glass. It doesn't matter where you are in the park—nobody can ever escape the sound of that laugh. It follows your every step.

You wave to her as you disappear through the front door.

Inside, the place smells of dust and stale popcorn. You like it more than you should. As you tiptoe through a maze of mirrors, you don't bother to look up at your reflection. You're probably not waiting there for you anyhow. You navigate narrow corridors and romp alone on rides with funny names like Human Laundry and Fun Wheel and Staggering Stairs until you don't know which way is which.

When you're done, you slip back outside and start walking down the midway. Past a row of abandoned games and concession stands that are emptier than your heart and a photobooth that keeps flashing, even though no one's inside. You can go any way you want now, but whatever you do, don't slow down.

And don't look back.

2. RIDE THE DODGER BUMPER CARS (EVEN IF YOU RIDE ALONE)

Take the first car you find. It's bright blue, clear as the ocean that whispers to you across the sea wall. Your thin hands stretched out in front of you, you can't quite grip the wheel—of course, you can't, you're a ghost, what did you expect?—but all the cars start moving anyhow, crashing into each other with a delirious kind of elegance.

One after another, the bumper cars jerk back and forth, worn metal screeching together, and your body going limp as you blink beneath the garish lights, the world becoming a little clearer. Your memories are clearer too. You still don't remember who you are, but you remember other things. Nixon's in the White House, troops are in Vietnam, and the city streets are awash in bell bottoms and pot smoke and the broken promise of free love and peace. There are a lot of broken promises in San Francisco, and Playland's just one more of them.

It's 1972, the end of Labor Day Weekend. The end of Playland too. When the streetlamps go down tonight, that's it—curtains for the year-round carnival at Ocean Beach. The rides will go silent, and so will Laffing Sal, her playful shrieks lodged in the back of her throat, the joy suffocated out of her heart. Out of your heart too.

It didn't have to be like this. In its heyday, thousands of people swarmed this midway, their silhouettes stark as ants in the unforgiving California sun. That was a long time ago now. Everybody who's anybody has heard the news that Playland is closing, but it hasn't made much of a difference. The rides are still empty, the darkness settling like a heavy veil over all the games and concessions. Even nostalgia can't lure the city to this boardwalk anymore.

But you're not entirely alone. There are a couple kids here, one in a green bumper car, another in the red, their tired parents watching nearby behind a rusted metal fence. Out of the corner of their eye, they sometimes see you, just for a moment, just long enough to question themselves, but mostly, you're left

on your own, drifting this way and that, invisible as a lie.

And really, why would anyone see you? You hardly see yourself. Who are you now? You wish you knew. You could be so many different ghosts. Maybe you died in the earthquake that shook the coast. Or maybe you were a hippie on a bad trip in the Haight who never came back down. This city's always had more than its fair share of tragedy. Maybe every city's like that. You can't be sure, because you're dead, which means you don't get to explore those cities. You only get to explore this one.

So let's make the best of it.

When the bumper cars finally lurch to a halt, the two children scurry off, and their parents herd them away. It's dark now, and they're headed home. But you're not sure you've got a home, so you keep going, deeper into Playland.

Deeper into the shadows.

3. Knock down all the fuzzy cats at The Cat Rack

Don't worry; no real-life cats were hurt in the making of this one. The Cat Rack's just a run-of-the-mill shell game, the kind where you toss a baseball and try to knock down a row of makeshift cats limned with fringe and filled with buckshot. It's a silly game, but it's your favorite. Not that you can play it anymore—the same as the wheel of the bumper car, your spectral fingers go right through the ball, your body less than air, less than nothing.

So you watch and wait and hope someone else comes along to play the game, so you can stand beside them, whispering in their ear, pretending you get to play too. But it's the last day of this broken-down amusement park, and there's nobody else left who's eager to have fun.

As the shutters start to fall on the other games, you step back, the night closing in around you. You still wish you knew who you were. There are so many possibilities.

You could be the heiress of Chambers Mansion, who quarreled with her sister before being found cut in two in an upstairs bedroom.

Or the ticket taker from the Curran Theater, murdered on the job back in '33, forever destined to wear his chic usher's uniform.

Or maybe even the Stow Lake Ghost, San Francisco's most famous specter who never stops searching for her lost infant, her tears thicker than ectoplasm, thicker than heartbreak.

You tell yourself you could be any of these phantoms, and maybe you're right. In this moment, it feels like there are a thousand voices bubbling up your ethereal throat, but when you part your lips to speak, no sound comes out.

So you just continue walking, even as the moon disappears from the sky.

4. DO YOUR BEST NOT TO LOOK OVER YOUR SHOULDER

There's nothing behind you, we promise. Or at least there's nothing you want to see.

5. TAKE A RIDE THROUGH LIMBO (AND TRY NOT TO LAUGH AT THE IRONY)

As midnight edges closer, you get in line behind what might be the only two patrons left in Playland. As you wait, a giant skeleton looms over you, its bones in a tangle, its hands folded as if in prayer. You keep staring at it, and it keeps watching you too, through the vast blank sockets where its eyes should be. The skull is so towering, so oppressively huge, you could practically slide through those sockets and disappear to the other side. You wonder what's waiting there. You wonder if you should find out.

Your body starts to drift forward, but a line of blue cars suddenly arrives on a rickety track. Murmuring to yourselves, you and the other patrons climb in. With the push of a button, the weary operator sends you on your way, the darkness ready to gobble you up.

Inside, the ride is fusty and strange, the air smelling of burnt sugar and melancholy. Above you, a witch's latex face drips thick with blood, a collection of baby doll heads lined up in front of her. Her latest kills, you guess. Everywhere you turn, there are tiny imps made of plastic and resin. That's to be expected, you guess. This place is called Limbo after all, and it's certainly living up to its name.

They call this a dark ride, because it's almost pitch-black inside. You get a light here or there, just the flash of it, just enough to see something waiting for you in the gloom.

Mostly, it's silly figures or rotating spirals or even a giant octopus, but on

one wall, it's something else. Something worse. A mural of sorts, arrayed with images of naked bodies, their flesh rotted away, the delicate cages of their ribs exposed for the world to see. They're suspended by ropes, sprawled out on the floor, even tucked inside another giant skeleton's mouth.

And they're all women, dead and nude and trapped in purgatory.

You shake your head, as the car keeps going, as if it was nothing at all. As if we're all meant to forget the women writhing in the afterlife. You can't understand how this place ever got away with a mural like that. The ride was built in the 1950s, in the *Leave It to Beaver* era, those so-called halcyon Eisenhower days when America was supposedly perfect. But in a way, you think Limbo might be onto something. It can see the horrors where they've always been hiding—right here in plain sight.

A final turn, and your car emerges back into the night. "Thank you for riding through Limbo," the operator says in a monotone, as the ride lurches to a stop.

Your head dizzy with darkness, you climb out and stumble through the park, still not sure who you are.

A lovelorn teenager who took a swan dive off the Golden Gate Bridge.

The headmistress who never stops haunting the Queen Anne Hotel.

The nobody, the one who isn't remembered, isn't mentioned on the ghost tours, isn't commemorated in spooky tales around a bonfire.

You think you could be any of them, or none of them at all. How many lives can one ghost lose? Too many to count, you suppose.

The midway stretches out in front of you, a ribbon of shadows, a maze of possibility. You wander along it, and you're sure this time you'll be able to call out, to howl at the moon, to speak to someone, anyone.

But your voice falters again, and you find yourself lost on a familiar path.

6. GO FOR A WHIRL ON THE MERRY-GO-ROUND

When you finally regain your bearings, you find you've circled back around, back to the Fun House, and across the way, you see it.

The carousel, already in motion, the painted figures a beautiful blur before you.

You don't wait for it to slow down. Instead, you close your eyes and materialize aboard the revolving platform. With the music lilting around you, you run your fingers along the frozen animals. Pretty ponies and a skulking tiger and a ram with curly horns. There's even a pale green dragon leading a miniature chariot. You smile, because they're all so glorious and fearsome, their teeth so much sharper than yours, their eyes open wide, scrying into worlds you can't even fathom.

You should probably leave now, the same way almost everyone else has. But you want to visit each remaining ride while you still can. You want to relive this place one more time. That's because you feel like you belong here. Like there's something waiting for you around every corner. A piece of you that's missing. A piece you're almost too afraid to reclaim.

A shadow starts to close in on you, but you won't wait around for it. You're on the midway in a flash, and this time, you don't look back.

7. Try to outrun the darkness that's always one step behind you

Faster now. The evening's wearing down, and you wouldn't want to overstay your welcome.

8. Disappear into the shadows of The Mad Mine

If you can't escape the darkness, perhaps you should simply join it. The Mad Mine's one of the only rides left that you haven't tried tonight, and it's a little like Limbo. It's a dark ride, built of heavy wood, with a sign out front that says Our Monsters Welcome All Visitors.

(You wonder for a moment if you're a monster too. What's a ghost made of anyway?)

You climb aboard, and the ride starts without fanfare. It turns out the operator has sneaked off for another Marlboro, forgetting to flip on the meager lights inside, the ones that are supposed to illuminate the nooks and crannies. Sure, it's a dark ride, but it's not supposed to be this dark.

Yet as you drift through the gloom, you think maybe this isn't so bad. You're a phantom, after all. Shadows are your specialty.

And in here, your last ride at Playland at the Beach—perhaps the last ride

anyone will ever take—the shadows are following you. They dart back and forth, dancing at the edges of your vision, always just out of reach. You even hear a small giggle nearby, though it doesn't sound so bad. It sounds almost welcoming.

You reach out for it, but by the time it starts to reach back, you take the last turn on the track, and you're back out in the night air, all alone all over again.

9. Wander the Midway Until Midnight

Until the lights have faded like distant stars, and all the rest have gone. You should be gone too. Even a ghost ought to have a curfew.

But as you get to the edge of the midway, you seize up, the glimmer of your heart heavy inside you. You know you should keep going. Besides, you only have one rule: to never look back.

But what good is the afterlife if you only spend it following rules?

With the waning September sky above you, you whirl around and stare into what's left of Playland at the Beach. That's when you see them. All the spirits waiting for you. In an instant, something stirs within you, the universe searing through your ephemeral body, and at last, you remember who you are.

You're all the ghosts, every last one of them. Every dirty secret of the Bay City. Every whisper, every tragedy. Every voice that was silenced before its time. Every voice you can now reclaim.

And tonight, you've come to collect a few more, the ones the world wants to leave behind at this rundown amusement park.

But not you. You part your lips, and this time, you find your voice, all the voices, eager and waiting.

"It's all right," you whisper. "You won't be alone now."

You open your arms, and with a soft giggle, the ghosts rush into you. They aren't at all what you expect. They're soft and sweet, the echo of patrons who never wanted to leave, of long ago summers you wished never ended. The specter of Laffing Sal too. All the ghosts of the living and the ghosts of the never-living, of the things we love and lose, of our hopes and dreams, faded and forgotten. Time has a way of erasing everything, but you won't let it. You'll remember this time. You'll remember forever.

Wrapped together as one, the ghosts brim within you, and you tip your head to the sky, as an uncanny aria rises up with the bay mist, everything in you ready, everything in you complete.

And as you disappear down the midway, a final laugh rings out into the air, sharp and jubilant, and for a moment, in the winding streets of San Francisco, you can hear it anywhere.

UMBRA   ARCA
C A S E   N O T E

AGENT No.

DARK WATCHERS

Giant observant entities, described as large silhouettes, who watch travelers from the distant horizon.

Described as wearing top hats and using walking sticks.

Only seen in the hours of twilight or dawn.

LOS VIGILANTES OSCUROS

Angela Yuriko Smith

Santa Lucia Mountains, California, USA

I aim not to be
a gift wrapped in shallow grave.
I keep my eyes down

and never tarry
in the Santa Lucias...
where shadows have eyes.

Hush when you see them.
Towering, they blot the stars
that glimmer awake.

Reflection of us
those without respect get none
from Los Oscuros.

Against the twilight
they appear from silver mist...
like ink stains on smoke.

On the edge of night
framed in red from setting sun.
Los Vigilantes...

those that watch and wait
for the end of times… and us.
Sentinels of shade

they guard the west sea.
Best to hush and hurry through…
away from their gaze.

UMBRA ARCA

C A S E   N O T E

AGENT No. _____

SAND AND SALT

Mercedes M. Yardley

San Rafael Swell, Utah, USA

"YOU DON'T BELONG HERE," Moira said.

Imogen wanted to respond in kind. She wanted to say something like, "The pot is calling the kettle black," or something biblical about motes and beams, or even resorting to the childhood taunt of "I'm rubber and you're glue." But she said nothing. She often said nothing, especially when she had to agree.

This pleased Moira. She floated around Imogen, her ethereal hair waving around her face as she rode the waves in the air. She turned her dead eyes to the harsh desert sun and squinted.

"I don't know why you stay here," she said.

Again, Imogen said nothing, but her heart answered silently for her. *I don't have anywhere else to go.*

Imogen was hiking this morning. She had a baseball cap and a bottle of water as she faced down the San Rafael Swell. She had left sunscreen and her phone behind in her neat little house with its neat little yard back in the tiny town ringed with desert paintbrush and juniper trees. She had hoped to leave Moira, too, but that hadn't happened.

Moira swam through the air, kicking her bare feet through the dusty currents.

"I hate this place," she said. "I wasn't meant to be here. I miss the cliffs and the sea and the moors of Ireland. I miss the scent of salt water, of spray against my face. This place is my private hell."

"You can leave," Imogen said. Her sneakers barely left tracks in the hard red dirt. She smelled sagebrush and stone and the wild things that lived under the ground. She saw cactus flowers and jackrabbit scat. Her skin was brown and hard due to the sun that beat, beat, beat down on her every day. It was relentless. The desert was relentless. The town was relentless.

"You know I can't," Moira said. "You're the last one left of your family line. You belong to me."

"I belong to no one," Imogen said, and the words didn't feel empowering or brave; they just sounded sad. This made her frown. "Maybe you belong to me," she said, and Moira bristled and growled and rent the air with her gray hands.

"Insolence!" she howled. "Disrespect! I am a regal bean sí from Éire, and I will not deign that a mere human should speak to me so!"

She screamed and cried and wailed, opening her mouth horrifically wide in a way that would have chilled Imogen's blood if she hadn't seen it so often. The banshee's voice rolled over the mesas, stopping desert foxes in their tracks and causing mule deer to flee.

Imogen just sighed.

"Sing for me," she said, and Moira stopped mid-curse.

"What?"

"Sing for me. Keen. Herald my death. If you hate it here so badly, let me go and be done with it."

The banshee sniffed. "That isn't how it works."

"Then how exactly does it work?"

"A mortal wouldn't understand such mysteries."

Imogen continued to trek, walking into the sun until her legs shook and her skin felt hot to the touch. But she was still well. She continued to live. Moira floated along behind her, chattering and complaining, but refusing to lift her voice in a death song.

———

Imogen worked at a tiny restaurant in the middle of town. She was quick on her feet and steady with her hands. She smiled, and smiled, and smiled. Waves of power and rage were held back by the bright, shiny pebbles of her white teeth.

"Poison them," Moira suggested. "Make them stop asking you for things. Put a little something special in their meal next time, and you'll be free of this place, servant girl."

Imogen ignored the banshee hovering over the ice cream machine. As usual, it was broken. As usual, everyone wanted ice cream cones and shakes and sundaes. Imogen dipped her head again and again, as she said *I'm sorry. I'm sorry.*

"If they were to die here, would you sing for them?" Imogen asked under her breath. Her face was red from exertion and the heat in the kitchen. Her hair was tied up in a hairnet under a red baseball cap.

"Of course not, child. I would only sing for you."

"Would anyone sing for them? Anyone at all? Are there other banshees here I can't see?"

A heavy hand came down on Imogen's shoulder. It weighed too much and pushed too hard.

"Talking to yourself again, are you, girl? Ain't nothing wrong with you, right? Get your head out of the clouds and back to work."

"Yes, sir," Imogen said demurely, but her eyes flashed fire and lightning and all manner of desert storms. They were fevered and bright.

"No, I'm the only one here," Moira answered, and floated through the window and into the clear blue sky. She missed the storms from home. The black skies, the voices of her sisters as they whirled together in the night. This place was lonely and harsh in a completely different way than the high cliffs.

After her shift ended, Imogen punched her card, gathered her things, and rode her bicycle home. The air was hot and fetid even in the dark. Her house was still full of her parents' old things. Why give them away? Why keep them? Why do anything but curl up in the rooms at night and watch the stars from the window? Why even do that, or really, anything at all?

Day in and day out. A month passed. Two. It was winter, and Orion and his glorious belt were high in the sky.

Sometimes snow graced the sage. It fell hard and fast, and Imogen felt something akin to delight when her car stopped, buried halfway up its wheels on the old desert dirt road. She could see the faint glow of the town miles away.

"You know better than this," Moira chided. She floated outside the car, pressing her face to the driver's side window. Her clear voice cut through like a bell. "You'll freeze if you sit here, and it will take all night to walk back to town."

"I'm not heading to town," Imogen said, and kicked open the car door. It pushed the snow aside, and Imogen clambered out. She pulled her coat tight around her.

"Surely you must be mad," Moira said. She shimmered, ethereal and gray, as beautiful and deadly as the snow itself. She and the white flakes filled the air.

Imogen took a step forward. She left the car door open, the ceiling light glowing weakly. The sound of the flakes pattered on the ground, onto the car seat, into her hair. Her lashes were soon long and voluminous with frozen water.

"Where are you going?" Moira demanded. "What are you doing? Get back in that car and figure out a way to stay warm."

Imogen took another step. Her feet sank in the drifts and soaked her pants halfway to the knee.

"You obstinate child!" Moira shrieked, and back in the small town, children shuddered in their beds when they heard her hideous call.

"I don't understand you," Moira spat. She bobbed along above Imogen, who was taking step after step out into the darkness. She walked by the light of the moon, predatory and bright, and by the light of the stars, which were carnivorous and licked their lips at the sight of her silvery skin. "So many people fight for their lives! They plan and twist and connive. They do horrible things, make deals with the djinn, and sell themselves to the universe. Why are you so intent on throwing yours away?"

"What happens to you if I die?" Imogen's voice came hard as she puffed and gasped. The snow came up to her knees, now, and every step burned her frozen feet like a funeral pyre.

"What?" Moira stopped short. Her face was beautiful and terrible. Her eyes were wide and shattered like glass, and her teeth were sharp needles in her perfect mouth. "Whatever do you mean?"

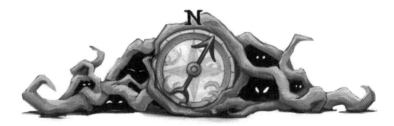

"I mean," huffed Imogen as she struggled, "you followed my family here from Ireland, right? I know you hate it here. You hate it here like I hate it here, but somehow the desert has marked my heart, and I cannot leave. But you? When I, the last descendant from my clan, die, what will happen to you?"

Moira was silent. Her eyes filled with sea. They were the color of froth and foam and stinking dead things that floated in the waves. She turned her face toward home, miles and miles from here.

"Do you go back?" Imogen asked. She was shivering in her thin coat and had stuffed her hands under her armpits to warm them. "Do you go home?"

Moira's voice, usually so great and terrible, was soft, nearly delicate. "I don't know," she admitted. "Maybe I go home. Maybe I cease to be. But if you would just get married and have a child, then..."

Imogen's laugh was dark and angry. "Get married and have a child? Send this sickness on to another generation? I couldn't do that. My parents shouldn't have done that to me. That was cruelty, you know."

Moira was silent. The shrieking wind blew through her like life itself. Her skirts danced, and her hair twisted prettily and horrifically.

"Keen for me," Imogen begged. Tears were running down her cheeks. The wind licked them off eagerly. "I'm begging you with everything I have to let me go."

"I keep telling you that it doesn't work that way."

"Take me like you took my parents, Moira. Please."

She started. "Moira. Is that what you call me?"

Imogen's teeth chattered. "It means 'bitter.' It always seemed to fit. 'Ghost' or 'demon' or 'the scary, beautiful thing outside' seemed wrong somehow."

"Humans were never so impudent as to give me a human name before," Moira said. She sounded almost haughty, but the tone fell a bit short.

"You'd never tell me your real one," Imogen said.

"I...don't remember," Moira answered, and the salt water in her veins ran cold. She could slice her wrist and pour it onto the broken ground, she knew it, and small fish and creatures of the sea would course out and flop upon the ground.

This human girl...

"S-sand," Imogen chattered. "Cut my wrists and I would bleed sand. It's in me like the sea is in you. I can't leave here. I belong to the earth, and it belongs to me. The stars fill me up. I'm full of mud and dirt and tumbleweeds. I'm a golem of this land. I want to leave here so you can go back home, but I'll die. I'll turn to dust. I'm sorry, Moira. I wish I could be stronger for you. I've tried. You're all I have."

Moira thought. She remembered Imogen booking a plane to the ocean, but she became violently ill before boarding. She had tried to drive to Oceanside with friends but was overcome with seizures hours from her destination. She had tried to learn to kayak on the reservoir, scuba dive in a small lake, swim in a pond, kick in a pool. She had vomited caked earth and worms, scorpions and red dirt. A small rattlesnake had slithered from between her teeth, chirring its tail.

"I'll never go home," Moira said thoughtfully. She stared out at the desert, which had been the sea once, a long, long time ago.

"Unless I can free you."

Moira shook her head. "That's not for a human to do. You don't free us. You don't do anything to or for us. We just...are."

Imogen's hair lay limp and wet on her soaked coat. "I heard you sing for my parents, you know. It was the most beautiful and horrible thing I had ever experienced. It made me...I wanted to..."

Moira slid down to the earth, then, walking in bare feet through the snow with Imogen. She left no footprints.

"That song wasn't meant for you to hear," she said gently. She took Imogen's freezing hand in her own. "When the time comes, you'll hear your own song. It will be just as heartbreaking."

Imogen's face ran with frozen tears. "Why won't you do it for me now? Why won't you let me go? I'm already crazy like my father. I'm talking to a banshee. I'm struggling with my temper at work. What if I snap and do terrible things, just like he did? What if I..."

There's an expression that humans use. They say that something dawns. It starts slow, like the stony, early morning sun, and it rises, and rises, becoming more and more until it somehow fills its vessel. It's like the sea in that way. It

fills the world with daytime, or it fills a being with understanding. Moira felt this dawning, and it was strange.

"You are afraid that if you love somebody, you will kill them like your father murdered your mother last year," she said. Her ghostly voice was dampened by the snow.

Imogen winced. She touched her chest, trying to rub the ache. Her heart was full of tumbleweeds and briar. Coyotes loped inside.

"This is why you drove your friends away. This is why you won't marry. This is why..." Moira would have gasped if she had been able to do so, but instead the air ran through her ethereal lungs in a peculiar way. "This is why you're ending the family line."

"I don't want to be alone," Imogen said, and her lips were blue. Her steps were slow and shaky, and Moira held more tightly to her hand. "I'm afraid to live. I'm afraid to die, but it won't be so bad if you're here with me. Won't you please sing?"

Moira wanted to open her mouth. She wanted to rock and keen and herald Imogen's passing, but the music wasn't there. Her breath didn't carry song.

"I can't," she said, and Imogen slowly pulled her hand away.

"Why won't you let me die?" she screamed, and for a second, her wail was so loud and full and strong that Moira nearly floated into the air again, to sing with her earthly sister, drawn to the anguish in that cry. It was nearly the cry of a banshee, but it was made from a human being with a throat created from meat and bone. She continued walking through the snow.

"I don't control it, Imogen," she said. She picked her words carefully, talking around her sharp teeth to explain the way of her kind. "I don't sing and cause people to die. I foresee their death and know it's coming. I'm looking at you, and there's no death. I know you're cold and you're sad and full of despair, and truly your suffering is delicious. But I don't see your death just now. I look at you and I see...nothing."

Imogen's face twisted in grief, and her mouth moved without sound. She was the inverse of a banshee, a monster who could not sing, who could not herald anything. She fell to her knees in the snow and sobbed.

Horror is cold, but grief is warm. Imogen wept and howled silently, and the fevered shuddering of her body melted the snow around her. The icy water fled from her until the ground was dry and she twisted her fingers into the red dirt as she cried. Her tears ran out, and sand rustled down her cheeks instead.

The earth moved carefully beneath her as something awakened. Bleached bone slid quietly from the ground and wrapped itself gently around her fingers. Imogen wiped her eyes and blinked at the skeletal hand that held hers.

Bones and starlight. Calcium and moonshine. The ground parted like the Red Sea, the dirt shifting reverently to the side, and the rest of the body climbed out of the packed earth, elbows and scapulas, patellas and fibulas. Great bony wings stretched and unfolded, and darkness flooded into them like marrow. The craggy skull glowed under the filtered moonlight of the sky. Its eyes were full of starglow, red rock, and wonder.

"It's older than I am," Moira breathed, and she felt it, the primitive power of this being that was older than rock and somehow more ancient than the seas. She almost felt like curtsying, but her kind never curtsied, and she wasn't certain she even knew how.

"Hello," Imogen said politely, as if the world hadn't just shifted and a Great Thing hadn't emerged from its slumber. "My name is Imogen."

"Imogen," the thing said, and its voice was hollow and full and tasted like Rabbit Mesa before the first rain. "Imogen," it said again, trying it out in its shattered teeth, and it liked the way it sounded because it said it one more time. It was the first thing it had spoken in a million years. It was the only thing it ever wanted to say again.

Imogen looked at the being of bone and the cosmos swirling in its eyes. It looked at Imogen and saw her humanity and her past and her parents. It licked her pain and tasted everything. Emotions and rage. Sorrow and tears that tasted like salt and sand. It tasted like youth and vitality and life that eluded it so very long ago. Something like springtime, but sharper. Like the footsteps of the great lizards and the old things before they all went away.

"Hope," Imogen told it, and twined their hands tighter. "I think the word you're looking for is hope."

"Yes," it said in its voice older than time itself. Something black and made of dust slipped through its ribs while it spoke. It grinned with all of its teeth,

and Imogen grinned back.

"There are two of us now," she said.

"Three," Moira said, but Imogen was already walking hand-in-hand with the Ancient One, toward the horizon where dawn would break soon. Moira watched them until she took a deep breath, threw her head back, and began Imogen's song. It was the first time she sang of rebirth.

A NUGGET OF WISDOM

Sean Eads

Superstition Mountains, Arizona, USA

T**HIS OLD-TIMER WILL DIE ON ME BEFORE THE HALFWAY MARK,** Russ thought, side-eying his customer as he pretended to give their provisions a final once-over. Luka Welser had paid in cash for a six-day round trip experience in the Superstition Mountains. Some people never got too old for an adventure, and Russ admired that despite his concerns.

"Here, Mr. Welser, I'll boost you up," he said, seeing Welser struggling with the stirrup. He stood about 5'6", and those eighty-year-old muscles lacked the strength to pull his sparrow weight into the saddle. Russ was just estimating the man's age. If he wanted to question people about stuff like that, he'd have gone to work in a liquor store instead of running a horse expedition company for the last twenty years.

After getting Luka situated, he got on his own horse. "It's going to be hot as hell out there. Sure you want to do this?"

"A little heat just reminds me I'm above snakes."

"Pardon?"

Luka Welser laughed. "That's a fine old expression from a forgotten time. It means I'm still alive."

"Forgotten times is what the Superstitions are all about. Let's go find ourselves a mine."

As they set out, Russ thought maybe Welser's company wouldn't be so bad. He'd always liked listening to older people's stories. That went back to hearing about the Old West from his grandpa, who started the horse packing company in 1901, when he was just 19. Journeying into the Superstitions always made him feel closer to those stories. It felt like turning his back on modernity as he renewed a kinship with the arid terrain. It was not a place of trees, but the canyons surprised many with generous greenery from cactus slopes.

They weren't a quarter mile into the journey before Welser brought his horse to a halt. He handed Russ a map and nodded with a recognizable solemnity. Hundreds of past customers had made identical gestures involving family heirlooms such as maps passed down from great uncles, drawn on paper furred thin as toilet tissue by time and obsessive handling. Sometimes it'd be diaries rather than maps, their pages filled with confessions about finding the Lost Dutchman's Mine and offering codes and clues about its location.

Russ realized right away Luka Welser's map wasn't some aged document claiming secret knowledge. It was, in fact, a souvenir from the Lost Dutchman's Mine Museum gift shop. They sold cartoon topographic maps showing the Superstition Mountain range and famous landmarks like Weavers Needle and the three lakes formed by the Salt River to the north.

In terms of accuracy and scale, the souvenir map had as much use as a child's coloring page. Russ laughed, shook his head and offered it back. Luka Welser refused it, making a slight nod at the paper. Russ gave it a closer examination and saw a squiggly line drawn through the mountains, leading toward Apache Lake. Before the lake, however, the line made a sharp 90-degree angle to the right and terminated at an asterisked, hand-written annotation: *Lost Dutchman's Mine.*

"That's the trail I'm hiring you to take."

"Mister, that's a doodle, not a trail. We're sticking to the path I know, or I'll be happy to end the venture before it starts. Don't you worry none, you'll get your fill of adventure on this trip. Plus, I can talk your ear off with legends about the mine."

Luka Welser smiled. "That will be most welcome."

Russ made good on his word, telling Welser all about such famous fortune seekers like Adolph Ruth and the number of prospectors who'd turned up dead over the years. Some were victims of poor planning, some were killed by partners they shouldn't have trusted in the first place. Some might even be suicides. As for the others—who knew?

Luka Welser rode beside him, listening with his eyes shut. Sometimes he was so quiet Russ had to look over to make sure he hadn't died in his saddle. Then he'd stare at the landscape, wishing he could see the saguaros as he'd seen them as a boy, when his father ran the business and he came along as a sort of mascot. God, how those cacti had seemed like forlorn guardians to a

child's eyes, soldiers and bandits and anything else the mind wanted to conjure.

Russ sighed. "You know the one thing that kills a mystery? I was going to say growing older, but it really isn't. You can be old and still have enough imagination to enjoy the unknown. The real answer, I think, is a museum gift shop. A museum by itself isn't the worst thing. It can be a shrine to a mystery. But once it gets a gift shop tacked on, you know the thing's become stupid."

"Debased," Welser said.

"The area got itself an official Historical Society, and the Historical Society decided they needed a museum. Some of my grandpa's stuff is in the museum, in fact."

"And then came the gift shop."

Russ spat. "Like a flea on a dog."

"The old man I spoke with at the register bore a passing resemblance to you."

Russ looked up at the cloudless sky, its cobalt blue as deep as outer space. "That's my dad. Spent decades leading bored tourists, adventurers and—"

"True believer crazies?"

"Now I don't go around saying that. But he sure got hired by a lot of people looking for that goddamn mine. In his prime, you could blindfold him, spin him around a hundred times and give him a push, and he'd still find Weavers Needle. He's proof about what I said. You can grow old and not lose your imagination. Maybe that's Dad's problem. He got too feeble for his passions. He can't do work like this, but he loves the idea of the mine so much that he'd do anything to stay close to it. That means working in the museum gift shop and making sure no one steals a refrigerator magnet. It's a sad thing. It won't happen to me."

"Sad things happen to everybody," Welser said.

On the third day, nearing sunset, Welser stopped his horse. Russ looked back and said, "What's wrong?"

"We've arrived."

"Where?"

Welser pointed to an opening at the base of the mountain. Russ squinted. For all of his long and hard-earned familiarity with the landscape, he felt certain he'd never noticed it before.

"The pass is right where the map showed it."

"Mr. Welser, that was just a scribble you or someone else made. We haven't been following any pretend trail."

"All paths start out as pretend. It's only later, after enough people have joined in the pretending, that they gain authority. Let's make the campfire."

Welser slid down from the horse, his feet dangling a little before he trusted himself to the drop. Russ looked toward the unexpected opening and wondered how he'd missed it all this time.

Tomorrow we turn back anyway, Russ thought. It didn't matter where the hell they camped, and if Luka Welser wanted to mess around with the pass, he could do it on his own. The horses weren't his, and the pass didn't look wide enough to get a horse up anyway.

"Fine," he said, dismounting. He made the fire, and they sat down opposite each other, regarding themselves over the flames.

After several minutes, Welser got up and said, "Will you have a drink?"

"I seldom do."

"But we must celebrate," he said, producing a flask from his saddlebag. "Right up that path is the Lost Dutchman's Mine."

Russ laughed and craned his neck to look up at the vast, gathering dark. "I wish that were true. I wish the sky was full of shooting stars, too. But every time I think I see one, it ends up being a damn satellite."

"You're the last of a kind," Welser said, sitting down with the flask. "You could do as well in 1890 as you do in 1990. You might even have done better. Drink with me. I'll tell you a story."

Russ grinned and accepted the flask. He expected whiskey, but the liquor had a cinnamon taste, closer to Schnapps.

"The Dutchman wasn't Dutch. He was German."

"Hell, I know that," Russ said, passing the flask.

"Did you also know there were German mercenaries who came in with the

conquistadors?"

"I thought they were all Spanish."

"The Welser family were powerful merchants and financiers. They helped fund the Spanish voyages to the New World, receiving certain benefits in return. This fact has been lost to time, I suppose."

Russ received the flask. The liquor was even better than before. He began feeling and enjoying its effects.

"History's written by the winners, right?"

"But it's underwritten by bankers."

"I hate every damn one of them. Damn leeches."

Russ leaned forward to pass the flask to Welser. When he sat back, he had trouble staying upright. He looked skyward and saw a shooting star. He pointed and laughed.

"Your Dutchman wasn't just a German. He was a member of the Welser family."

"You're wrong on that account. His last name was Waltz, just like the dance. I'll tell you something I've never told anyone before. My grandpa was there when Jacob Waltz came staggering out of the desert in 1891."

"I know."

"The hell you do."

Luka Welser smiled and got up. He didn't stagger at all as he strode over to the horses. He opened the saddlebag again. This time he produced a knife. He came toward Russ bearing the blade, and Russ discovered he couldn't move.

"I know all about your grandpa," Welser said, placing the knife to Russ's right arm. The slit was as violent as it was short. Russ tried to scream, but his pain came out in a series of squeals, thwarted by his clenched jaws. Welser tossed the knife aside, placed the lip of the flask to the cut and began milking Russ' blood into it.

"The ancient natives on this continent had only a shadowy knowledge of rock magic. Even in these mountains you'll find petroglyphs meant to invoke good luck in the hunt. Simple and of the moment. I come from a stock more imaginative and long-sighted, a people schooled in the power of timeless shaman words written in living ink upon dead stone."

Welser went to the start of the pass, bent toward the rock face on the right and began to draw in blood. Russ could do nothing but watch, and as the campfire died the runes Welser had drawn on the rock assumed an unmistakable glow.

ᚷᚨᛏᛗᛈᚠᛁ ᛏᚩ ᚦᛗ ᛗᛁᛏᛗ ᚩᚹ ᛇᚩᚾᛚᛋ

Welser came to stand over him.

"I'm going to reclaim what's mine now. Your lore calls it the Lost Dutchman's Mine. I know it as the Mine of Souls. Thank you for helping me reach it again."

Russ fought and failed to move his body. He could only watch Welser disappear up the pass. He was sure the rock would close up behind him, but it remained, as did the fiery runes. As the hours passed, his joints and muscles unthawed in fractions. At last, close to daybreak, he could stand up and move on legs that felt like stilts.

An approaching figure caught his attention. By instinct, he bent and picked up the knife Welser had cast aside. Then he saw the stranger's face.

"Dad?"

His father wore his usual clothes, faded blue jeans and a brown shirt from the gift shop that showed an image of Weavers Needle and the words *Lost Dutchman's Mine*.

"Dad, what are you doing out here? Where's your horse?"

Russ reached for him but his fingers passed through his father's body as he started up the pass.

"Wait! Don't go up there!"

His dad kept going. Russ pocketed the knife and moved after him, staggering on his stiff legs. The pass went into a steep ascent that had him gasping after a minute. He stopped, amazed at his dad's pace. Yet his footsteps made no sound.

Russ pushed himself forward but the incline had become more of a scramble than a hike. He slumped to catch his breath again as his dad moved out of sight. He panted and stared up at the rock walls, which extended so

high on either side that he felt like a rat in a maze. There were names on the rock face. They appeared in countless columns. About five years ago, around the time Dad began accepting that his horseback days were ending, the two of them took a trip to see the Vietnam War Memorial in D.C. Dad wanted to pay his respects to those who, in his words, "never got the chance to hate getting old."

Seeing over 50,000 names cut into the granite was disorienting, but not as dizzying an experience as the list he confronted now. God, how many people did the rock face tally? 100,000? 500,000?

Lon Solfko	Chalipun	Adolph Burr	George Fitzhugh
Jesse Capen	Jose Peralta	Brian Stewart	Itza-chu
Robin Bremmer	Micah Schrum	Rich Calhoun	Marley Williams

Recognition shocked Russ into muttering two names aloud. He couldn't know how many people he'd led into the mountains over the years, but some customers stood out in his memory. George Fitzhugh was a banker from Montana, broken by his job. Russ led him into the Superstitions ten years ago and soon discovered looking for the Lost Dutchman's Mine was just Geroge's way of renewing himself. Marley Williams had been an unwilling atheist looking for a mystery to exercise the muscles of faith. Russ had never had so many philosophical conversations over the course of a few days, and when they returned, Marley shook his hand and thanked him. *"Looking for God is too abstract a thing. You can't hunt for a lost mine from your armchair."*

The Lost Dutchman's Mine had attracted more than its fair share of scoundrels, but Russ knew George and Marley were good men. So why did he get the feeling their names—and every name—was on a list of the damned?

He resumed the climb until he came to a flat place that led to a mine entrance. He crept toward the opening with no intention of entering, but the sound of pickaxes compelled him. Even accounting for echo, it seemed there must be thousands of miners working inside.

The rough-hewn rock had the milkish transparency of quartz. Light shown from the other side, though Russ couldn't determine its source. He was too stunned by the silhouetted palms pressing and beating as if pleading for his help. Every slap sounded like a pickaxe striking stone.

He stumbled from hand to hand, drawn ever further down the shaft. The internal descent proved just as steep as the external climb. At one point he lost his footing and tumbled, rolling until the shaft spilled him into a room that seemed as vast as a desert plain. Its walls had the same bright gauziness and were as high as a canyon. Dark impressions of pressing hands winked in and out everywhere like black stars. The pickaxe sounds overlapped and became a sustained ring.

There was a single chair, a rock throne about fifty yards ahead. Welser perched upon it, and Russ saw his dad sitting in the old man's lap, whispering in Welser's ear like some absurd parody of a child's visit to Santa Claus. Welser nodded and laughed. "Yes, tell me more. Tell me everything." Dad kept talking, and as Welser listened his features changed. He grew younger, more robust.

"Get away from him!" Russ said, coming forward. He tried to pull his dad free, but his hands again passed through empty air.

"I've long dreamed of the time I'd enjoy the nuggets of wisdom someone's life experiences provide," Welser said. He grinned, his gaze making a broad sweep of all those pressing hands. "How my mine has grown!"

Russ again tried to touch his father. His failure had him on the verge of tears.

"It's of no use," Welser said. "He died during the second day of our trip. A heart attack in the gift shop you loathe."

"I don't believe you," Russ said.

"The mine called to his soul, as it's called to the thousands upon thousands who've sought it at some point in their life. One day it will call yours too, Russ, and this will be your fate."

Welser left the chair and steered Russ's dad to the nearest rock wall. His father passed through it as a slip of paper might disappear into a crack. Then the shadowy shape of his palms appeared on the other side.

Russ ran and placed his own hand against the rock. There looked to be almost nothing keeping them apart, but there felt like a million miles of space between them.

"He belongs to the mother lode now," Welser said. "A vein that feeds straight into me. The genius of this mine is that it gathers its riches rather than yields them. All who seek it give themselves to it, and therefore to me. Their experiences, their stories, their essence. I am restored at last."

He went back to his rock throne and settled into it.

"There are a few places across the Earth that have special properties under the right circumstances. My family used the conquistadors to quest for them in the New World. It was a generational search, and at last the responsibility fell to me. I couldn't have done it without your grandfather's help."

"He'd never help you do whatever this is."

"He thought we were looking for gold, and he'd do anything to make that dream come true. Including giving me his blood for the rock ritual when the time came. I was prepared to share the treasures of this place with him. When we arrived, of course, the mine was empty. Your grandfather thought I'd tricked him and he attacked me. Knocked me unconscious and dragged me into the desert to die. Then he returned home and concocted his story of the Lost Dutchman's Mine. I think he meant to cover up my murder, but as word spread and people came, he saw the chance for a different kind of fortune. The irony is his actions were just what I needed to save my life and fill the mine."

"If Grandpa left you in the desert, you should have died of thirst."

"I would have. But the first men to hear your grandfather's story were very old locals who set out searching for the mine without forethought or provisions. They died looking, with the idea of the mine consuming them. That's the tether between this place and the souls of those who seek it. The mine claimed its first nuggets into the mother lode, and provided me with a basic sustenance. But I could not find the pass again. I can't say how many years I wandered these mountains, in essence becoming the very figure your grandfather concocted. Over the decades, I encountered parties of prospectors, lone adventurers, feckless fortune hunters. These men I killed when I could, both to obtain whatever physical possessions they had and to speed the mother lode's growth. Then I found the pass but couldn't enter it. The blood ritual needed to be performed again, and I tried several times to no avail. Magic is a fickle master. I'd made the original runes with your grandfather's blood. To make them again, I needed to obtain it again. From his posterity."

Welser got up, went to the rock face and inspected the pantomime hands. "So many souls, so many stories. I will enjoy these nuggets one at a time, savoring them for an eternity, knowing the mother lode will always be replenished. Even today it's said there are 8,000 people a year who search for the mine. The legend remains more powerful than ever."

He touched the rock, and his hand passed through it. He seized one of the palms and began pulling a man out of his confinement.

Russ reached into his pocket for the knife. If Grandpa had knocked Welser out once, there must be something flesh and blood about the man. The knife's 6-inch blade seemed so little against the mine's vastness, like trying to kill a man with a safety pin.

He clutched the haft in both hands and plunged the knife between Welser's shoulder blades. Welser screamed, slumping forward against the wall with the blade embedded in his back. Russ yanked the knife free and stabbed again, over and over, sobbing, his mouth dry, heavy mucus running from his nose. Blood, hot and all too human, splashed his skin and soaked his clothes. Welser quit moving.

Russ thought it should have been a quiet moment, but the mine was not silent. The sound of pickaxes continued, as did the motion of the slapping hands. Russ dropped the knife, turning, looking at the vast pantomime.

"I don't know what else to do," he said, whispering. "I don't know how to help."

Welser got up. Russ stooped to retrieve the knife, and then realized Welser's body still lay on the ground. What stood was something else, a shade of Welser with blank, unexpectant eyes.

Russ shook his head. "You've doomed yourself, haven't you? No one sought the mine more than you. No one was more obsessed. You thought you were its master, but now you're just...another nugget. God help you, if there is a God. And God help me, too. I don't want to end up in this place when I die. I don't want that for anyone."

He touched his hand against the rock where his dad's hand pressed from the other side. Then Russ left the mine, thinking about all the people who

were at this very moment getting off tourist buses at the museum or musing over the gift shop trinkets or looking toward Weavers Needle and thinking about the possibility the mythology might be true.

Russ went home wondering how to defeat a legend.

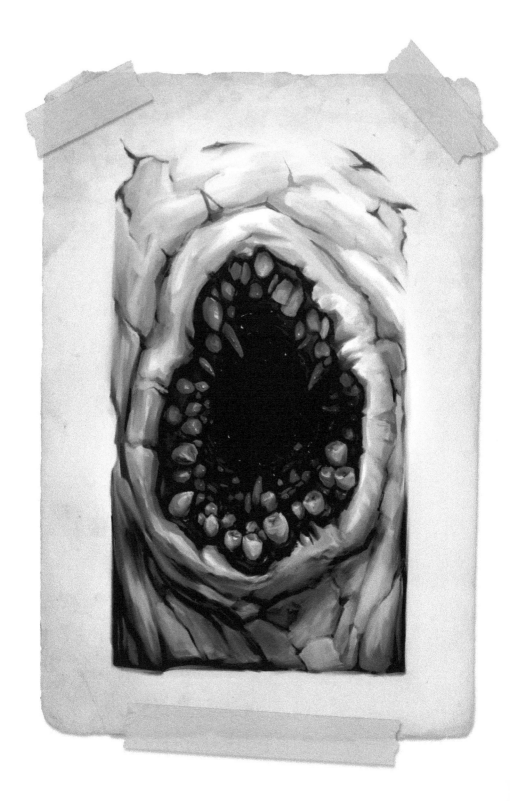

YOU OUGHT NOT SMILE AS YOU WALK THESE WOODS

Annie Neugebauer

Piney Woods, Texas, USA

THERE ONCE WAS A WOMAN WITH A VERY HAPPY GRANDSON. Truth be told, he was simply too stupid to be sad. He was too oblivious to see others' suffering, and so he thought the world was quite wonderful.

On this particular day, once upon a time in the Piney Woods of East Texas, the grandson went to visit his grandmother, who lived in a house, cabin, or cottage in the green shadowy woods filled with creaking pines and gnarled oaks. He was to stay with her for the summer, but being a modern young man of perhaps twenty, he did not relish the stay, despite contributing nothing for her trouble.

His grandmother was a staunch woman of Czech-German descent who knew her grandson was a fool and loved him anyway, because it is actually quite difficult not to love one's only grandchild, and what's more, to dislike someone who is perpetually happy.

After a few days of sleeping in and eating far too many kolaches, the young man desired to go on a hike through the beautiful woods surrounding the home. The grandmother, however, begged him to stay. "The woods are not safe for someone like you," she told him. "You ought not smile as you walk these woods."

"Alright, Grandmother," the man said, as he spoke very formally despite being a modern young man. "I will stop smiling as I get deeper into the woods."

"I have never known you not to smile. I do not think you're able to hide your teeth, and the fairies are plentiful here. You cannot smile as you walk through these woods, Grandson."

The man smiled, nodding, and promised her that he would not show his teeth, even though he knew that the fairies of East Texas are scavengers and opportunistic carnivores. The small flying mammals posed no threat to a big, strong, young man such as himself.

Even still, he had grown up hearing about the creatures and their peculiar habits. They preyed mostly on dead animals, feasting on the fatty tissue of the gums, lips, cheeks, and occasionally other soft areas. They were known collo-quially as teeth fairies because they loved to collect all sorts of teeth from all sorts of animals to adorn their homes.

A tooth fairy, though, is a small thing, and cowardly. The only real risk to a human from a tooth fairy is circumstantial: legends of drunks passing out snoring in the leaves, waking up with no teeth; small children left to wail outside their houses in the evening. Grandmother swore she knew a man who'd broken his leg and lost consciousness. Folklore said they had a literal sense of fairness, and that only thieves and trespassers were attacked. Others believed a pocket full of coins could protect the properly prepared. Myths, tales, stories to frighten and excite, bestowing magic and morality on a real animal. It was common for Texans to warn visitors not to smile in the Piney Woods, but it was only taken seriously by old-timers and tourists.

Truth be told, the grandson suspected that older people simply object to younger people having fun. His father often told him that smiling so much would rot his teeth, but seeing as his grandmother never smiled and had a mouth almost devoid of teeth, that didn't seem likely. (What the grandson didn't know was that his grandmother used to smile as well in her youth and only stopped upon the death of his grandfather.)

So, smiling at her foolishness, the young man promised his worried grand-mother that he would take great care once he got beneath deep trees and took off on a hardy stroll.

The woods of East Texas are tall and lovely, with shade from the large pines and constant noise from the small animals. The young man loved to be outside, and he enjoyed himself immensely as he walked farther and farther into the wild, paying no mind to trampling the delicate lichen and flora on the ground. He spotted birds and squirrels and all sorts of critters, but no fairies.

Until, from the corner of his eye, he saw what he at first took to be a large wreath hung on one of the live oak trees. He ventured nearer to see what it could be.

It was, he soon found, a shape created of the tree itself, having once

grown around some foreign object or barrier and made an enormous ring that extended out beyond the width of the rest of the trunk. Inside this ring was a hole that he recognized from photos as a fairy knot.

The young man grinned in delight to have found one of the animal's nests at eye-level. Knot peeping was an elaborate hobby of some Texans, but the grandson had yet to enjoy it for himself.

The visitor information for the area emphasized that the fairies are endangered due to their false reputation as violent, and that under no circumstances should this fragile species be approached. But locally it was said that if you snuck a tooth from a fairy knot and did not get caught, you would have luck for the following year. However, if a fairy spotted you stealing from their home without leaving fair trade, you would be cursed. Some old folks like his grandmother even left little dishes of coins and sparkling objects out as offerings, claiming it brought them good fortune.

The grandson did not believe in luck or curses, and he failed to see how a life like his grandmother's could be called fortunate, but he did want to see a fairy knot.

Thrilled with his sneaking, he looked around for any of the animals. Seeing none, he approached the hole with care and stood on his toes to peep.

The knot was three or four feet across, and deeper than he expected into the flesh of the tree. The opening itself was lined all the way around with sharp white canines and incisors from all manner of animals, arranged to defend the dwelling. This was very effective, as the young man could not put his hands on the edge to balance as he peered inside.

The bottom of the hollow spread level but bumpy with molars worn down over time, like enamel cobblestones. Some were darkened with rotted pits, like tiny potholes.

On one side, an entire jawbone sat with teeth still attached, propped up perhaps for lounging or resting against. The grandson didn't know what type of animal it was—maybe a deer.

At other edges inside the knot, tidy piles of objects balanced like strange sculptures: fangs, claws, delicate bones, a single white shell, even a sparkling crystal.

The young man was delighted to see such treasures. He had never considered the beauty of teeth, but looking now he could see why the fairies coveted them. Come to think of it, didn't he enjoy showing his? The very constancy of his smiling was surely what angered his father so.

The day was growing late and warm and the young man was hungry, but as he turned to leave, an object glinted in a ray of sunlight. He paused, bending to peer in and up into the knot, and he saw a chunk of gold floating near the ceiling, seemingly hovering in the air, turning slowly this way and that, glinting over and over in the sun.

A small gasp of awe escaped the grandson, as he had never seen a thing float before, much less a piece of gold, much less in a fairy knot in the Piney Woods of East Texas. There were, of course, those who swore the fairies had magic, but since the young man believed in a just and balanced world, he knew that if magic existed he himself would be deserving of having it. Since he did not, he knew magic could not be real. He wanted very much to touch the gold, to see if it would fall or continue to hover, and to figure out what it was so he could tell his grandmother about it as she baked him more kolaches.

The sharp teeth around the opening made it quite tricky, but he managed to balance with one hand against the rough trunk of the oak and reach the other carefully through the hole to poke the glistening gold.

It fell but didn't land on the cobblestone molars as he expected. It stopped just shy, and the young man gasped in glee, for it was suspended now from his own finger, as if by some invisible thread.

The grandson was too foolish to realize that it was, in fact, suspended by a fine strand of spiderweb, and instead came to believe in a single moment that magic must be true after all and that he possessed some of it, and that if that were true he had as much right as any to keep this gold. More, even. So, he decided to take it.

He heard, at some unknown distance among the noises of the living woods, an unfamiliar sound, and he looked round for fairies. He saw none, although they are notoriously fast in flight and camouflaged in stillness. He began to withdraw his finger from the knot.

The spangling hunk of gold floated far enough below his finger that in

lifting it over the bottom of the knot he scraped his arm against the top row of sharp teeth. A small line of wounds reddened, making it seem like the tree itself had bitten him for his trespass. But the young man smiled, because he had succeeded in retrieving the gold, and placed it in the palm of his other hand to examine.

This particular young man possessed a set of teeth inside his mouth that were so strong and healthy that—despite his general neglect—he had rarely known a dentist, and so it didn't occur to him that the irregular gold object he held was a filling.

The sound came again, from the side, and the grandson looked to see what caused it.

A tooth fairy buzzed nearby, its wings so fast as to be nearly invisible, merely a blur of anger around the small rodent.

The young man smiled at the animal, having never seen one so close, realizing that the sound was not just its rapid wings but also its strange speech, something between a chipmunk and a bird, with a cricket's chirp mixed in. There are some who think teeth fairies charming, but the grandson found it quite ugly, like a bat or a possum, with its face all twisted up and strange.

He didn't want to return the gold. The fairy was just a dumb animal, protective of its knot, and he, it turned out, merited magic. Besides, it was small and alone, and he was big and strong. Clutching the gold in his fist, the grandson walked through the woods back to his grandmother's house.

At first the critter followed him, fussing and darting in and out around him. The young man laughed to see its antics, kept his fist tightly closed, and continued on.

Eventually the fairy returned to him less and less, until its wings were a distant buzz, and then lost entirely to the noises of the Piney Woods.

His grandmother's abode was a dwelling of antique quaintness, with wood walls and scalloped trim, and a chimney made of stone that puffed out aromatic smoke even in the summer months. He could hear her humming in the kitchen, and so he went inside to show her his find.

Remembering her admonition not to smile in the woods, the man tried to cover his teeth as he walked into the house, but he found it harder than he'd have thought. How could he not be happy when he had come home with gold and magic? Despite his best efforts, he grinned as he approached where she worked dough on the counter.

She turned, took him in, saw his grin, and shook her head with a tight-lipped smirk. "Boy, you probably smile in your sleep. Was your walk pleasant?"

His grin brightened even more with excitement as he held out his palm to show her the gleaming hunk of gold.

The old woman gasped, spreading flour on her weathered cheeks as she covered her mouth. "Where did you get that?" she demanded with fear and awe in her voice.

Surprised by her tone, the grandson realized she would be unhappy if he told her the truth. She was too superstitious to appreciate it if she knew it was from a fairy knot. Running his tongue over his teeth to stall, the young man swallowed and lied a very stupid lie. "I found it along a dirt trail. Just sitting on the ground. It belonged to no one." Seeing her face still clouded with concern, the grandson got an idea. Never having needed to know the value of objects or money, nor really needing this trinket, he added, "And now it belongs to you."

He gently took her shaking hand and turned it so he could place the gold in her palm.

The grandmother, too stunned and touched by his rare show of generosity to further question him, slipped it into her apron pocket to be hidden with her other savings later, and turned back to her dough. "Which filling do you want?" she asked, and the grandson grinned.

That night the old woman slipped the piece of gold beneath her mattress where she kept a few silver coins, the cash she'd saved, and her late husband's watch. Her grandson, she knew, was dull and spoiled, but she didn't think him bad. She couldn't believe he'd have stolen the gold from anyone, and so she let herself believe he'd found it as he said. Suffering and hope, as you may know, can also make a person quite foolish.

She slept the deep, hard sleep of the very old and hard of hearing, snoring loudly, dreaming of roses and copper and someone screaming in the distance.

In the morning, she woke to throbbing pain. Her whole head pounded, and she opened her eyes a slit, squinting against the horror of how she felt.

Her ears and temples ached. Her jaw hung open in a stupor. A fog of confusion hazed her mind, but through it pierced a sharp fear, like cold air on an exposed nerve.

The grandmother heaved herself out of bed and looked under her mattress. The bills were still there, but before she could feel the relief, she realized that the coins, watch, and piece of gold were gone.

In their place was a pile of detritus. Bending over to get a closer look despite her aching face, she recognized them as teeth. From all manner of animals, it seemed. Teeth and a jawbone, talons, fragile bones, a seashell, and a crystal. But mostly teeth.

The woman couldn't close her mouth for the pain, nor could she bring her fingers to press against whatever made her ache so. She stumbled to her dressing mirror.

Her jaw dangled like a loose hinge, and her usual view of empty gums was obscured by white doused in gore. She leaned forward and tilted her head up to see.

Teeth, wide and white and straight, but out of order, and too big for her face. Beautiful, white teeth stained pink, lined up as if someone had forced a puzzle together incorrectly. Her head pulsed, her mind screamed, and she knew that she recognized the teeth.

Through the wall, she heard the distant whimpering of her grandson. She grimaced at her reflection, and not even the stupidest boy in the world could have called it a smile.

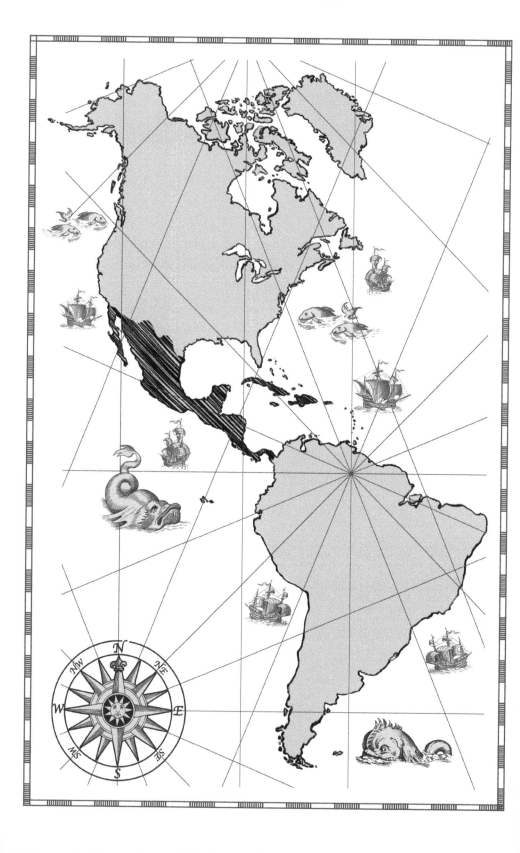

MESOAMERICA

II

THE SHADOW ATLAS

is read on Sunday mornings,
when the light shifts left
to balance its politics
and the world's corrections
which are written in blood.
Its citations are numerals,
poems, lore of the folk.
It speaks in the old tongue,
through hieroglyphs,
and higher maths.
Only priests are allowed
to turn the pages.
Women can read it but only
in the red tent.
Children can dream
what it truly means.
The rest of us must guess.

-Jane Yolen

VISITORS

UAP or UFO sightings in the Yucatan region trace back to the ancient Puuc Route.

Some believe Mayan architecture was inspired by "visitors from above."

INVASION

Angie Hodapp

Yucatán Peninsula

She doesn't understand, she says, why they
revised the maps, the globes, the compass rose,
erased the only latitude she knows,
and made the poles' magnetic pulls obey

the physics of the world from which they came.
It's not, she thinks, as if they had a right
to take her sense of touch, her sound, her sight,
but still they did. They also took her name.

Unanchored now, she wanders crowded crypts
in temples where the overlord surveys
the chaos he created, and she prays
and cries I'm sick! to every life he stripped.

You see her there? She cowers in the tomb
and waits for Puuc's destruction in the gloom.

XIPE TOTEC

Mario Acevedo

Aztlán (Northwestern Mexico/American Southwest)

"WE'VE BEEN HERE BEFORE, ESE."

I look at Neto. He tends to talk crazy.

I reply, "I've never been here before."

We're in Ascensión-Agua Prieta, barely more than a tight bend in the two-lane asphalt road—Mexican Highway 2—that runs just south of the U.S. border. The only reason I've teamed up with Neto is that I've been told he's as familiar with this desert as a rattlesnake.

"Sure you have, ese," he insists. He points to the wadded hills of the Sonoran landscape surrounding us. Sunglasses protect me from the summer glare. The awning we're under provides a patch of merciful shade. "We started here."

"We, who? And what did we start?"

"Our journey. This is Aztlán."

I shrug. *Aztlán.* Big deal. This swath of cactus and sand—the four corners area of New Mexico, Arizona, Chihuahua, and Sonora—is the mythical homeland of the Aztecs. "I see why they left. If it wasn't because of money, I wouldn't be here. Hell, who would?"

Neto gives a big grin, a grill of frighteningly large teeth, stained dark yellow.

My iPhone chimes. Elba. *Estamos cerca.*

Neto glances at me. I nod to confirm that it's time. He drapes a hand over his chrome-plated .38 Super, shoved into the waistband beside his belt buckle. One of the pistol's mother-of-pearl grips is decorated with the Aztec calendar, the other with the seal of Mexico. For my part, I pack a basic Smith & Wesson Shield 9mm. If you're a coyote, you don't trust anybody.

Two Dodge vans, one white, one blue, cruise into view and turn off the highway straight toward me and park side by side.

Elba Castro steps out of the white van. She's a bottle-blond güera and adjusts her goggle-like sunglasses. "Hola Viktor, que calor."

It's the standard summertime greeting.

The cargo doors of both vans bang open. Elba's gamberros hop out. Barking orders like dogs, they herd the migrants spilling from the vans into the building behind me, where we all gather inside.

Elba says, "Nueve cajitas." All kids. Four boys, six girls. Dressed in Walmart discards. The youngest I guess is eight, the oldest, maybe sixteen. Each carries a backpack.

She huddles with the two teenage girls. From her purse she hands out balloons the size of large grapes. The girls sigh heavily, then mouth the balloons to swallow them, one-by-one, easing the process with a swig from a water bottle. Each gulps ten balloons.

Mules. For now. Then street walkers. They might have other ambitions but they'll learn that as chicas indocumentadas the fastest way to American dollars is through a man's zipper. They—I mean the heroin in their bellies—are the true reason for this trip; the other kids, they're just extra money.

Elba hands over the down payment for our troubles, five thousand.

When I show the bills to Neto, he shrugs like it doesn't mean much to him.

Her business concluded, Elba pivots toward the door, her driver and two of the men following. They climb into the white van and drive off.

The crew from the blue van are Paco, Chuí, and Rey. I have them hand out snacks to the kids, keep them believing nothing bad will happen. They remain placid as hamsters in a pet store. The *squeak, squeak, squeak* of a rusted swamp cooler marks the passing of time.

Around five, the heat breaks. Neto and Paco go to the van and disconnect the back-up and brake lights and remove the bulbs from the interior lamps.

I text Beltran, the chequeador in charge of the punteros up the trail. Andamos.

Neto and I pack everyone into the van. Paco drives. Neto guides him onto a dirt road that detours around a ridge before swinging north. The path isn't much more than two parallel ruts through weeds and dirt. Cottonwoods scratch the van. Twilight darkens, thickening into one continuous murk. We poke along as best we can without headlights. Even with the windows open,

with so many of us crammed in the van, it reeks of sweat, farts, and desperation.

A few minutes later, Neto slaps the dashboard. "Llegamos. La frontera."

I scope out the terrain. It's nothing but blackness under a shroud of stars. I trust Neto because he has this uncanny ability to keep oriented like he's wired with GPS.

The plan is to hike through the Animas Mountains in the Boot Heel of New Mexico. Fifteen miles is a long haul for these kids, especially the youngest, but no matter. They're just Honduran or Guatemalan campesinos, so far down the social pecking order that even we Mexicans call them mojados.

Everyone climbs out and inhales fresh air. Each of the smaller kids gets two bottles of water. The rest of us gets a gallon jug each to haul in our backpacks. Rita, the teenager with long black hair and neon green nail polish, whines, "How come we have to carry something so heavy?" She points to the kids. "They don't have to."

"How about you carry no water," I scold. "And get nothing to drink."

"How about you carry my water, and I'll make it up to you." She makes duck lips.

"No thanks." I push the gallon jug into her hands. "I've seen what you put in that mouth."

She starts to sass back when the other teenager, Lourdes, nudges her. "Ya, basta."

Paco turns the van around and motors away.

We hike up an arroyo. Behind me, small feet stumble but no one yelps. These kids have made it up the spine of Mexico, and the long journey has weeded out the weak and delicate. Along the way, we find discarded water jugs—spray painted black—a telltale sign that other coyotes have been this way before.

Time for a radio check. Since the gringos are monitoring cell phones, we use walkie-talkies with text scramblers.

Beltran advises: La migra.

Mierda.

A mile to our front, a *chop-chop-chop* echoes from a blip with green and red lights. *Helicopter.* A searchlight stabs the ground and rakes across the terrain.

I watch, clicking through plans in case the copter comes close. I tell Rey to select the two smallest of the kids in case we have to send them running as decoys. The migra will have no choice but to stop and rescue them while the rest of us get away.

For now, everyone sits and waits. And waits.

The minutes pass, stretch into an hour. Two hours. Still nothing from Beltran.

The moon arcs above and sinks toward the mountains. Sunrise in a little more than an hour. Bats and bugs flutter about. As the sky lightens and the stars wink and disappear, lizards scurry across the open ground. A mouse darts from under a creosote bush, snatches a beetle, then rushes back under cover. A sidewinder twists toward a crack in the ground.

The eastern sky turns purple, red, orange, yellow. The sun peeks over the horizon and just like that, the landscape snaps with vivid color. Javelinas scurry through a sandy trough. Sparrows flit overhead and vanish.

Then stillness. Seems everything in nature has gotten the word to stay out of the sun but us humans. There's no breeze. Only the sun moves, rising, powerful and merciless.

Probably not a worse place to be on Earth than in the middle of the Sonoran Desert in July. Everyone wears baseball caps with handkerchiefs hanging from the back, French Foreign Legion style. The heat builds and saps our enthusiasm. Feels like a tourniquet tightens on my skull. I should've brought aspirin. I sip water and moisten a rag to wipe my face and neck.

To the north appears a dirty haze. I can't tell if it's something moving or a heat mirage. The blur gets closer. I see people. Marching. Out here? In this heat?

They trudge toward us. Slowly, as they approach, I count ten adults. The one leading carries a pole with a standard made of woven grass. Painted on the banner is a crude rendition of an eagle perched on a nopalito and eating a snake.

The image startles me. Legend is that the Aztecs left this land in pursuit of a new home, Tenochtitlán, whose location would be marked by the eagle,

snake, and nopalito, and the motif would become the seal of Mexico.

These wanderers are Aztecs? Or re-enactors? They wear simple tunics made of the same woven grass. Skin the color of mahogany. Dark hair gathered into knots. Some carry primitive backpacks filled with provisions. They heft two litter poles with some sort of animals swaying beneath.

They continue past, oblivious to us. I want to hail them and find out who they are. But they possess an ethereal quality, like they aren't supposed to be here.

I scrutinize the man carrying the standard. In profile, he so resembles Neto that they could've been twins. No surprise really, because Neto, like many Mexicans, is puro indio.

These Aztecs, or whoever the hell they are, continue, their sandaled feet churn the sand with a muted *scrit, scrit*. They wander along the curving basin, blending into the lines of brush until they're gone.

I blink and blot my eyes, convinced that I'd been hallucinating. I find Chuí squatting in the narrow shade of a saguaro and swigging from a gallon jug. He had the same vantage I had of the arroyo, so I ask, "Did you see them?"

"See who?"

"Los indios. Los aztecas?"

He looks at me like I'm an idiot. Maybe I have been hallucinating, but it isn't yet hot enough for that.

Neto approaches. Unlike the rest of us coyotes, he doesn't wear sunglasses and the corners of his eyes are etched with sun-squint wrinkles.

I ask him, "Did you see the indios?"

"All the time, ese."

"What do you mean, all the time?"

"Exactly that. The indios never went anywhere."

His answer gives me the sensation that reality is shifting, tilting out of balance until the buzzing of my radio brings me back to center. A text from Beltran: Seguin.

I find Rey. His expression is pained, and I assume that his headache is as bad as mine.

Until he says, "We lost two. Los mas chicos. Los señuelos." He gives me the rundown. Apparently, they died of heat stroke. "What do we do?"

Nothing much. We didn't bring shovels, so we can't bury them. The best option is to cover them with dirt and rocks, hide them from the vultures. A flock of them circling would invite the Border Patrol.

The flat valley scrolls before us, mountains to the west, hills to the east. The open landscape is overwhelming, unreal. Moving in daylight seems like an obvious way to get spotted, until you come out here and see how big and expansive the desert is. Add haze and heat mirage and everything smears into a beige mass.

Clouds float majestically above, enormous mountains of white. Their shadows, refreshing pools of dark cool air, tease around us. Dust devils dance across the sand.

As we trudge for miles, time swirls around me. My mind flits between the present and the past. History feels as tangible as the heat. I ask myself who we are and what makes us different from the many who trekked for centuries across this forbidding ground. People were here before there was a Rome, an Athens, a Troy.

Neto leads our column into an arroyo that cuts back and forth. A sound, half shriek, half gasp, echoes from up ahead. I sprint to see what happened. The cajitas have stopped where the arroyo widens. They're facing five men slumped against the wall of packed dirt, heads down, faces hidden by the brim of their helmets. All wear armor breastplates, the steel battered and rusted. Threadbare trousers are tucked into boots coming apart at the seams. Swords, lances, muskets. Peaked helmets. Spaniards, no...conquistadores!

Despite their antique garments and equipment, the men appear recently dead. Who are they? Why are they dressed like this?

I tug on a man's breastplate. His hips shift, and from under the armor, a mass of intestines spill. Everyone gasps. I stumble backwards, heaving, and choke on the bile flooding my throat. When the tangle of guts plops around the man's boots, the sludge of maggots brings a second wave of nausea.

The conquistador's helmet tips loose and clatters to the ground.

Rita shrieks. "Chui."

The face, though green and mottled, is that of Chui. But it can't be.

A miasma of dread settles over me, bringing gooseflesh in spite of the heat.

"Vamanos," I order before everyone freaks out even more.

Rey trots after me. "Bad news, Viktor. Three more of the cajitas are dead."

"What's going on? Where's Chuí?"

I have Neto watch the remaining cajitas while Rey and I separate to find Chuí.

A soft sobbing draws me to the edge of a large rock. On the other side, the ground slopes into a depression. Chuí's lying in the weeds, legs twitching, head lolling side to side. Drool leaks from his mouth, and his eyes bulge.

Even though it seems pointless, I ask what happened. He doesn't answer, instead wheezes and gulps like he's not getting air.

I step close, and from the shadow around his boots, a scorpion the size of my hand skitters away, tail curved menacingly over its back.

I crouch beside Chuí, carefully, so I don't get stung myself by another scorpion. He trembles, suffering in a palsy of agony. I look around for help, but there's nothing but desolation.

Neto saunters close and stands so his shadow falls over me. "You got no choice, Viktor."

I know what he means. I say, "Bueno, dale."

He shakes his head. "Chale. Eres el jefe. Es tu tarea."

A hard knot forms in my throat. I regard a large rock by my feet and contemplate using it to smash Chuí's head. However, that seems too cruel, even for me. Instead, I risk the noise of using my gun, rise to my feet, draw, and aim the Smith & Wesson.

The report echoes and fades to nothing like Chuí never existed to begin with.

Neto and I throw dirt on him and the cajitas to hide their corpses and continue. It's the hottest hour of the day but at least there's the promise of cooler temperatures. So, it can't get any worse.

Lourdes runs to me. "It's Rita, she's sick."

My first thought is sunstroke. Lourdes leads me to Rita, where she's collapsed next to a cactus.

Her face is gray and clammy. The pupils have shrunk to dots. Overdose. One of the balloons she swallowed must've burst open. She chokes and spits foam. I got paid a premium, not for her, but to make sure her heroin gets to Beltran. Regardless of what happens to Rita, I have to account for the dope or the cartel will dissolve me in acid.

Lourdes stares, paralyzed in shock. I chase her off and settle into my grim task. Rita's backpack lies where she'd chucked it. I dig out her jug of water and take a pull to ease my nerves.

After clamping a hand on her throat, I feel for her pulse. If there is one, I can't feel it. I yank off her blouse, snap open my knife, clench my teeth, and get to work. Her belly slices open likes it's been expecting the blade. I try to be neat, slipping my hands into her organs. I've done a lot of bad things to women over the years but no violation feels this obscene. I pinch the length of her small intestines, warm and slimy, groping for the telltale lumps of heroin. Flies buzz around my head and cluster on my hands.

I recover one lump after another. When I collect nine, I sigh in relief. I pour water into Rita's blouse to wash my hands, scrubbing them harder, harder still until I realize it's not the blood I'm trying to cleanse. I stash the heroin in my backpack then kick dirt over her corpse, scattering flies, who circle right back.

I'm dizzy with confusion, disgust, and despair. We came across the five mysterious conquistadores and then Chuí and five of the cajitas died. Then Rita. What the hell is going on?

Years ago, I rejected the idea of God, proclaiming that He was a figment of our delusions, an excuse to justify our actions. Now I stagger forward, knees weak from the weight of an enormous guilt, as if God was saying, *You want to live without Me, this is what you get.*

I meet with Neto, and he can tell that I'm losing it. He claps my shoulder. "We can only go forward, ese."

Only two kids plus Lourdes remain. Rey and I nervously palm our guns. His eyes tell me that something stalks us. We scope out the surroundings. Nothing but desert and more desert.

The march continues. My thoughts swim in a delirious daydream where I find myself in an air-conditioned room, one hand clasping an ice-cold beer, the

other resting on the cool thigh of a spent whore.

Rey shouts, and I'm back in this hell. Pistol in hand, I run toward his voice.

He and the cajitas are facing four soldiers, their corpses pierced with arrows. They wear blue trousers tucked into tall boots, stained shirts with bandanas knotted at the collars. The brass buckles on their leather belts are stamped: U.S. They're American cavalry. Mangled hats obscure their faces. My nerves draw tight with dread. I reach for the closest soldier and lift the brim of his hat.

It's Rey.

I feel the skin peel back from my eyeballs. I fall backwards a step and whirl around to look at Rey. His face is ashen, horrified to see his dead self.

Lourdes and the remaining kids stare. They begin to sob hysterically.

"What's going on?" Rey asks, his voice cracking.

This must be a prank, and my mind stutters, *It's a trick, a trick.* I howl into the wilderness, daring the phantom joker to show himself.

Lourdes squeaks, "La Llorona?"

I pan our surroundings. "Don't be stupid. She's only around water. We're in the desert."

Lourdes' lower lip quivers. "Then what? Chupacabra?"

I'm so off balance that I laugh. "What does a chupacabra even look like?"

"El cucuy?"

Neto steps close. I shout at him. "Have you seen el cucuy?"

"You mean monsters, ese?" He grins sardonically. "The only monsters here are us."

No truer words. Rita's blood still stains my fingers.

Rey stares at me, and I can see in his wild eyes that he's lost all hope in what we're doing. Neto sidesteps behind him. Rey backtracks from me when Neto trips him. Rey stumbles, spins, and as he straightens, he gropes for his gun.

I beat him to the draw and fire twice. The bullets hit him square in the chest. He sinks to his knees, too slowly, so I shoot him again. When he plops on the dirt, Lourdes and the two kids are screaming.

I aim my pistol at them. "Shut up! Shut up!"

They go quiet, paralyzed with fear.

Nothing makes sense and in wrestling with this chaos, I lunge for the next dead soldier and yank off his hat. "Maybe this one is me?"

It's Lourdes.

I jerk the hat off the third soldier.

It's one of the kids.

Turning in place, I stare at Lourdes and the two kids.

I hesitate to remove the hat of the final soldier. A gust of wind knocks it off.

It's the last child.

The paralysis gripping Lourdes and the kids gives way, and they bawl in terror. Their screams tear at my sanity like broken glass.

"Shut up!" I keep screaming, "Shut the hell up!" and fire into their midst. The bullets hack at them, and they collapse in a heap. I keep shooting until my pistol is empty, smoke swirling from the ejection port and the muzzle.

Neto's watching me, his expression enigmatic and opaque.

Fear and confusion give way to despair. My mind sinks into the practicalities of the situation. "The cajitas are dead," I tell him. "We've lost that money, but we still have to account for what's in Lourdes' belly."

Neto blinks like he's weighing the moment, weighing me. He grins and says, "Do what you have to do, and I'll make sure no one is coming."

Robotically, I set to work. I move like my brain has been disconnected, and it's not until I'm stuffing the balloons of heroin into my backpack that I'm aware of the cool twilight air and the sticky blood covering my hands.

Neto steps out of the darkness and leads me into the velvet gloom where flickering lights—votive candles—beckon us into a narrow arroyo. This trip has turned so inside out that I don't question what's going on. The tiny flames waft the smell of sage and rotting meat. Something about the candles draws my eyes. On the sides, instead of the Virgin of Guadalupe, or Jesus, or some other Catholic saint, the decals are of Aztec deities. Strange characters in stiff poses with angled limbs.

"What's with this?" I ask.

"Vato, don't you know your indigenous supreme beings?" It's Neto, his voice like gravel. "That one is Huitzilopochtli, god of war and he who led us to Tenochtitlán."

"Us?"

Neto ignores the question. He goes down the line of candles, naming each. "This one is Mictlantecuhtli, god of the dead." At the last votive in line, he says, "This one is Xipe Totec, the Lord of the Flayed. God of death and rebirth."

Neto waves his pistol like it's a wand. There's a shimmer, and now he's wearing some kind of a sheath. A tight-fitting garment made of freshly flayed skin. Human skin. A second pair of hands dangle from his wrists. He reaches behind his neck and pulls what resembles a hood, stretching it over his head until I'm looking into the grotesque, misshapen face of Lourdes.

I shrink from him. "What...what...what are you?"

"It is what we are, Viktor."

"What do you mean?"

He tugs at the corners of the mouth, ripping it apart until his face emerges anew, but not as a human but as an upright gila monster with the muzzle, eyes, and ears of a wolfman. "I am el cucuy."

Recoiling in horror, when I raise my arms to shield myself, an extra pair of bloodied hands hang from my wrists. Delicate hands with neon green finger-nails.

Neto holds up a shard of glass—a mirror—and I see my reflection.

"And now, so are you."

11 August 1982

"That one is Huitzilopochtli, god of war and he who led us to Tenochtitlán."

Huitzilopochtli, the Aztec god of war and patron of the city of Tenochtitlán, is still recognized by his demands for human sacrifice. The blood of war captives is known to feed his strength and his will supreme. This deity led the México from the legendary Aztlán cave in the northwest desert on a great migration, a time-warped procession observed by the coyotes Neto and Viktor. The later appearance of the conquistadores suggests that the party of illegal immigrants wandered too close to a dimensional shift. One of my colleagues, in fact, has spent considerable time mapping out such dimensional oddities as are found in the Aztlán. Huitzilopochtli has made several appearances in the society records, most notably in 1752 when an agent reported on an in-depth encounter while seeking refuge at a Spanish mission. At the time, the agent classified the god as a Level 10 being.

UMBRA ARCA
CASE NOTE

AGENT No. _____

THE GHOST PYRAMID

Quetzalcóatl—
"The Feathered
Serpent"

THE HOLLOW PLACE

Gerardo Horacio Porcayo

Apatlaco River, Tamoanchán, Mexico

By the Apatlaco River, in the land that scorches,
there used to stand an unusual pyramid, ancient by far, hollow by design.
Lonely witness of the dust and the blood,
of the starvation of the people, paradoxically condemned not to touch food
even in the very center of Tamoanchán,
the Eden on Earth, doomed by the arrival of the comet in the sky,
of the ships at the coast, of the fake returning of the great Quetzalcóatl,
the feathered serpent, the one that was called Cortés,
dressed in metal, riding the tall beast that eats distance and directs the army.

The gods never liked to be confused, never liked to be switched.
Battlefield soaked in blood, desert soil inhabited by bones,
was rapidly converted to a road for the silver to be enriched.
And the Momozoc—the pyramid—lies there,
dedicated to an unknown god. Hollow, vengeful, silent, it patiently suffered reconstruction
and the words: "Purify the temples, do not destroy them. As long as the people
can see their old praying places, they can be gained for the true God."
And in the day of Pentecost of the year of the Lord 1642
it was consecrated to the Holy Ghost and therefore, condemned to its future.
Deformed by a spiral keep at the top, and finished by a campanile,
it endured the new days and the new wars to come.

Brother against brother, pawns of the people in power,
Insurgents came back to hide in the hollow pyramid,
running from the mighty Royalist Army.
Again and again, so many times until nothing else mattered
but the war, and when the temple of the Holy Ghost went down
so did the entire pyramid, leaving only hollow ground
in a hollow town that once the people called Nahualco,
the Place of the Wizards, the site that keeps the magic.
The emptiness was renamed, the stones used to build
the Municipal Palace of Jojutla, the same one that came down,
bell first, in the earthquake of 2017.

Since then, some people say, the pyramid is still there. Ghost of a ghost,
people can barely see it by sunset,
against the calm waters of the Apatlaco River,
when the Sun is climbing down to Mictlán, whenever
the pain is wandering over the hollow place of the hollow pyramid.

UMBRA ARCA
CASE   NOTE

AGENT No _____

Dead Doll Island

Island of the Dolls

UMBRA ARCA CASE FILE

Isla de las Muñecas
Mexico City, Mexico

Field Report #SW109:2262-59:44089
Coordinates: 19.290128, -99.096807
Date: 20 September 2009
Agent: B. Carerras

Location: Xochimilco Canals, Mexico City, Mexico
Colloquial: Isla de las Muñecas (Island of the Dolls), Isla de las Muñecas Muertas (Dead Doll Island)

Description: The site is located on a chinampa island in the Laguna de Teshuilo, part of the network of ancient Aztec canals within Mexico City. The "island" is actually a small peninsula located within the Xochimilco Ecological Park, traversed by tourists on a daily basis via ferry and by local farmers via canoe. Typical tropical flora of agricultural wetlands in evidence, including willow, cypress, and wild celery. The entirety of the island--trees, bushes, posts, fencing, the small structure--is hung with dolls of various ages and in various states of disrepair.

Background: The story of the dolls centers around a man named Don Julian Santana Barrera, who claimed to have discovered the body of a young girl who had drowned on the site where Island of the Dolls sits today. As he was mourning her loss, a doll is said to have floated by on the canal, and upon seeing it, Don

Julian was overcome with the notion that the doll was possessed
by the spirit of the girl. To appease the spirit and offer
protection to others like her, he began to scavenge dolls from
around the city, hanging them upon the trees and surrounds of
the island site. In 2001, Don Julian was discovered drowned in
the exact spot where he reported to have found the body of the
young girl some fifty years earlier.

Phenomena: Since Don Julian's death, the site has become a
popular tourist attraction. Visitors claim to have seen the dolls
turning their heads, blinking their eyes, or raising their small
limbs as if to say hello. Popular legend claims that the dolls
are repositories for the souls of lost girls.

Observations: The island was divided into quadrants, quadrants
C and J being measured and mapped to note locations of dolls,
photographs taken to capture positions over a 36-hour time
period. During hour 16, doll 52 was noted to have moved its head
a fraction of an inch to the right. Otherwise, no changes.

UMBRA · ARCA
C A S E · N O T E

AGENT No. _____

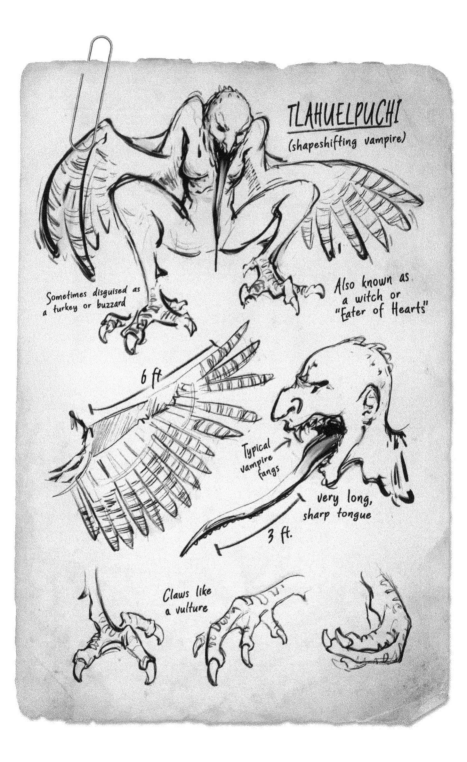

TLAHUELPUCHI
(shapeshifting vampire)

Sometimes disguised as a turkey or buzzard

Also known as a witch or "Eater of Hearts"

6 ft

Typical vampire fangs

very long, sharp tongue

3 ft.

Claws like a vulture

BLOOD OF ANGELS

Owl Goingback

Tlaxcala, Mexico

In the state of Tlaxcala, east of Mexico City,
in the shadow of the Volcano La Malinche,
the night belongs to Tlahuelpuchi,
shapeshifting vampire, eater of hearts.

When the weather turns cold or rainy,
when the men have gone off to work
and the village lies silent and dark,
she separates her body and flies.

Disguised as a turkey or buzzard,
or maybe even a tiny insect.
Her glowing aura illuminates the blackness,
her breath smelling faintly of blood.

Soaring over simple adobe homes
she makes the shape of a cross,
north to south and east to west,
marking her prey in an unholy ritual.

Young mothers sleep deeply,
victims of her paralyzing mist,
while the vampire sucks their babies
with a long, needle-like tongue.

In the morning, women grieve
over infant bodies bruised and lifeless.
Seven in one night near the village of Xolotla,
small sleeping mats left empty and forlorn.

The doctors gather, shaking their heads.
And upon death certificates they write
chupado por las bruja, sucked by the witch.

And the newborns become nameless,
no prayers said over petite caskets.
No songs for their funeral processions,
or flowers on their graves.

And the chill evenings will come again,
mothers wrapping onions and garlic in serapes,
placing metal scissors beneath meager beds,
hoping to ward off Tlahuelpuchi, the vampire-witch.

19 January 2017

"Volcano La Malinche"

It was late in the evening on an October in 1979.
The date is lost in the desert of my remembrances
during that particular sun-scalded expedition. My guide
led me to a precipice overlooking a parched and
crumbled canyon, across from which, he pointed out
a singular cavern opening high up the volcanic face.
We spent days, weeks searching for a way up, but
although countless paths were trod, innumerable walls
scaled, we were never able to discover the entrance
itself. Low on supplies, we were forced to turn back.

WÁAY CHIVO

(Also known as "Huay Chivo," meaning "sorcerer-goat")

Half-man, half-beast.

Evil being that feeds on livestock.

WÁAY CHIVO

Jimena Jurado
Julia Rios, translator

Cuernavaca, Morelos, Mexico

It blew slime and blood
—Cristina Sánchez-Andrade

We saw it once. It came like a bleat on the wind.

With its chrism, from which there surged fingers or spirals of bone,
the chivo came to open the early doors of fear.

Grandma and I froze behind the scrubby bushes,
caught in the wave of our shuddering screams,
like our legs were made of wicker.

How to fight against that fury, if its eyes alone,
prisms of an ancient light among the pines, are two fists
against our own; if they seem to keep a pact with an ulterior red,
beyond the mountains of shadows, where
a different light boils. This is how the chivo looks at us,
with that color of suns suspicious of the plow.

How, if its kicks sound like digging a grave
in the full light of town in Coajomulco,
and to it, we are a noise that grows inside,
and inside that noise grow nights of black blood
where other still-beating viscera ferment in its slime.

It came earlier than early, goring the air in grief,
its strength doled out in jumps, as a consequence
of the country fever.

The chivo had escaped, in the dark, from the earthy corral of the mountains
which the goatherds found blown wide open.

A single corral for its fury. Far from the lambs
it seemed, better than it rubbing shoulders with the beasts.

Only then did they find the fracture
in the timbers, the trail of sweat and a pasture trodden by hoofs.
And word of its absence went
from mouth to mouth. The people said that this thing was not an animal
and that its drool burned on their hands every time they tried to tame it.
Later we learned that this chivo, master and lord of the goatherds,
herded its people.

We did not see the goat again, but one day
the rain came from the east and we heard it
before feeling it, with its smell of petrichor, and its voice of multitudes
brought us omens.

How to quench its thirst so vast.
The thirst of its ancestors on its tongue.

The livestock lay still the morning after,
horizontal with the grains of dirt and the hard water,
licked by a hunger that is not of this world, for something that chose
only the strands of their blood,
and left them stretched out like palm leaves for a petate,
reduced to skin and bones until they looked
like a taxidermist's masterpiece.

Since then, I understand
that sticky color of slime that is sometimes there
in the middle of the road, before the crime,
like a cloudy, viscous turpentine,
that leaves a trace even in dreams, after the bleating
of the night winds.

Then, beneath the silence of my pillow, and Grandma's: the possible
violence
just imagine that figure, stuck deep down inside in the fear,
has the same shape as the chivo that left
running into the night,
or, perhaps, it incarnates in another incomprehensible body
and we will never know.

XTABAY

Julia Rios

Yucatán Peninsula, Mexico

Y FATHER WAS SEVENTEEN when he left Yucatán. He went to study engineering at Mississippi Southern College, shedding his tropical childhood like a too-tight snakeskin. He spent all his attention on assimilating, scrabbling for purchase on the idea that a medium-complected mestizo from Mérida counted as white. Because in Hattiesburg in 1953, you were white and allowed to attend college, or colored, and not.

It wasn't long before he moved north, as though cold winters could freeze out the jungle of his memory. In Illinois, he married his first white woman. Her name was Bella, which meant beautiful in Spanish, though she was descended from Germans.

They had four children, one after the other, like stair-steps. Miguel Jr., Gustavo, Carolina, and little Freddy. They rented a cheerful yellow house, and Bella's dad's friend at Schmidt's Car Lot gave them a deal on a station wagon that was only a few years old. Life was good.

And if my father had to ignore slurs from people on the street, or the occasional unmarked envelope that came through the mail slot, so what?

He belonged there, he told himself. He had to.

By the time I came along, I was an only child. My father had been divorced from Bella for decades, and his other children (who no longer spoke to him in any case) had all grown. Except little Freddy, of course.

My mother, so young that she might as well have been his daughter, was a perfect English rose. Blonde-haired and blue-eyed with porcelain-pale skin. It was only a shame, my father said, that I had come out with his brown eyes.

Still, I was light-skinned enough, and so many years had gone by, that he figured it was safe to tell me about the past.

They had gone out for ice cream the day little Freddy died—a special treat since all the older kids had gotten to go to summer camp and little Freddy was still too young. He was hyped up on sugar and bouncing on the station wagon's bench seat. My father, not even thirty, hair gleaming with pomade and a smile that melted all the ladies' hearts, looked over for an instant. Just one instant.

"Shush now," he said. "You're like a screaming monkey." He winced at the way the words sounded in his mouth, the vowels all stretched out instead of clipped short like the square hedges in front of Bella's parents' house. *Scree-meen Moankee.*

Then three things happened all at once. Little Freddy shrieked and bounced harder, the light ahead turned red, and a man on the corner yelled, "Go back to your own country! We don't want you here!"

All of this combined was too much for my father to handle with grace, and, in his panic, he slammed on the gas instead of the brakes.

When the windshield shattered, and little Freddy flew out into the street, my father saw his own broken heart in the fractured glass.

Of course, little Freddy wasn't wearing a seatbelt. No one wore seatbelts back then. But would he have survived if he'd been strapped in? No guarantees. The passenger side of the car was completely crushed in the impact.

My father would walk through that day over and over whenever he'd had a bit too much to drink, clutching his chest like his heart was physically breaking. It was, of course, but I didn't know that yet.

When I was twelve, I found out that wasn't even the first time my father had wrecked a car. There had been an earlier accident, too, before he left home. I only learned about it because I found an old picture of him with another boy, labeled *Adolfo y Miguel.*

"That's your tio, Adolfo," my father said. "He was my cousin."

"What happened to him?" I asked.

My father's eyes looked haunted, and he said, "There was an accident. Crashed the car. The Xtabay."

He refused to say more about it.

Tio Adolfo was the one who goaded my father into finding his first love.

It was August. The days were scorching, the nights sultry, and my father felt keenly his lack of experience with girls.

The church said no woman was worthy unless she maintained her purity, but the word around school was that no boy was worthy unless he did the dirty.

Answer? Find a girl from a lower class. A pretty one selling tortillas in the market, or a weaver, maybe, or a servant.

Adolfo had already made two conquests, but my father had made none. This is how they talked about it: conquest. Like they were Cortés pillaging the land and taking the women. Like the violence that had happened through the centuries and led to their own mestizo existence was admirable.

Adolfo left a trail of broken hearts wherever he went, but my father was not comfortable enough with lies to convince a girl that he was going to take care of her when he had no intention of following through. Because of that, he was coming up on the end of sixteen, and still had nothing to show for himself.

He tried going to Progreso to find a girlfriend on the beach, but it didn't work. The next week he decided to go the opposite way, inland to swim in the cool, still water of a cenote. Cenotes were deep and dark, and some adults said they were dangerous, but rumor also had it that local village girls liked to hang out in them. And to my father's astonishment, before he even reached the cave where the cenote was, he found the most beautiful girl he had ever seen.

She had deep brown skin and long black hair that shone against her white huipil. She rested in the curved roots of a ceiba tree, and her hands were full of white flowers. My father pulled over and flashed her a smile.

"Do you need a ride somewhere?" he asked.

"I am exactly where I need to be," said the girl. The flowers in her hands were attached to vines, he saw, and she was twisting them together to make a garland. They smelled sweet like honey.

"I'm going to the cenote. Do you want to come?" my father asked.

He expected a no, but she said yes. And when he asked her for a kiss, she said yes to that, too.

They swam and they kissed, and they did more than kiss. And my father couldn't believe his luck. But when he asked her name, she said, "They call me Xkeban."

My father drew up short. "Like the story of the two sisters?"

"Like the old word for whore," said the girl. "Do you think I'm a whore?"

"I think you're perfect," said my father. And in that moment, he meant it with his whole heart.

———

Every day that week my father went back to the jungle to see the girl. They swam, and they loved, and they swam again.

Every day my father asked her name, and every day she deflected, answering instead with another question.

"Will you come back tomorrow?"

On Saturday, my father said, "I have to go to church with my family. Don't you?"

"No," said the girl. "I don't go to church."

"Do you not fear for your immortal soul?" my father asked. He meant it to sound light and playful, but it came out sincere instead.

"My immortal soul will not be helped by going to a place run by colonizers who've taken everything we have to give and more."

My father was pulled in two different directions in that moment. On the one hand, this girl had just given him the best week of his life, and this righteous passion made her look even more beautiful than before.

On the other hand, her words went against everything he had been taught.

"The church isn't all bad," he said. "It helps the poor."

"Would there be so many poor people if the church hadn't come here to take all our livelihoods and make us convert to serve it?" the girl asked.

"I don't know," my father said. "Maybe?"

"The church says it is wrong to love like I love you. Do you agree with them? Or can you look past their colonizer morals?"

My father thought about what his grandmother would think, and his face grew warm with shame.

"Is following the church worth denying your pleasure and your Maya roots, mestizo boy?" the girl demanded. "If they asked you, would you tell them all I'm a slut? Would you call me Xkeban like the rest of them, or would you see that things could be so much better if you stopped pretending the oppressors have our best interests at heart?"

"I wish you would tell me your real name," he said. "I could bring you home with me. You could meet my family." But even as the words came out, he knew they weren't exactly true. This girl was not the kind of girl his parents would approve of. She was poor, and from the country. With her dark skin and Mayan nose, she surely didn't have any kind of claim to a lineage with Spanish nobles in it.

"That's not an answer," said the girl, and her eyes swam with tears.

That Monday, when my father went back to the cenote, the girl wasn't there.

I spent the summer I was fifteen in Yucatán. My parents had sent me away while my dad got specialized treatment for his heart. It was a last-ditch effort to fix a problem we were all pretending wasn't going to kill him. I played my part, acting like this was a normal summer vacation.

All the teens at the condo complex hung around in a pack. My cousin Yessica was the same age as me, and she had eyes that were silver. Ethereal. They made her the most popular girl at the pool. I had my first bikini, and I wore it, shyly, but I checked every so often to see if any of the boys were watching me. I might not have silver eyes, but I was blonde and foreign, and that had to count for something, right?

Sadly, the only person who ever seemed to pay me special notice was one of the ladies who worked in the garden. She dressed in a traditional white huipil and tended the flowers. Once I looked up from applying sunscreen to find her glaring at me, as though I had personally done something unforgivable.

I shivered despite the tropical heat, and turned to nudge Yessica with my elbow. "What's the deal with that lady in the garden? Does she hate kids or something?"

"Who are you talking about?" Yessica asked.

When I turned back to point her out, there was no one there.

One night after the pool had closed, we gathered around the fire pit.

"Let's tell scary stories," said Yessica. I was sure she'd be shivering in faux fright soon. The only cure for that was having a cute boy's arm around her, of course. I sighed, wishing any one of them would look at me with half as much interest as they showed in her.

Javier started the storytelling. He swore his grandfather saw the wáay chivo, a sort of sorcerer weregoat dude with glowing red eyes. No one else witnessed it, but the next day they did find three dead cows in the area.

Ernesto made a big show of yawning. "Probably just a jaguar," he said. "I know a guy who got kidnapped by the Xtabay."

A chill ran down my spine. This was only the second time I had ever heard that word. "What's the Xtabay?" I asked.

"She's a beautiful woman who seduces men and then eats their hearts," said David. He sounded dismissive.

Yessica clucked her tongue, exasperated. "If you're going to tell it, tell it right."

Once in a village near Timucuy, there lived two sisters. They were each beautiful on the outside, but on the inside, their hearts were as different as day and night. Xtabay was kind and would help anyone she saw in need, animal or human. But she also fell in love too easily. She had boyfriends in all the surrounding villages. Women shunned her, and made their husbands do the same. Everyone began to call her Xkeban, which meant sinner, instead of her real name.

Her sister, Utz-Colel, was pure and chaste. She did not favor any man with inviting glances, and for this the people celebrated her. But inside, her heart was cold, and she thought the poor and the sick were repulsive.

One day, everyone noticed a sweet smell, and when they followed it, they found Xkeban's body, dead, but not decomposing. Animals guarded it, and all around it were vines full of fragrant white flowers.

Some called it miraculous, but this made Utz-Colel jealous. She reminded everyone that her sister was impure, and swore that when she herself died, her own corpse would smell much sweeter. They buried Xkeban in an unmarked grave, away from the other villagers, and only the poorest people attended to her. The next day, though, the spot was covered with new growth—vines of white flowers, and it smelled luscious.

Utz-Colel died not long after, and almost as soon as her heart stopped beating, her body began to reek. Flies converged upon it, and no one could bear to stay near for more than a breath or two before they wanted to throw up. The whole village turned out to bury her though, and they decorated her grave with flowers of every color and size, for she had been a model citizen. So pure, so chaste.

The next morning, all the fresh blooms had withered, and in their place grew a thorny cactus with foul-smelling flowers.

"They say Utz-Colel made a deal with the demons to come back so she could be more alluring than her sister. And then she stole her name. So if you see a beautiful woman near a ceiba tree, you better not go near," Yessica concluded.

"The ceiba used to be a sacred tree," said Isabel, who came from a family of professors. "My mom says when the Spanish brought Catholicism over, they started the rumors about the Xtabay to stop people from going near the tree and practicing their old faith."

"My mom says the Xtabay lies in wait for men who go out drinking when they're supposed to be at home with their families," said Javier.

"I say bring it on," said David. "I can think of worse ways to die."

"Gross," said Isabel and Yessica in unison.

I thought of the disappearing lady in the garden and didn't say anything at all.

The next day, I called home. "Dad," I said, "you have to tell me everything."

My father went to the cenote every day for the next week after the Monday when his love didn't show, but she never reappeared. Well, that was okay, he thought. Maybe even good, since he wouldn't have to have more uncomfortable confrontations.

Even after he stopped trying to see the girl, he kept their trysts a secret for a while. What he'd had with her seemed too special to share as a conquest story. But, as time went on, and Adolfo ribbed him again and again about his virginity, my father began to feel like he had to say something.

"I did find a girl," he said one day. "She's gorgeous. And so wild. I bet *you've* never done it under water."

"Yeah, that doesn't sound made up at all," said Adolfo.

"I'll show you the cenote where it happened," said my father. "Maybe she'll be there."

As they drove, the road ahead grew dark. It was afternoon, but heavy storm clouds blotted out the sun, and then opened in a violent burst. Rain lashed the windshield and cut visibility to almost nothing. My father thought he should pull over, but at the same time, he was afraid to go off the road and into something worse, so he drove on.

When the girl appeared just in front of the car, soaked through so that her huipil was nearly transparent, my father swerved wildly.

The car hit a ditch, lurched to one side, then bounced back and rolled. The windshield sprayed shards of glass everywhere, mingled with rain and blood. Adolfo was thrown from the car entirely, and he lay in the road like a broken doll.

The wet girl stared at my father, her eyes so cold and hard she seemed like a different person. "I knew you were as bad as the rest of them," she said. Her mouth curled into a sneer, and she pitched her voice lower like his. "So wild. I bet you've never done it under water."

"I didn't mean anything by it," my father said.

"You meant to take and take, and only for your benefit, not caring how it feels to be the one being used. You made me think you loved me, but you didn't listen to anything I said! And then you bragged about it, like I was a whore. Well, at least your colonizer friend won't be spreading more tales about me."

"I'm sorry," said my father. "I just wanted to fit in. I ... you didn't have to kill him..."

"I don't care that you're sorry," said the girl. "He deserved to die. And so do all like him! And you? I curse you! I curse your oppressor heart a thousand times! May you always find that the harder you try to be one of them, the more you will feel your own heart being devoured! And when it happens again, remember me."

"You're white, though, like your mother," my father said. "You're not really like me at all. Everything will be different for you."

The next day, my mother called in tears to tell me that what we all knew was coming had finally happened. My father was gone. His heart had stopped in his sleep.

I stared out at the garden, which was full of sweet, white, flowering vines.

I thought about my mother's blue eyes, the ones I didn't get. And Yessica's silvery ones, which I'd been envious of as recently as yesterday. Was *I* trying to be something I wasn't? Was *I* as bad as the rest of *them*? And what, if anything, could I do to fix the centuries of injustice that led to me being born? What could I do to stop my own heart from being devoured? I didn't know the answers to any of these questions.

As the first sob wracked my body, I saw, out of the corner of my eye, the distant figure of a brown-skinned woman dressed all in white, watching.

UMBRA ARCA
C A S E   N O T E

AGENT No _____

ALUXOB
(Alux)

Mischievous dwarf creature. Invisible but can take physical form. If treated with respect, the aluxob can be helpful. If they are angered, they will happily wreak havoc.

Stands 1.5 – 2ft

GUARDIANS OF MUNDO MAYA

Gerri Leen

Yucatán Peninsula

Tiny houses pepper the lush Maya landscape
Homes to the mysterious aluxob
Dwarfish creatures, descriptions vary
But all agree they're fierce defenders
And wicked mischief makers
Run afoul of one, pay the price
Sickness, injury, property damage
Even death, if an alux is pushed too far
So offerings are made: tiny houses erected
With care as tributes or perhaps prisons
Alux origin legends vary
Born long before man and free
Or created by man from clay and owned
But with the same purpose: guard the
Land, the water, even the crops and animals
Drive out interlopers, those who hunt uninvited

After seven years, the houses are sealed
Aluxob get restive, protection turns to
Mischief if they're not allowed to return
To the forest, to trees and earth and water
Freed of their houses, they escape
Tucking into cenotes, hiding under bushes
Their small frames mimicking lost children
Men go missing trying to help them

Show up days later with no memory
Families leave offerings, thanks for protection
Bribes to keep malice away
Even archeologists rarely start a dig
Without a ritual honoring the spirits of the land
Asking permission to dig, to wound the earth
Those who don't, learn the hard way
Tools go missing, passages collapse
Until a priest is called, the ritual performed
And the aluxob, as always, have the last laugh

UMBRA ARCA
CASE NOTE

AGENT No. _____

Vanilla

golden syrup

aspoon soda

da last

I cup oats rolled

place s ma ll balls flattened with a fork

ke in mod. oven 350° for 12-15 mins

UMBRA ARCA CASE FILE
Vanilla Origin Myth
Mexico City, Mexico

It is a well-known fact that Quetzalcóatl, the god of wisdom, gifted the Mexica with cacao seeds. In fact, the word "chocolate" comes from the classical Nahuatl word chocolātl. It is said the Aztec Emperor Moctezuma II (1502-1520) drank up to fifty cups of chocolātl each day. He called it a "divine drink, which builds up resistance and fights fatigue." In the book *History of the Conquest of Mexico* (1838), William Hickling claims Moctezuma "took no other beverage than the chocolātl, a potation of chocolate, flavored with vanilla and spices, and so prepared as to be reduced to a froth of the consistency of honey, which gradually dissolved in the mouth and was taken cold." Moctezuma later served this special drink to the conquistador who would become his nemesis: Hernán Cortés.

Unlike cacao seeds, the divine origin of vanilla beans has yet to be confirmed despite claims that the chocolate-brewing witches of colonial Latin America employed the power of wisdom paired with love stolen, a betrayal of the darkest sort. They knew that without the enhancement of vanilla, chocolātl is just another beverage. I hope to discover evidence to support this claim.

Rudimentary research shows that the Totonacs were the first to cultivate vanilla pods, a vine-like member of the orchid

family. According to legend, vanilla orchids sprouted from
the blood of a king's daughter dedicated to the goddess Tono-
acayohua. However, the princess fell in love with a mortal
man, and the priests demanded death as payment for the
forbidden romance. Where the lovers' blood was sown grew a
bush; clinging to the branches was the first vanilla orchid.
The Totonacs declared the vine and its flowers sacred, and
they called it caxixanath, the nectar of the gods. The Aztecs
later gave it the name "black flower," as the pods turn black
once they mature and are harvested. I intend to follow the
path of discovery wherever it may lead.

                              -Anonymous, 1956 June 21

Translated Recipe for Xocolatl

Archival note: The drink favored by Moctezuma II was bitter
and served cold. To adjust this contemporary recipe to
its more authentic flavor, the following substitutions are
suggested: omit milk and increase water to 2 cups; use 3.5
ounces of dark chocolate (chopped) or ½ cup of dark chocolate chips instead of semi-sweet chocolate chips; omit the
honey; and replace cayenne with 1 chili pepper, split in half
and seeds removed (chili pepper should be removed from the
mixture after the flavors blend).

   1 ½ cups milk
   ½ cup water
   ½ cup semi-sweet chocolate chips
   2 teaspoons honey (or more to taste)
   1 teaspoon cinnamon
   1 teaspoon vanilla
   pinch of cayenne pepper

Warm the milk, water, and chocolate chips in a pan over low
heat until the chocolate melts, stirring often. Once the
chocolate is melted, blend in the honey, cinnamon, vanilla,

and cayenne. Allow the mixture to reach a low boil, and then
remove from heat. Allow mixture to sit for 10 minutes to
infuse the flavors. Add more sweetener if desired. Serve warm
or chilled.

CHOCOLATE BRUJERÍA

(Chocolate-brewing Witchcraft)

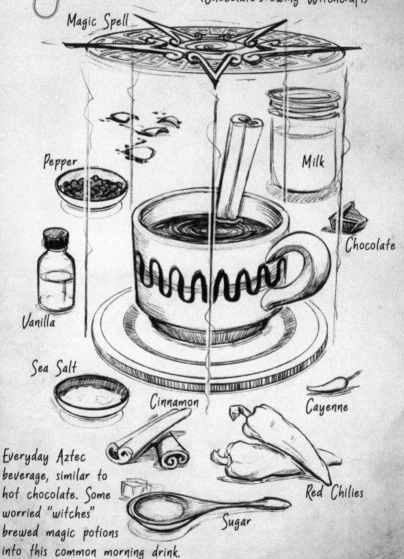

Magic Spell

Pepper

Milk

Vanilla

Chocolate

Sea Salt

Cinnamon

Cayenne

Red Chilies

Sugar

Everyday Aztec
beverage, similar to
hot chocolate. Some
worried "witches"
brewed magic potions
into this common morning drink.

BLOOD, LIKE CHOCOLATE

Stephanie M. Wytovich
Guatemala

Dawn breaks like the bones in my cheek,
I fold like bedsheets, like chocolate into
warm milk.

I wash blood off the walls, blink back
my grandmother's words, rewrite the recipe
in my head.

    ¼ teaspoon of vanilla
    a pinch of sea salt

You wait in the kitchen,
a ticking clock, a lit fire.

I pull knots from my hair,
rip my nails out with my teeth.

    2 red chilies
    cinnamon to taste

Urine runs down my leg, hot like a
blessing, strong like a chamuco's
bite.

I spit in the pot, stir it backwards
with my hand, a protective circle,
a banishment.

> 2 cups of milk
> 1 ounce of chocolate

You're annoyed I'm late,
a cockroach, a pig.

I prepare your cup,
trace the rim with my tongue.

> a dash of cayenne
> a sprinkle of sugar

I become the whisper, the witch,
the cocoa my armor, its bitterness
my sword.

You drink, you swallow, the sweet
scream of ritual in your veins,
heat on your lips.

> add pepper to garnish
> a cinnamon stick to stir

I paint over my bruises
Readjust my spine

You leave the house alive,
I make myself coffee.

> 1 step to safety
> 3 days, a widow.

UMBRA ARCA
CASE NOTE

_____

_____

_____

_____

_____

_____

_____

_____

_____

_____

_____

_____

_____

_____

_____

_____

_____

AGENT No _____

La Lluvia de Peces en Yoro

UMBRA ARCA CASE FILE

La Lluvia de Peces en Yoro

Yoro, Honduras

The journal of a certain Father Francisco Garza was recently discovered in a sealed container unearthed by a farmer near Yoro, Honduras. The date printed on the inner cover is April 13, 1873 (Easter Sunday), and the last entry was made on July 11, 1873. Records show that La Lluvia de Peces en Yoro occurred in the afternoon the following day on July 12, 1873. The majority of the pages were ripped out, but a few of the more recent entries remain intact. Along with the damaged diary was a compass bearing the Umbra Arca sigil and a handful of small bones wrapped in a pouch stitched together from leathered fish skins. An analysis of the bones confirms the reconstruction of two human hands. The subject is believed to have been an adult male. Also inside the packet was a scrap of paper inscribed with the lines: La venganza no es de Dios. Me pertenece. ("Vengeance does not belong to God. It belongs to me.") The words are written in a feminine hand, but there is no signature to confirm the agent's identity. Cross reference the archives for a match. La Lluvia de Peces en Yoro continues each year as it has for over a century. Case remains unsolved.

—Archivist Gwenifer Reading, April 22, 1973

May 15, 1873

It is said that it rains fish in this small village. Locals
name this phenomenon La Lluvia de Peces en Yoro. The coming
of this peculiar storm is presaged with a sudden darkening
of the sky, which is quickly followed by severe lightning
and thunder, violent winds, and a downpour so dense a person
cannot see past the length of one's arm. The locals say this
has happened for years now, always occurring when the rains
come in May or June. It is reportedly as predictable as the
seasons, yet it still has not arrived. Soon, I will discover
the secret. And then I will make it my own.

May 28, 1873

Even though I long for civilization, I dare not stray lest I
miss the very reason for being in this unholy region in the
first place. I am more determined than ever to prove that
Father José Manuel de Jesús Subirana subverted doctrine to
summon the first fish rain in 1856. His converts and their
children still call his name in faithful gratitude, but soon
my name will be on their lips instead. They are as blind to
truth as the fish that sacrifice their bodies to sate the
hunger of these heathens who would dare to worship their
pagan gods at the altar of the Almighty. These people once
starved, and they will starve once more. I am secure in the
knowledge that the glory of God will grant me the power to
take this blessing with me, and I alone will have the power
to confer the bounty on those I see fit. This travesty has
continued long enough. It must stop, and by God's grace this
will come to pass. And I will be the hand to see it done.

July 10, 1873

Today a woman showed up in the village. Although she is not
someone I've seen before, she is as brown-skinned as the
natives. This whore wears her pride as easily as the veils
that obscure her face. I am certain she is a Jezebel sent by
Satan to lead me astray. But like Jesus, I will not succumb.
I conquered those base desires more than a decade ago. I am
pure, sacrosanct. The angels call my name alone. They tell me
the time is nearly upon us, that I am a vessel and my wrath
will scour this nameless harlot's presence from the world as
surely as the sun conquers the sky.

July 11, 1873

Blasphemy! This woman knows no shame! How else to explain
the actions of a whore who would dare to approach a holy man
such as myself? And then, she demanded that I leave this
place when all here know I am on a mission bestowed by God
himself! It is as I suspected when I first saw her. Even when
called to repent her true nature, she attempted to keep her
face hidden from my sight. Despite the ordeal that followed, I
remain pure and untouched by evil. Thanks be to God!

I first discovered her following a golden compass near the
headwaters of the Aguán River two days ago. But when our
paths crossed today, she claimed that I was following her!
Can you believe such an accusation? The harlot told me the

fish rain would arrive tomorrow, but that I would never see
it. She demanded that I leave today or suffer the conse-
quences. As if a jaded woman such as she was in a position
to make demands or threats. I left her there, sprawled in
the mud where she belongs. I've safely returned to this
hideous hovel I've been forced to endure these last weeks,
yet I cannot make the compass work. It just spins and spins
and spins - as worthless as the woman who once carried it.
Outside, I hear the natives' voices calling peces over and
over again, and I wonder if the fish rain will finally fall
in the morning. It's a pity that my hands were damaged during
my battle to remain chaste. No matter. Holy fire will heal
the scratches on the morrow. Glory be to God!

UMBRA ARCA
CASE NOTE

AGENT No. _____

THE SUGAR CASTLE OF ST. LUCIA

E. Lily Yu

Caribbean Sea, St. Lucia, West Indies

ALL OF THE SPARKLING, SHINING MAGIC had been knocked out of Gloria long ago, which is what happened to most Black girls in Tennessee in those years, including April and Pauline, but as their wedding-cake of a cruise ship docked at Castries, she swayed side to side, almost dancing, in the clean sea breeze.

This cruise was the bonbon the three widows had saved for themselves, after decades of feeding their men and children before themselves and mending their dresses until the cloth was thin as ghosts, so the men could buy themselves new shoes. However much drudgery, however many cruelties they endured, their gloves were spotless on Sundays and their lips pinned shut.

This last, glorious, extravagant reunion, which Gloria had suggested on a giddy whim, had taken them through the Windward Isles over the past three days. Setting aside the small impairments of arthritis and suchlike, everything they'd tried and tasted had been exquisite.

Junior pursers raised aloft the previous night's sign-up sheets and shouted names as the *Queen Anne* disgorged its passengers. Arm in arm, April and Pauline decamped for Castries' art galleries, street markets, and duty-free shops, worrying the clasps of their purses. Gloria, whose child was slightly less successful, and whose spending money was correspondingly less, followed her excursion group onto a bus headed for the northern beaches. She was not sorry to have an afternoon on her own; all night long, April's tiny, glassy snore had stuck in her ear like a large mosquito.

All the boat tours running from the north of St. Lucia were five-star operations with freshly painted fiberglass hulls, Yamaha motors, and clean canvas canopies—all but one.

Once Gloria stepped off the bus, shielding her eyes from the sun, she stood a little out of the stream of cruise passengers, most of whom moved much more quickly than she did. A young man who had been lying in the shade of an upturned dinghy stood up when he saw her, brushing the sand off his legs. While the other boat tour operators wore fresh red polos embroidered with logos, this man, barely out of boyhood, wore an overlarge sports jersey in eyewatering yellow. The threads were fraying at the hem.

"Come with me," he said, with a courtliness startling in one so tall and ragged and young. "I have been waiting for you."

"Get away, I'm much too old for you!" she said, laughing, but he only bowed and swept one arm out toward his dinghy.

Gloria wasn't sure the patched and faded inflatable boat, with its suspiciously young skipper, was a registered business, much less one approved by the cruise company, and she wondered vaguely about the reaction of the list-checking assistant purser. There were rules, after all; she had lived her whole life by them.

She eyed the straggling strand of cruise passengers headed from bus to boat, raised her chin, made her hands into fists, and strode toward the dinghy as fast as the powdery white sand would let her.

The young man handed her in gently, with the help of a plastic stepstool, and she perched on one of the crosswise seats.

Then he pushed them free of the sand, levered himself in with an oar, and spun up the motor. They drifted away from the beach at the thrilling rate of five to seven miles an hour, or so Gloria judged. By the bus, the purser was glancing up and down from his clipboard, beginning to frown.

"So," she said. "What's your name?"

"My name?"

"If you're kidnapping me," she said, "it's only fair."

"Epiphane," he said, sliding a white cigarette out of its box. His fingers were long and thin, and she wondered what instruments he might play. "Do you want to go back?"

They were barely fifty feet from the shore. Gloria shook her head.

"How much will this cost? The cruise pays the tour operators, but I don't think you're one of them—"

He flapped his hand at her, the one holding the cigarette. With the other,

he steered them away from St. Lucia. "Free. Gratis."

"Well, that doesn't seem fair."

"Family curse," Epiphane said, half smiling.

Though Epiphane sweated and shone in the hard light of the sun, under Gloria's broad-brimmed hat, all was gentle and warm. She wanted to ask him about his family, about school, about what St. Lucia was like beyond the polished places set up for show. But the boat rocked, and the warm air made her yawn, and the sunlight curled up in her lap like a cat. She closed her eyes.

When she next opened them, the points of St. Lucia's two mountains had dropped out of sight below the horizon. The engine cut to a hum.

"Hm?" Gloria said, almost toppling forward. Epiphane stopped her.

"We are here."

"Where?"

"Where you wanted to go."

Before she could form the next question, he pointed to a low rock protruding from the waves. It was gritty and quartzlike, with a slight translucence.

"That was a castle of sugar," he said. "Before a hurricane comes, it rises up. Then the sun and the sea melt it again."

"Sugar—"

"Taste it," Epiphane said. "Put out your hand, like that—"

The rock was not as cold as quartz. It was wet with sea spray. She put only her smallest fingertip to her mouth.

"It's sweet," she said. "And salt."

"Yes, the salt is of the sea. The rest—I will tell you, if you don't mind."

And she listened as they floated over the blue belly of the world.

Four hundred years ago, tall ships sliced through the thick sargassum on the jewel-blue sea. Going west, their holds were full of stinking, dying bodies; going east, they held sugar, rum, tobacco, and cotton. Gloria's parents were sharecroppers, and so she knew the lines that tobacco and cotton had cut into faces and histories. But Epiphane was talking about sugar, and the sticky-sweet, fly-specked floors of sugar mills, and the bloody reek of copper molasses cauldrons.

The sugar that was fed with blood and came out so white and clean, he said, built houses—mansions—fanciful architectural confections, all across the islands, Trinidad to Cuba. Little French and British princelings in exile, second and third sons without inheritances to look forward to, lived in them for as long as the hurricanes permitted, and by hurricanes he meant both weather and people.

And on Trinidad, in a very, very fine house like one of the sugar trionfi on the tables of the rich, or the pastillage sculptures brought out on cruise ships for midnight buffets, there was a princeling with a gay laugh. And he met in Martinique a white woman whose love he did not deserve. He had all the black bodies he wanted, you understand. At any time he wished.

He did not marry her.

So she invited herself to his island estate while he was back in France on business, dressed in her finest, waving a letter from him.

In the way of white women who discover the injustice boiling around them only when their own fingers are scalded, she had found common cause with the slaves he whipped. For the child growing in her was a half-sibling to several of their children.

It was suicide to help her, madness just to listen, and many did not. Those who broke their backs turning bitter to sweet every day of their lives did not need another cupful of bitterness. But one of them did not care much for this world, nor mind the hellfire of the next. When the white woman came to the fires between the shacks, this woman told her about Mami Wata and her lwa and showed her the secret altar she kept.

The white woman offered up to Mami Wata all the jewelry she had, which was not much, in exchange for a curse. And her offering was faithfully given to the sea, because it would have been fatal to find even one pearl among the slaves.

When she left to go back to Martinique, the priestess of Mami Wata thought that was that.

But no, the white woman had gotten drunk on her own despair. The slaves had told her about Mami Wata's riches, garnered from all the shipwrecks in the world. A little gold bracelet and pair of carnelian rings was not enough to buy her favor.

The moon filled up, and so did she. In time, the child came.

As soon as she could stand, this woman went down to the sea cliffs with it. Doing what she recalled the old priestess doing, clumsily and not well, she gave the child as an offering.

Then she gave herself as well.

When the princeling hove back into port, the woman's curse caught upon him like a knotted net, though he felt no more than a roughness in his throat. From then on, though the air might be dry and still, one could smell storm winds around him, if one were familiar with storms. And the priestess burned her altar and buried what could not be burned, for she knew how blame roves about and seeks a body like lightning.

When the princeling heard of the white woman's death, he shrugged and refilled his coffee and sugared it. He remained on his Trinidad estate for three months. At the end of it, he signed a bill of sale for his palace, the plantation, and all the slaves there. One signature was all it took. He loaded his last shipment of white sugar and dark rum onto a ship set for England, and booked passage on that ship for himself as well. He took the money with him, the whole price of his sugar castle.

The ship stopped at Barbados and St. Lucia to take on more passengers.

And then, not far from here, on a clear blue day like this one, the sky suddenly went black, and the winds whipped the sea into mountains. There was a hurricane, such as the islands might see once every hundred years. Like a great hand pressing down from the sky, it flattened many of the sugar castles on the islands and blew the splinters into the sea. All kinds of bodies too: white, black, Carib. A curse does not make fine distinctions.

On the princeling's ship, the sails were shredded at once, and the scraps flew about the sailors' heads like gulls. The tall, grand ship was a small nothing in the vastness of the sea.

It foundered and sank with all hands, its hold full of sugar and rum. The waters there tasted like sweetness and death for days after. Or so they say.

They also say, though not one soul escaped, and I do not know how *they* should know, that before the ship went down, all those on it could hear the laughter of a woman—wild, triumphant laughter—and the cry of a child.

Even now, though it should not be possible, they say that on certain nights, when a hurricane is coming but not here yet, and the moon is full, you can see a ghostly palace of sugar upon the water where the ship went down. My cousin was night fishing, and he saw it. He tied up his boat and walked inside. Big as any of the fine old castles on Trinidad, he said, but made of pure white sugar. The doors inside were sealed shut. No light but the moonlight shining through the empty windows. He was going up some stairs when he heard a woman laugh, and it was not a good laugh. The shadows seemed to stretch out their hands for him. He turned and ran to his boat and tore off across the water.

We all laughed at him and his story. He was drunk, we said. I have never seen this castle myself. It comes and goes as the sea pleases, I think. If it even exists.

But I come out here in my boat, and I find this pillar of sugar, and I do not know what to think. Except that it looks like an altar my aunt used to keep, that I saw when I was a boy.

———

"That is a very good story," Gloria said. "Did you bring me out all this way just for that?"

"It is an explanation," Epiphane said. "You brought me out here."

Gloria fanned herself. "Me?"

"Some hundreds of years ago, a priestess was sold from Trinidad to St. Lucia to pay a gambling debt," he said. "My family, we are all good Catholics now. But one of us still, always, sees and hears when we are needed, in that other way. Someone has taken your life from you. A sweet singing voice. A love of dancing. All gone. What is his name?"

"He's dead," Gloria said. "And sometimes he was good."

"Still. We are here. Where the sea is sweet and bitter both. There is some-

thing loud in your heart. What is your wish?"

"I have a daughter," Gloria said. "She is smart, and has a degree, and did not make the mistakes I made. I wish I had my life back, all of it, all the time I gave away, that he did not see, that he did not think about. All the ironing, the laundry, the cooking, the weeping over the women he did not care to hide well. But for my granddaughter and grandsons, let everything remain as it is."

"Time moves only forward," Epiphane said. "I do not think you could stop any of them from existing."

"Then there's no harm in wishing."

"No harm," he agreed.

She plucked her coral earrings from her ears, the ring from her finger, and the tiny gold cross from her neck and put them on Epiphane's open palm. "There," she said. "I bought those earrings for myself and pretended they were from him. Give those to Mami Wata and ask her to give me my life back, if she likes."

Epiphane stretched out one long, skinny arm—she wondered briefly how much he ate—and dropped them on the flattish face of the sugar rock. Then he unrolled another of his cigarettes and sprinkled the brown flecks of tobacco over the coral and gold.

A swell of water passed over the rock, taking the offerings with it.

"I am sorry to be telling you all of this," Gloria said. "And him dead and unable to speak for himself. Everyone thought so well of him."

"Some things must be said," Epiphane said. "Or even bones will cry out. Even birds and stones."

She opened her mouth to tell him to take her back to land, and indeed he was already reaching for the boat's motor, but the sun had become unbearably hot, the air unbreathable. She sputtered and choked. What she needed, what she desperately needed, was—

The sea.

The water was cool against her face. Weightless in that water, her limbs no longer ached. Above her, a young man whose name had left her looked down in horror, shouting for her to come back. She did not know him anymore. She gnashed her new, sharp teeth and turned away and swam down in a slow spiral around the pillar of sugar.

As she descended, her weariness floated off her shoulders.

The pillar grew from the seafloor like the spike of an orchid. At its roots, she found her new sisters.

They were old as time itself, and armored like fish, and their slender fingers and sharp teeth worried the bones of princelings long drowned. They called to one another like St. Lucia's parrots, who throughout the island's forests now fluttered their wings and cried as one. In Castries, April and Pauline looked up from displays of earrings and wood carvings with a sharp pang of hunger, though for what, they could not say.

Around and around Gloria the sea folk swam, and their dance was a dark and silver braid. They stretched out their hands and beckoned to her.

And Gloria joined them.

UMBRA ARCA
CASE NOTE

_____

_____

_____

_____

_____

_____

_____

_____

_____

_____

_____

_____

_____

_____

_____

_____

_____

AGENT No. _____

LA CIGUAPA

Long, glistening hair

Inhabits high mountain regions. Nocturnal habits.

Mangled legs

Backward-facing feet

LA CIGUAPA

Christina Sng

Dominican Republic

In the Dominican forest
On a felled, rotted log—
That was the place

Where I was brutally maimed,
Feet twisted all around
As they held me down, laughing.

I could not forget that day.
I was only seventeen,
Betrothed to the chief's son,

Another kind of prison
But I accepted my fate.
It couldn't be that bad, I thought.

I should have run while I could.
I tried—
They caught me,

Desecrated my body
And left me for dead,
Lying in my own blood.

Before I faded into darkness,
I promised I'd serve any god
As long as I had my revenge.

One god brought me back,
But he couldn't fix my feet
Nor restore my body to what it was.

I wept after seeing myself in the river,
Rage building like a gale force
In the maelstrom of my mangled body.

I rampaged over the monsters
Who did this to me,
Cut open their chests,

Snapped open their ribs,
And ripped out their hearts
While they were still beating.

I ate them while they watched,
Until they stopped begging,
Until they stopped moving.

Centuries later, I was satiated.
Revenge was a pointless game
When all your enemies were dead.

I'd lived in peace since,
In quiet solitude
Up in my mountain home

Until the monsters came back for me
With their axes and knives, determined
To dispel the myth of La Ciguapa.

I moved faster than them, knocked
Their weapons from their hands,
Ripped the arms off the closest man

And tore into them, before turning
To the rest who ran and tripped,
Falling off the mountain.

Two smashed their skulls to pulp
On rocks paving the way down
While the third survived,

Hobbling into the deep forest
Where I followed, my feet
Making backward footprints.

I'd long considered
Acquiring a companion
And this man seemed able.

I took what I needed
And kept him air dried,
The thin mountain atmosphere

Desiccated things well.
He fed me for a time before
I made toys from his bones.

Soon after,
I gave birth to my first child.
She was tiny and perfect.

She had her father's eyes.

UMBRA  ARCA
C A S E · N O T E

AGENT No. _____

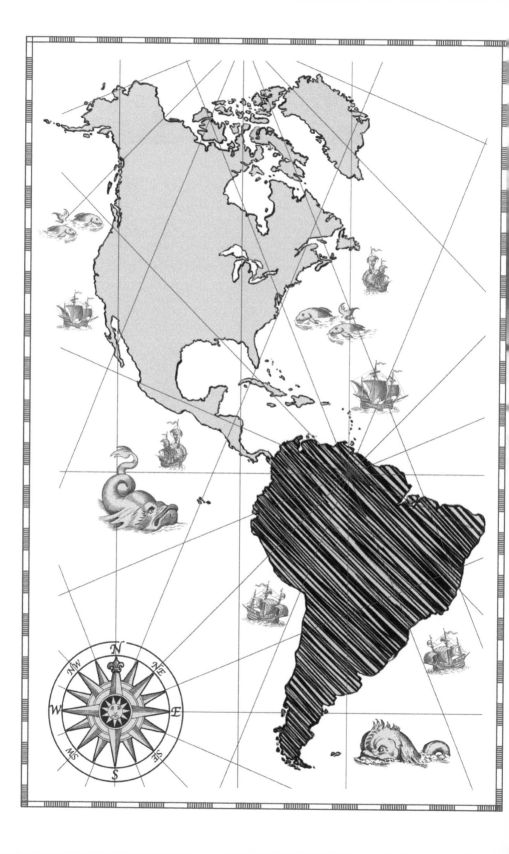

SOUTH AMERICA

THE SHADOW ATLAS

is a myth, a metaphor,
a false memory, a mistake
that has been raised to a stature
no book can maintain.
It instructs unreliably,
proves nothing, improves less,
lifts spirits falsely, sets no courses.
It does not instruct, only entertains,
yet declares it is the true way.
It is like a dream, a wish,
of shadow lands and shallow.
We follow the maps therein.
We have no others in hand.

-Jane Yolen

LA SAYONA

Appears to unfaithful husbands.

Animal-like claws.

Wears a long, white dress.

Uses her beauty to lure adulterers to a horrific death..

LA SAYONA

Christina Sng

Venezuela

Each generation tells my story
With new embellishments.
Each generation retells it
Through its own lens.

I've come out here
To set the record straight.
This is what really happened.
Listen...

Once, I lived in a small town
On the plains of Venezuela,
So quiet and peaceful.
My life was beautiful there.

I believed my husband
To be faithful and true,
A hardworking man,
A good, loving father.

But he hid his dark side.
He hid it so well—his love
For control and violence,
His love for desecration.

He unleashed his rage onto me
Whenever he lost control
Then lied and said he loved me,
Saying I was a broken girl.

There was no one to tell.
No one believed a woman,
Much less one
With no status, no position.

I quietly celebrated
When he left us
For another woman
And her children.

But my mother found out
On the day she watched our baby.
She confronted him,
Told him to think of our family.

Instead of remorse,
He killed her with a machete
Then smothered our baby,
Leaving the bodies in a pile

Before setting our home on fire,
And fleeing like a coward
With his new woman
And her children.

The townsfolk lynched me,
Citing the story you hear,
That terrible lie he cruelly spread
Before his planned departure.

My mother would never
Take up with my husband
Nor would she curse anyone,
Let alone her own child.

When they stoned me to death,
I swore I'd come back.
I made deals with all the gods
And one of them

Brought me back
With his power to resurrect
And granted me the ability
To shape-shift, to punish the wicked

And I have,
For generations now,
Destroying unfaithful husbands,
Starting with my own.

There was nothing left of him
To hold, let alone bury
When I was done with him
And his married harlot.

This is my true story.
Whether you believe it or not,
But if you stray,
Trust me when I say,

Wherever you go,
I will find you.

UMBRA ARCA
CASE NOTE

_____

_____

_____

_____

_____

_____

_____

_____

_____

_____

_____

_____

_____

_____

_____

_____

_____

_____

AGENT No. _____

EL MAYANTU

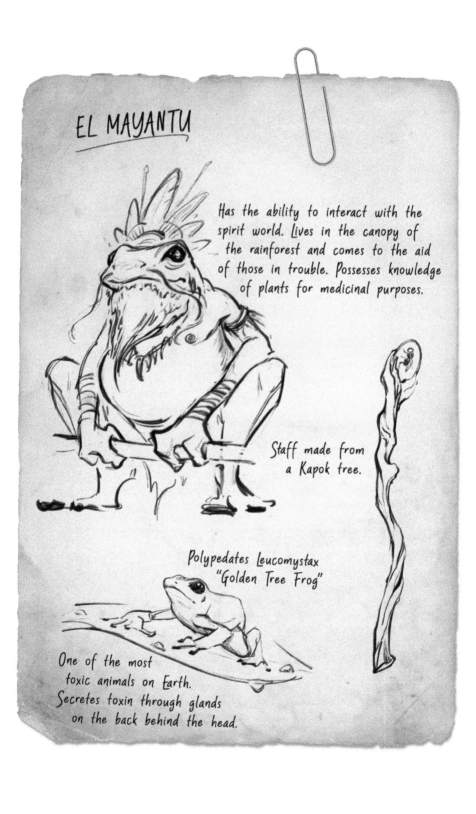

Has the ability to interact with the spirit world. Lives in the canopy of the rainforest and comes to the aid of those in trouble. Possesses knowledge of plants for medicinal purposes.

Staff made from a Kapok tree.

Polypedates Leucomystax "Golden Tree Frog"

One of the most toxic animals on Earth. Secretes toxin through glands on the back behind the head.

THE DRUG DEAL

Marge Simon

Valencia, Venezuela
1988

A certain ranch-style house overlooks a spacious beach.
It is wonderfully cool inside, with beautiful floors of sienna tiles.
Comes a black sedan covered in thick orange dust;
five men emerge, all swarthy, save for a blond American.
He's attired in a costly white suit and attended by a Yagua boy
whose tongue is newly missing, removed with a cuchillo
by order of his boss, ensuring he will tell no tales.

The men wear sunglasses, guns holstered inside suits,
but the one with yellow hair speaks English with their host.
At his signal, the boy lights the bong for sampling wares
and disappears to wait outside the kitchen door.

He sits cross-legged in silent prayer,
O Mayantu, lord of home and forest,
hear me, though you are far away,
guide me to break this cruel bondage
that I may return to my village.

A thunderclap, a flash—the air clings like a cloud,
suddenly hot and moist; then a breeze thick with smells
of rotting leaves and scents of strong, sweet flowers.
A tiny golden frog hops up to him and speaks,

"Mayantu sends me to die for you; kill me quick
and chop me fine, then add me to the stew.
Fear not, my poison shall not harm you."

When Cook's back is turned, the frog goes in the pot.
For lunch, there is paella served in steaming earthen bowls.
The boy must taste it first, ensuring it is safe, but he is fine.
Soon howls of pain replace the house guests' pleasured smiles
as one by one, they fall to writhe upon the floor.

A dark survivor drives off in a cloud of dust, as
homeward bound, the Yagua sends a prayer of thanks.
Deep in the Amazon, the frog-faced god of mercy smiles.

UMBRA ARCA
CASE NOTE

AGENT №. _____

BLOOD SISTERS

Christa Wojciechowski

Columbia

W E FLEE OUR PILE OF CRUSHED BEER CANS, giggling wildly through the rows of coffee trees who stand like a dark army under the ghostly blue-white moon. Clouds stretch beneath its cold glare, illuminating great swathes of enchanted mist that slide over the black hilltops. Wind lashes the overgrown branches, their leaves smacking into our backsides like the palms of angry fathers.

Plock, plock, plock.

There's the sound again, the one that made us take off like spooked horses. But we haven't put any distance between us and the drumming. It's following us in the row to our right.

"Fuck, Tina. Go!" Beatrice squeals.

The soil is loamy and damp. My feet lose traction every time I push off. A moonbow appears in front of the clouds. A rainbow inverted, the colors are decayed—dried-blood maroon, bruised violet, and putrid green. It's like a giant bridge to the underworld, conjured to guide us. I wonder if Beats sees it.

Plock, plock, plock.

Now the sound comes from the left. We run faster—adrenaline sizzling through our beer buzz. I grab Beats' wrist and yank her with me. I take a sharp left where I feel the incline. We clamber up the ridge where we find the road back to town.

It all seems comical back at the hostel, as we take turns pouring shots of aguardiente. Beats and I, in the middle of a spooky plantation, getting freaked out just like when we were twelve. We'd hike into the woods behind her house, dance around small fires in our floral print briefs, a ritual for a panel of exclusive gods, ones who created us separately from the rest of the world. Whenever we'd hear knocking, we knew our gods were talking to us, a phantasmic Morse code that made us bolt through the trees—free and naked and frenzied. Blood oaths, razors to palm. Matching charm necklaces. *Best Friends Forever.*

But we have to "adult" now. Beats is engaged. She is going to settle down and have a family. By default, I'm settling into what's expected of me too, off to manage a new branch of Dad's insurance company. I wonder how, after so long together, this could be the end of our story. Our last girls' trip before we're cleaved apart, rambling around the mountains of Colombia, pretending we'll survive this.

In the morning, we gulp several cups of scalding local coffee—black and bitter—till our hearts palpitate at a delicious, frenetic rate. A breakfast of arepas and chicharron soaks up the hangover. We walk from downtown to a neighboring indigenous village, hoping to loop up to the entrance of a hidden trail I discovered on a travel forum that is rumored to take us up a ridge to a rock formation that juts thousands of feet over the valley.

"Where are we going?" Beats asks.

"It's a surprise," I say.

On a desolate patch of road lined with endless coffee plants, I duck into a finca to pee. I walk a few rows until I can't see the road or Beats anymore, pull my jeans down and squat. The wind breathes through the massive trees that border the farm to shade the coffee plants. A lone black vulture circles overhead. My urine makes a soothing hiss as it trickles into the roots. I feel alone even though Beats is yards away.

Plock, plock, plock.

Goosebumps prickle over my exposed backside.

"Beats?"

I yank up my pants and swerve my head to home in on the sound. Between the shiny leaves, I see an indigenous woman in a bright purple smock. An infant cocooned in a scarf hangs on her back like a growth. At her waist is a red plastic bucket hanging from her neck by a colorful woven strap. She reaches up to pluck a handful of bulbous coffee cherries and drops them into the pail.

Plockety, plock, plock.

"Hola," I say in the way of a tourist that always sounds patronizing. She acknowledges me with an unfriendly glance and goes back to her work, the infant gazing at me with matching hostility. I look beyond her at a man's hard,

black eyes. Behind him, more workers mill through the trees. Coffee cherries drum into their buckets, rolling into a percussive cacophony.

I retrace my way out of the maze of shadows into the sun-blanched street. Beats is at the curb blocking the sun with her hand to look at her phone.

"Dude!" I whisper-yell. "There are people in there!"

"What?"

"People ... in there!"

"Guess you better not pee on the coffee," she says, half-distracted, thumbing a message. No doubt, she is texting Bob. She looks up. "Ready?"

An arid north wind pushed out last night's cloud fronts, and the sun sears my cheekbones. My sinuses are powder-coated with fine, pungent dust from the disintegrating pine needles piled along the drainage ditches that line the road. We hike up and down the foothills, past crystalline creeks, ancient water-falls, indigenous shanties, tortured volcanic rock formations, past endless rows of coffee, heavy with swollen, blood-red fruit.

It's not fun though. It aches.

Since seventh grade, Beats and I were one soul in two bodies. Her freckled limbs—the scar on her right knee from falling on my driveway—were as familiar as my own. My voice came out as hers. The smell of her body, dryer sheets mixed with the funk of her greasy old shepherd, was my smell. Our periods were always in sync.

There is no way it will ever be the same with a man in the way, and lately Beats uses phrases that are foreign to our lexicon, things that Bob must have brainwashed into her. *Don't you think you're being compulsive? Stop making yourself the victim of this situation. I feel like you're trying to manipulate me, and I don't appreciate it.*

This is how I've always been, and she never said anything about it before.

"So. How is *Bob?*" I ask.

"Fine," she says. "And you can quit emphasizing his name."

"I still can't believe you're with a guy named *Bob-buh.*" Her face twitches. I know it's not funny to her anymore. His head is shaped like a mallet. I looked it up. People with flat heads were left on their backs too much when the skull is soft and malleable in infancy. Knowing he had neglectful parents makes me almost feel sorry for him. I imagine him and Beatrice in bed when she wants to face him for a kiss good night. He can't turn his head to the side because it's geometrically impossible to roll a cube. He's just stuck there, looking at the ceiling.

"I know I promised I wouldn't be online with him during our trip, but I do have to let him know I'm still alive. Okay?" She stops walking, hands on her hips. "So don't be a dick. He was just wondering why we chose this place."

I shrugged. "Just seemed like a cool place. Mountains, jungle, mystery..."

"I guess so. I mean, it's gorgeous. So much green. Life exploding everywhere."

As we walk, our talk becomes forced—inane comments on the warring hummingbirds, the butterflies being knocked off trajectory by the wind, or the malnourished puppy, covered in scabs, sidling up to us for a pat. We're already acting like different people. It makes me angry.

"You know," I say. "Last night? The sound that freaked us out?"

"It's never left me. Our gods following us."

"Oh, come on." I push her. "You don't still believe in that stuff? It was workers harvesting coffee. Throwing beans into their pails."

"They can't pick coffee at night."

"The moon is crazy bright out here."

"Maybe. Must not be fair trade then."

"Nope. Probably not."

We spot the opening of the trailhead. It funnels into a narrow footpath, so steep that we have to climb with our hands. As we clamber upward, the temperature cools. I don't tell Beats that I do believe in our gods. In my mind, I'm in a constant conversation with them. It's as if they circle us in the fog that creeps up from its secret source, filling the dark spaces between the trees. They know why I chose this place. This mount is legendary in Colombia. If an unwed person stands on Piedra de la Tristeza, they will never marry.

I know it's wrong to bring Beats here, but my inner child, chubby little Tina who sat alone at the lunch table, is wishing with all the power she imagines she possesses that the gods help make this work. The full moon and the night rainbow are signs that all is converging to knock us off this doom trajec-

tory to a life without magic.

With every step, I expect us to reach the summit, but we're blinded by a wall of white mist, its microscopic droplets collecting in my nostrils, condensing, and running down into my lips.

"How far is it supposed to be?" Beats asks.

"I think it said an hour at the most." My voice is too close to me, the mist insulating the sound.

"Do you think we should turn back?"

"No way," I say. "We must be nearly there."

She grabs ropy tangles of vines with raw palms to hoist herself upward. I strain to keep up as her murky form disappears into the mist. I feel like she's deliberately trying to lose me, to put distance between us. But I won't give her the satisfaction of knowing I'm struggling. Just like when we were kids racing our ten-speeds.

The wind whispers against my neck. Leaves clatter at us. Branches sway impishly as if vying for our attention. The unrelenting power of the cloud forest hums beneath our feet, an infrasound that puts me on alert. The animals and plants here have been stewing in this environment for eons. One bite from an equis viper or a pounce from a jaguar will end our story in minutes. I glance at my phone. No cell reception. No data. We're only here because the forest is allowing it.

As we gain altitude, the air thins. My head buzzes, and my lungs feel like they will collapse and stick together. My wet clothes cling to my skin, sucking the heat from my blood. What if I lost Beats? Lost the trail? I imagine being swallowed by the clouds, how hypothermia would sink into my bones, leaving me cold and blue at the foot of one of these ancient trees. The rufous-tailed hummingbirds would flit above my body, deriding me with their impatient, clipped chirps. An indigo butterfly would alight on my nose to make sure I've stopped breathing. Beats will not even realize I've been left behind and will continue with the forest in fierce and beautiful apathy.

But the cloud disperses. Beats looks back to check how far back I've fallen and gives me a challenging smile. The sun flickers through the small spaces in the shell of the canopy, its fingers of light ferrying my anxiety skyward. We step onto the flat plate of rock, like an altar in the sky. The countryside unfurls before us, verdant and choked with life.

"Wow! Look at this," she says.

"It's our throne."

"You just said the gods were our imagination."

"I didn't mean it."

The moment is too heavy. I can't stand the tension between us as the forest drips and stretches and curls around us. I hoot as loud as I can. Birds explode from tree branches.

"You had to," she said.

"What."

"You had to make this about you."

I shrugged.

"It's okay. I'm going to miss this." She embraces me with a quick, light squeeze. Like she's afraid to give too much of herself. "Whatever it is."

We take dozens of pictures on the summit with our phones—gang signs, high-fashion, bitch face, goofy smiles. We have to slide to get down the steep path, and our asses are shellacked with mud. We pollute the cloud forest with profanities, and it feels like before. Running through the past, riotous with sarcasm and laughter, so quick that life couldn't catch us. As we get closer back to civilization, I am filled with noxious anticipation.

But nothing happens after we stand on that rock.

Our last days pass quickly. Beats still jabbers on about wedding plans and regularly texts with Bob. I listen to everything she says closely, to the subtext of their conversations, but I don't detect any discord. I accept it and my desperate, childish attempt to keep my blood sister with me. There is no other way to handle the last hours with her except to get obscenely anesthetized.

We walk to a dance hall at the edge of town, a framework of steel beams and corrugated tin with a concrete floor layered in glossy, chipped paint. We end up sitting with two grimy locals who say they have coke. We do shots and

take turns ducking behind each other to snort powder off the bar. Beats tells her guy, Alvaro, about how this was our last trip before she gets married and that we hiked through the cloud forest and stood on a rock above the valley.

"You went up there?" His eyes widen, and he turns to his friend, Tiago, who doesn't understand any English. "Oye, estás locas subieron la piedra."

Tiago balks.

"Why? What is it?" Beats asks.

"That place is cursed. Anyone who goes there will suffer. They will always be alone."

"You're kidding." Beats glances at me. "Did you know that?"

"Of course not."

"What do you think *Piedra de la Tristeza* means?" He chuckles. "The Stone of Sadness."

"It's not funny," Beats says.

"We don't believe in any of that crap," I say.

Beats' smile never turns my way again. She leans on Alvaro, whispering in his ear as if they are conspiring. I feel the axis of the world shift, that we are operating in an inverted version of it. I remember the dark rainbow, the hard eyes of the coffee workers. Maybe we weren't supposed to come here after all.

I drink aguardiente until my veins are on fire. Tiago tries to teach me to dance the cumbia when I notice the barstools that Beats and Alvaro occupied are empty. The room whirls. The accordions grate my ears. Tiago's smile flashes white. He grabs me as I double over and guides me toward the bathroom. I look up between sticky, sweat-soaked strands of my hair. A man pins a woman against the wall near the bathroom. Entangled, they writhe in the shadows like one monstrous creature, silent except for the rhythmic metallic clang of his belt buckle and the slip of his cowboy boots against the gritty concrete. I stumble to the slimy stall. Tiago holds my hair as I vomit. I casually note that the porcelain says *American Standard*. He gives me another bump off his calloused knuckle. It does little to sober me.

A black gap spans the time between the bathroom and the moment I'm following Beats' feet to the street, watching the hem of her dress swing. I'm still hunched over, being supported by Tiago. We get into a jangling cab. My head lolls back. Streetlights smear over my body.

At the hostel, we collapse in our bunks, sweating liquor and too drunk to sleep. It's impossible to think of tomorrow—packing, airport security, and catching a flight. I listen to Beats' controlled breathing. She is ready to say something. I want her to say it.

"You knew, didn't you?"

"It's not real," I tell her.

"It doesn't matter if it's real. Just like the placebo effect. Homeopathy. Does it matter that it's a sugar pill if people feel better? Does it matter that faith healing is all in someone's mind, a way to break the psychological blockage? Hypnotism and suggestion. *All in the mind* is all there is. If we believe in our gods, they help us. If we hear about a curse, then part of us conspires to make it come true. It's not magic. It's unconscious. Our inner world splattered over reality. That's how anything, everything works."

"So, you're blaming me because you fucked that guy?"

She pauses. She didn't know I saw her. "I'm blaming you for betraying me."

"Does that mean you're going to cancel the wedding?"

"No. But I could've been happy, and this trip has tainted everything."

"These are your last moments as a free woman. Embrace them. I swear on our blood that your secret is safe. You know me."

"No, I don't think I do. I don't even know who I am now."

I try to think of something to say, something that will bring her back to me. "Alvaro is a cool name. And he's got a nice-shaped head. Round."

"You're a toxic person, Tina."

I twist in my blankets and smile bitterly in the dark. Silence. Then snoring. Beats' hand falls and dangles from the top. I grab it and squeeze. It's a limp dead thing. Her phone dings, and I know it's Bob wondering why she's been MIA all night. I picture him in bed, forced to stare at the ceiling as tears slide down into his ears.

The liquor in my blood is waning and allows the cocaine to surface. The moonlight deceives me, makes me believe we're on the constant cusp of dawn though the night has just begun. In a timeless space between bad dreams, I hear the dull, random drumming again. It's angry, like an executioner's march.

I pray it's rain on the roof, or the pounding of the booze in my temples, but I know we've slipped out of our skins, emerged as impostors. Our private gods needed us to exist as much as we needed them, and they weep in some dark grove, cursing our names as they disintegrate and seep into the lightless void of wet, black soil.

DIABLO BALLENA

Jeanne C. Stein

Lake Tota, Columbia

I HAD NO IDEA MY WIFE Eleanor and I weren't happy. Most people would have thought us the perfect couple.

   We met as seniors at Cornell in our early twenties, both anthropology majors, both interested in studying the ancient Muisca culture in Colombia. We had different reasons—she because she was fascinated by their religious beliefs and ceremonies (including human sacrifice) and I because the time before the Spanish Conquest is rich with Muisca mythology—my specialty. After graduation, we were lucky enough to attach ourselves to an anthropological study at Lake Tota, the largest lake in Colombia.

   With the exuberance of youth we married, packed up, bid our families goodbye, and headed to Colombia. It didn't matter that we had no idea what to expect and had no clue what our living conditions would be. We were embarking on an adventure. We knew the town of Aquitania was a well-known Lake Tota tourist destination, popular for wind sailing, hiking, and trout fishing. Our accommodations turned out to be a single room shack far away from the tourist haunts, but that did not diminish our excitement. We were among fellow anthropologists living in our own village, if you will, with very little contact with the big city.

   We got right to work. You might think that my wife and I would work together, but mythology is different from religion. Religion is bound up with deities, temples, and rituals while myths are usually a combination of real events and people. The Spanish who made first contact in the 1530s left a record of the Muisca's mythological creatures, some of whom could change the order of things or bring the dead back to life using substances derived from different plants. But I wasn't much interested in them. I was interested in the

Monster of Lake Tota. The monster I was introduced to in a 1980s B movie called *Monstroid* and who had been the subject of numerous newspaper articles as recently as 2016.

So, each day Eleanor would set out with her guide to explore the remains of ancient temples, and I would travel by myself to a nearby village where there was a young boy Pablo, who in his halting English, would recount the stories told by his father and grandfather of the monster who inhabits Lake Tota.

That he believed these stories, I had no doubt. He was a quick, intelligent handsome eight-year-old who took great pleasure in describing a grotesque, striped-headed fish with a long, sinewy body and teeth that could tear apart an ox.

He explained how Lake Tota was formed by the monster. A high priest threw an immense emerald as an offering to the reptilian creature living at the bottom of a deep cave. When the stone struck the serpent, it became embedded in its skin and lost its natural hardness. The purest green waves poured forth and the vast valley filled with water.

The creature is believed to be living in the lake still, Pablo told me solemnly. Fishermen in his village claim to have seen it, this diablo ballena or devil whale. They stay away from the deepest inlets lest they awaken him from the depths and be swallowed whole.

An inlet like the very one I was living on. Pablo was quick to tell me I musn't do anything to capture the attention of diablo ballena. Never speak loudly on the pier, or fish there at night. I took copious notes, thinking how wonderful it would be to believe as completely as this naive boy in such a legend.

Meanwhile, Eleanor's work was progressing nicely, and she soon spent more time with her exploration partners than with me. At first, I didn't mind. I had my own studies to occupy my time, but truth be told, I began to realize it might not be the ancient religion that held her interest as much as the handsome professor who led their expeditions.

Professor Vega had been our faculty advisor at Cornell and I was aware that his relationship with Eleanor went back farther than that. Years before, he and his (then) new wife moved into the same neighborhood as Eleanor's parents and often spent evenings with them. His stories of exotic peoples and places sparked an interest in the teenager and, as I was soon to find out, sparked an interest in him for her.

But I get ahead of myself. We spent most waking hours apart, true, but our sex life hadn't suffered. We were newlyweds, and more nights than not we made love and fell asleep in each other's arms. Any misgivings I may have felt about the relationship of student to professor were assuaged by the fervency of our passion.

Then six months into our stay, Eleanor announced she was pregnant.

This was unexpected to say the least. We had decided to put off having a family until we had exhausted our anthropological wanderlust, something, as far as I was concerned, we'd hardly begun. And we'd been using protection. Eleanor was on the pill.

Now, I know the saying, man plans and God laughs. I tried to be as happy as Eleanor seemed to be. I even offered to cut short our time and head back home. She, however, was determined to stay.

Then I found her birth control pills, unopened, all twelve packs we brought with us for our year's stay.

When I confronted her about it, she laughed. She told me I needn't be concerned about the baby because it wasn't mine. I could go back home if I wanted. She was staying with the baby's father, Professor Vega.

It was then I realized luck had nothing to do with our being chosen for this expedition. She took great pleasure in telling me she and Professor Vega had been lovers long before she met me. His wife was the jealous type who insisted only married partners accompany him on his treks into the jungle. I played my part perfectly, besotted enough with her to never question her sudden change of heart to marry before we came to Lake Tota. Now that she was pregnant, and she was sure it wasn't mine, Professor Vega's wife would have to let him go.

She told me all this while she packed to leave my hut and move into his.

My brain reeled. How could she be sure the baby wasn't mine? We had been intimate. I challenged her, and she reached under the mattress on our bed and pulled out a diaphragm.

Confusion turned into anger, anger into rage. I stormed out.

There was a rickety old dock spanning the inlet between our hut and the forest surrounding the lake. Pablo said his great-great-grandfather had built it as a fishing dock used by the men in his family for five generations—used until it became known as the place diablo ballena was most likely to be found. I didn't care. I strode out to the end of the dock and sat staring into the murky water.

It was late fall. The pines nearest the lake's edge stood out in sharp relief, but the fern and brush beyond were shapes cloaked in mist. Outrage and indignation turned my thoughts dark with the need for revenge. I never considered myself a vengeful man but what Eleanor and Professor Vega had so calculatedly planned cried out for punishment.

But punish who? Could I harm Eleanor and her unborn child, the innocent in all this? I knew my heart. Probably not. But Professor Vega—a philanderer, a liar, a cheat? I would be doing his wife a service. And Eleanor, too. Once a cheat always a cheat.

Did I want Eleanor back? We had not been married a year and already she betrayed me. And so cleverly that I never had a hint. No, I wouldn't physically hurt Eleanor, but I could never trust her again either.

When I got back to the hut, Eleanor was gone. I trekked to the village to find Pablo. I had a very specific question to ask him. He looked startled that I would ask such a thing, but gave me the information I needed.

I began fishing on the dock, studies forgotten. When one of my classmates came to check on me, I'd make up a story of illness. As the story of Eleanor's betrayal with Professor Vega became common knowledge, though, the visits stopped. I was an object of pity.

The days passed. Every night found me on the dock. I brought a portable radio with me and played it as loud as I could. I wanted diablo ballena to hear, to be tempted by the bait I offered. I would watch the float bob and weave in the gentle current until my eyes grew heavy, and I leaned back against the boards. I tried every bait I could think of, from food scraps to minnows. Then, one night, when I'd actually fallen asleep, it happened.

A startled cry awoke me. I looked around until I realized the cry I heard came from my own lips. The fishing line had pulled so taut, it yanked the pole from my hands. I grabbed for it and managed to snatch it up before it disappeared into the murky water. Something big and silver flashed just below the surface before it was gone in a swirl of silt and debris.

I stared after it. Was this what I was looking for?

Excitement bubbled up. I had used chunks of raw chicken as bait. I got more from a local farmer. That fish would swim to the surface and taunt me by grabbing my line, run with it until he tired of the game. Then he'd snap up the bait and return to whatever depths he inhabited.

One day, a piglet had gotten loose from the farm where I got the chicken. I hadn't realized it was following me until I crossed the bridge and heard a startled squeal. I turned back. The piglet had slipped into the river and faster than a thought, the fish had snatched it up, and in a heartbeat, both were gone.

My heart pounded. Had I really just witnessed a fish gobbling up a ten-pound piglet?

Was it just a fish?

My mind raced. Could it be true? Had I done it? Had I awakened the devil whale? I did a little dance of glee and laughed into the darkness.

My plan came together. I had to work fast. The farm was more than a mile away from my shack, too far to walk for what I had in mind.

Steeling myself to remain calm, I went to Professor Vega and asked if I could borrow his Jeep, the group's only vehicle. I told him I hadn't been feeling well and had to drive to Aquitania to see a doctor. He looked at me with pity in his eyes and said he understood.

He understood.

I wanted to rage at him, bellow my disgust. It took everything I had to nod morosely, eyes downcast. If I looked at him, he would see the hatred that burned in me, the control it took not to strike him down. Eleanor joined us just then, and the fury her sympathetic smile ignited in me made me tremble. I had to hug myself to keep it in check. It was a relief when Professor Vega handed me the keys, and I could get away.

I was still trembling when I arrived at the farm. I asked to buy a butchered pig.

An entire pig.

The farmer's expression mirrored his surprise. I told him I was conducting a forensic experiment, and the flesh of a pig is closest to that of humans. Did he understand? Probably not, but he accepted it with a shrug, most likely because I was paying in cash—U.S. dollars. I suppose he'd grown used to the eccentricities of the foreigners who came to this region to study a culture as alien to us as ours was to him.

I wondered what he'd think if he knew the truth—that I was more like him than he realized. That I not only believed in the diablo ballena, but had resurrected the monster.

He helped me load the carcass into the back of the Jeep. It was wrapped in newspaper, still seeping blood and fluids. I didn't know how I would clean the Jeep after, or even how I would lift a two hundred-fifty-pound bovine by myself when I got it to my hut, but at that moment, I didn't care.

It was dark when I got back. I grabbed an ax from the wood pile, and then pulled the Jeep as close to the pier as I could. The night was moonless, the jungle, strangely quiet. An air of breathless anticipation mingled with the mist billowing off the lake.

By the time I had the pig on the ground, I was drenched in sweat. I stripped off my shirt, stained black with blood. I went to work with the ax, each blow severing a limb or a haunch or a rib until the pieces lay strewn before me. I picked up the head and walked to the end of the jetty.

I tossed it in.

The huge fish leapt to the surface. As if smiling, its wide mouth and sharp teeth flashed before it gulped down the offering. It paused, looking up at me, the stripes on its great bulbous head and long, eel-like body in full display for the first time. We stared at each other. A thrill rippled through me. I wished I could take a picture to capture the moment but I couldn't risk it. Diablo ballena had to remain a myth.

I tossed a second piece in, then a third.

It churned the water, demanding more.

Be patient, I told him. My plan was to feed him over two days until he came to expect the flesh of the pig. Then he'd be ready for the main course.

It took me three hours the next morning to clean the back of the Jeep. I had only pieces of my own wardrobe to use as rags. When I was done, a pair of shorts and some tee shirts were all that was left. No matter. As soon as Professor Vega was taken care of, I'd be going home.

Before I left to return the Jeep, I fed my new friend. He'd consumed half the carcass, and still he demanded more. I clucked my tongue at him and bade him again to be patient.

Next, I bundled the rags I used to clean the Jeep, weighted the bundle with rocks and threw it into a deep part of the lake on the way to Professor Vega's camp. Luckily, he and Eleanor and the rest had already left for their daily trek to the ruins.

I tried the door to the hut. It was open as I'd expected. I told myself I was going in simply to leave the keys where I could be sure he'd find them. But when I saw the rumpled bed where he and Eleanor undoubtedly slept together, I knew the real reason. I needed to confirm my lust for vengeance was justified. I could smell her in the room, and hatred hardened my heart. I couldn't imagine how Eleanor justified her actions or why she had no regard for the professor's wife waiting back in the states. What did she intend to say to her, a woman who she grew up knowing so well and who had attended our wedding? How would she explain to her own parents? Did these thoughts even cross her mind?

I threw the keys on the floor. It occurred to me that Professor Vega seemed unconcerned about any of this. Maybe his infidelity wouldn't have been such a shock to his wife because it had happened before. Seething at the thought, I wanted to take a knife to the bed, to set fire to it.

But I contented myself with the knowledge that my revenge was far more appropriate.

When I walked back to my own hut, I was surprised to see Pablo waiting for me. He stood over the remains of the pig, a puzzled frown on his face. He spied me, and the frown turned into a smile. I expected him to pepper me with questions, but he only asked where I'd been. He missed our conversations.

I paused before answering. Should I show him the object of the tales he'd shared with me? Prove that myths were founded in reality?

Or was that taking a chance he might piece together Professor Vega's disappearance?

I was so close now. Less than a day away from fulfilling my fantasy.

Soon the pig was forgotten. The very reason he'd come to find me, he said excitedly, was diablo ballena. The locals were saying there had been sightings, and many were afraid to venture out on the lake again.

I could hardly contain my glee. What perfect timing!

After Pablo left, I threw the remaining pig pieces into the lake. The water boiled as the monster thrashed, snatching the pieces from the air and shaking them the way a dog shakes a bone before gulping them down. His massive head lifted from the water, seeking more.

We were both ready.

I sent a note to Vega worded to be sure he'd come alone to meet me after dark. If he didn't, I wrote, I would tell his colleagues at the university about his affair when I returned to the States. Involvement with a student was frowned upon, especially when the affair began years ago when Eleanor was underage.

Then I waited for him at the end of the jetty.

Diablo ballena waited with me, there, just under the surface of the water, watching. His huge lidless eyes stared into mine.

"Soon, my friend," I whispered.

I smiled at the irony.

Eleanor was studying an ancient religion that practiced human sacrifice.

Her Professor Vega was about to become one.

20 January 1941

"Fishermen in his village claim to have seen it, this diablo ballena or 'devil whale.'"

According to the indigenous Muisca culture, the diablo ballena ("devil whale") has had a presence in Columbia's Lake Tota since the 1500s. This legendary lake monster was documented by conquistador Gonzalo Jiménez de Quesada in 1676 and again by French explorer Gaspard Théodore Mollien in 1823. Research indicates that the monstrous fish hibernates, sometimes for decades, before surfacing its black, oxlike head in search of fresh meat. Sonar shows Lake Tota reaching depths up to 190 feet. The cold temperature of the water and fresh influx from the Upia River invigorate this freshwater devil. Legend claims that those who wake the great black snake are doomed to cater to its monstrous appetite until the creature takes them as a final sacrifice before it sleeps once more in its great underwater cave.

It was December 1940, with the war raging in the background, that I encountered my first cryptid, the diablo ballena. I was on assignment — my first actually — as apprentice agent, under the supervision of Agent J. Falcio. The man was a domineering jackass, the kind that refused the work and hoarded the glory. We already had a personal conflict in full swing the night I was made to stand watch at the lake's edge, a task always assigned to me. The creature surfaced for the barest of moments — seconds really, in which I was able to capture but one photo. The next morning, when he expected me to report out, I lied and told him I saw nothing. When we returned to the Western Scriptorium, he was incensed when I made a full report to the head archivist, refusing to name him as partner. I was written up for that little stunt, but it solidified my reputation and, I like to think, made fellow agents think twice about trying to take advantage of me.

UMBRA · ARCA

CASE · NOTE

AGENT No. _____

TASTE OF SORROW

Warren Hammond

Guyana

I SCAN THE PALTRY COLLECTION OF BOTTLES behind the bar and see little besides the ubiquitous Bacardi and Captain Morgan. Shaking my head, I lament the fact that some of the best rum in the world is made right here in Georgetown, yet the bars are stocked like ill-bred frat houses.

I take a seat on a wobbly stool, mop my brow, and look out the window, where the sea breeze has evaporated into a clingy haze fueled by the Guyanese sun. I drop my hat on the bar and pull at the collar of my sweat-logged button-down.

The bar is unattended, but I can hear the buzz of refrigeration and know that a chilled bottle of Coke will soon be my reward. I have little hope this bar has what I've really come so far to find, but after dozens of fruitless stops, I decide this is as fine a place as any to wait out the most stifling hours of the day. I bet they'll feed me if I ask. Not that I have much appetite since I entered my eighties.

Outside, the Demerara River flows lazily by, and I pull a rag from my pocket to dry the back of my neck. I hear somebody speaking Creole nearby and get to my tired feet to peek out the open window. A man and a woman talk while she waters plants that hang from a wall painted Caribbean blue. I get the man's attention, and he offers a broad, welcoming smile before hustling in to fetch me the Coke I so desperately need.

"American?" he asks.

"New Orleans," I say before a long, sweet swig. I reach into my pocket and pull out my phone. I swipe away another message from my lawyer then call up the same picture I've shown to barkeeps all over Georgetown for six days running. It's a bottle with a handwritten label that simply says *rum*.

He reaches under the bar to pull out an identical bottle. "That's it!" I dance off my seat. "I've come all the way from America to find that rum."

"Are you a collector?"

"The finest."

He grabs two glasses. I'm already salivating. I have over two thousand bottles of rum in my collection: the fresh and grassy rhum agricoles of Martinique, the funky Jamaicans rich with hogo, and of course, my absolute favorites—the seductive and smoky Demerara rums of Guyana.

But this bottle before me is different. Special. I watch him pour two fingers. It has the color of a classic Demerara, dark and mouth-watering as a Vermont maple syrup. I put my nose into the glass and get a bouquet bursting with chocolate, vanilla, and toasted coconut.

This rum is the best I've ever had. I'm convinced it's the best that's ever been bottled.

Lifting the glass to my lips, I welcome the rum onto my tongue, where it tingles with nutmeg and citrus over a rummy baseline of treacly burnt sugar. I swallow and barely feel the burrs before it mellows even further into a warm finish that brings tears to an old man's eyes. "It's sublime," I say. "A religious experience."

"It's magical," says the bartender. "It's rare I meet a fellow connoisseur."

I savor another sip, and like every taste of the previous bottle I drank, I try to identify the mystery flavor. It hides in the background, barely perceptible. It's redolent of almond, but it's different. Unique. Otherworldly.

"What is that flavor?" I ask. "Similar to almonds, but not almonds."

"I don't know, but this rum is pure magic." He takes a sip and keeps it in his mouth for a long while before swallowing. "Just like the old legends that come from deep in the jungle."

I chuckle and hold out my glass for a refill. "Witchery and voodoo."

"So they say. How did you come to learn of it?"

"I bought a bottle off a Ukrainian sailor who works a container ship. Where does it come from? Who makes it?"

"It comes from Port Kaituma, just a few bottles at a time. I don't know any more than that."

"Where's Port Kaituma?"

"Inland. Do you want to go? I know somebody who can take you."

"Tomorrow," I say. "Today, I want to spend the afternoon and evening

right here on this stool."

"As you wish. But I'm not responsible if you have visions."

My head snaps to look at him. "Visions?"

A knowing grin breaks on his face. "That's the magic."

The river cuts a meandering channel in the jungle, and the fishing boat rides deep in the still water. The hard seat hurts my bones after a full day's travel. Jungle greenery thins, and I see houses of wood and cinderblock. Port Kaituma. The boat putters up to a dock, and the fisherman helps me carry my bags to his cousin's home, where I've been promised dinner and a room. I spend the last hour before bed on a second-floor balcony looking down on an intersection of dirt roads.

My phone gets no service here, which suits me fine. I don't need more warnings of liens and asset seizures. Blaylock, Blaylock and Finch can go screw themselves if they think they'll ever get a penny from me.

I sip on the flask I filled before departing Georgetown. The rum delight-fully reawakens the peppery aftertastes of my meal, and I keep tippling until my vision blurs.

Then I'm back home, back in my attic, surrounded by racks and racks of precious bottles. I know it has to be a dream, but it's so vivid. So real. The attic is alive with the smell of old wood and mildew. I run my fingers from bottle to bottle feeling a surge of pride at having amassed the world's most exquisite collection of rums. But the pride welling inside me quickly sours and spoils.

I push one of the racks over, and the bottles crash to the floor. Shattering glass unleashes the boozy, eye-stinging odor of spilt rum. I yank another rack over and my collections of Barbados rums shatter and splash across the floor. Moving faster than I have in years, I tip every rack, every shelf, until my collec-tion has been destroyed.

Finally, I eye the locked display case that hangs on the wall. I key it open and pull out the most precious bottle I own. An 1872 rum issued by the British Navy. I hurl it against the wall with such force it explodes.

I slump to the floor. My hand wraps the jagged neck of a corked bottle and I lift it to my face. A small puddle of a dark Demerara is trapped in the spout, and I pour that last sip into my mouth before jamming the sharp glass into my neck.

Warm blood spurts and spills, and I watch it mingle with the wash of rum seeping through the cracks between the floorboards. My life's work destroyed in a frenzy of righteous pique.

Take that, Blaylock, Blaylock and Finch! You may have won your lawsuit, but you'll never get your greedy paws on my collection. Bastards thought they could auction off my rum to pay their almost-seven-figure award? Screw them and their blinded clients.

I admit I feel bad for their teenaged clients, who I hired to paint the downstairs. Yes, I promised the underaged pair a bottle, but only after they asked for one. I didn't mean for them to help themselves to one of the boot-legged bottles of 1930 rum I keep in the basement. That batch blinded two dozen in Atlanta at the dawn of the Depression. I bought those cases for their historical significance.

Granted, I hadn't labeled them as dangerous, but what happened was an accident. How dare their lawyers try to take my life's work—my one and only passion—away from me?

I drop my soon-to-be lifeless fingers into a wet puddle of rum and smile at the beauty of it. Those suits won't get a cent. I'm the one who did the liquidating.

I wake. I'm standing on the balcony, still looking down on the dirt roads. That's the second time I've had that dream. A vision is what the barkeep in Georgetown called it. The first time it happened was when I drank the bottle I bought off the Ukrainian.

Whatever magic that rum holds, I can't wait to find out what it is. Then once this final itch is scratched, it will be time to go back home and make that vision a reality.

I step out of the jeep into a muddy rut. I thank the driver and turn to face the jungle. A path of overgrown stepping stones leads me into the trees. The canopy above is dense, only allowing a few sparkling beams of sunlight to fall all the way to the ground. The air is fragrant with vegetation that blooms, or wilts, or rots.

I keep to the path as a drop of sweat finds its way down my spine. Deep guttural croaks sound from somewhere high above, and I look up.

"Howler monkeys."

Disoriented, I look about for the source of the voice and find a woman coming from the trees. She looks to be in her fifties, a gray afro poking out from under a baseball cap. "The howlers are used to seeing me, but they make a racket whenever I have a visitor."

She labors to carry a bucket of water.

"Can I help you with that," I ask.

"Are you kidding? What are you, a hundred?"

"Thereabouts. I'm Jeffrey. I came all the way from Louisiana. I'm a collector of rare rums."

"I'm Barb," she says. "You're in the right place if you're looking for rare. I barely do a thousand bottles a year. How did you hear of me? Don't tell me my rum made it all the way to the U.S."

"It did. I'm so honored to meet you. You're an artist."

She laughs and shakes her head.

"Truly." I place a hand over my heart. "I've tasted them all, and you make the finest rum the world has ever seen."

"You're quite the charmer. Come, Jeffrey from Louisiana, let me give you the tour."

The distillery is a large one-room structure with a hammock and a kitchen consisting of a hotplate and a small refrigerator. Before I can ask where the power comes from, she says, "Solar panels." Then before I can ask how she gets enough sun, she tells me the panels are installed in a clearing about a hundred yards away.

A trapdoor sits in the center of the room, and she lifts it to take me down to a cellar where two dozen oaken barrels age. "I've been out here doing this for over nine years now," she says. "In two months, I'll be ready to bottle my first ten-year."

"What did I drink?"

"A five-year."

I can barely imagine what another half decade of aging can do to a rum that's already so incredibly perfect. "My god, can I try the ten-year?"

She chuckles. "Only if you stay until September."

I nod. "I'll earn my keep. I might be old, but I'm not afraid to work."

"Whoa," she says. "How about we take this relationship one step at a time?"

Chagrinned, I let it drop. For now. "You know, I barely detect an accent when you speak. Aren't you Guyanese?"

"I'm from San Francisco. Came to Guyana when I was fifteen, and I was orphaned at seventeen. Got my first job at the El Dorado distillery in George-town. They had me pouring sips in their tasting room, but I always felt more comfortable wearing overalls than a dress, so I coaxed my way into the produc-tion side of the business and worked my way up to becoming a master distiller."

"You left there to come here?"

"After learning everything I could working at another half-dozen distill-eries, yes. I also learned some incredible tricks apprenticing with the rumrun-ners down in the jungles near the Brazilian border. They're schooled in the old ways."

"The visions. What causes them? Did they teach you to put ayahuasca in the rum?"

"You get visions when you drink my rum?"

I nod. "And what's that mysterious flavor? It tastes like almond, but it's not almond."

She answers with a smirk. "You don't know me well enough to be asking such personal questions. How about you ask something else?"

"You said you were orphaned. How did that happen?"

"You don't know where we are?"

I shake my head.

She leads me back up the stairs then outside into the jungle. We follow the snaking trail of a power cord until we enter a clearing. Passing her solar panels, she leads me to a battered old sign that lies on the ground. She struggles to lift it free of grasping grasses that don't want to let it loose. I have to kneel to see the sign's underside. Painted in green lettering, it says, *Welcome to the Peoples Temple of Jonestown.*

I climb down the ladder and drop the wire brush on the workbench. I've been in Guyana for six weeks now. I spend my nights in town. My days apprenticing.

I rest a palm on the smooth copper surface of Barb's still. "The pot's as clean as new."

Barb hands me a cold glass of water. "The wash is done fermenting. We distill first thing in the morning, but we need to get one more ingredient first."

"The secret ingredient?" I ask with a hopeful rise of eyebrows.

"You've earned it."

I set my glass of water down. "Let's go."

She holds up a bottle. "Not yet. First, we drink. A lot."

I'm drunk. But I can walk and so can Barb, who carries a cooler. I follow her past the solar panel to where the Jonestown sign stands tall overhead.

Drunk as I am, I know that's impossible. "The sign, it was too badly damaged. You couldn't have fixed it."

She looks up at the sign, and her eyes mist over. The heavy burden of pain I know she carries every day is now bubbling to the surface. But then she lifts a hand to cover her heart and she smiles.

"Where are we going?" I ask.

"Home."

We pass under the sign and into the compound, which is bustling with late-afternoon activity. I see people working a field of crops. A bulldozer rumbles in the distance, perhaps leveling a plot for another wooden structure to go up. It looks just like I remember it from the TV news back in 1978, only this is before everybody died.

My knees feel weak, and I have to stop. Barb puts a steadying hand on my elbow.

"The rum," I say. "Somehow, it's brought me into your past."

"You call them visions."

"My god, what did those rumrunners teach you down at the border?"

Barb races ahead to hug a pair of young girls playing on a small playground. She introduces me to her little sisters. Amazingly, they don't seem to notice that Barb has aged.

The girls run back to the swing set. Barb says, "I should've never left them. Or my parents. But I was scared, and I ran." She points in the direction we came from. "I hid until it was over."

"There's nothing wrong with wanting to survive."

She leads me to a simple stilted structure painted sky blue. "I want to see my parents and my grandmother now." She beckons me to follow her in, but I decline. Being in this place, remembering the horrific images of what happened here, makes me maudlin. I find a stump to sit on and watch the children play as the sun sets behind the trees.

A tractor pulling a trailer arrives at the compound. Men armed with shotguns and rifles jump down, and I know they've just come from the Port Kaituma airstrip, where Barb told me a congressman and others were shot and killed while taking a group of defectors out of Jonestown.

Knowing what's to come next, my gut churns with dread. My head is still hazed with intoxication but I ache to sober up quick so this vision can end before the catastrophe.

Barb brings a snack to her sisters, and the trio chats and giggles. Barb sees me and waves. I lift a hand to wave back when an announcement comes over the loudspeakers. Everyone is to report to the pavilion.

Armed men herd people toward the center of Jonestown, and we find a place to sit just outside the pavilion, but well inside the perimeter formed by

armed guards. I can see inside, and on the low stage at the front, I can see him, sitting on a deck chair, speaking into a microphone. He wears sunglasses, and his beleaguered voice pleads and cajoles. The U.S. congressman is dead. The journalists in his entourage are dead. The government is coming for vengeance, and Jones wants to end it. Here and now.

Barb fusses with her sisters' hair and tells them how she plans to take them to Disney World. She's doing a fine job keeping them from getting scared. Righting the wrong of abandoning them in 1978.

When Barb and I work in the distillery, she often talks about Jonestown, most of it good. It really was home to her. The only home where she felt she belonged. Where she was a part of something greater than herself. Making rum is what she loves to do now, but Jonestown—she always tells me after a couple drinks—is the only place where she ever felt loved.

I listen as Barb continues to do a masterful job of entertaining her young sisters. I imagine she relives this vision over and over, her solitary goal to fill her sisters' last hours with joy instead of fear. When lines begin to form inside the pavilion, she tells her sisters to stay where they are before rising to go inside. She comes back with three cups of Flavor-Aid.

I tell her not to do this.

"It's okay," she says. "This was how my life was supposed to go." She drinks her share down before encouraging her sisters to do the same. Barb begins to convulse. I rush to her. I cradle her head as blood and vomit spill from her mouth, and she wheezes in pain.

Her sisters thrash and roll in the grass. Helplessly, I watch their agonizing passage from this world. All around, I spot so many babies and toddlers among the adults. I never realized how many of the 909 people who died here were children. I see a woman approaching with a tray full of cups. I leave Barb's unmoving corpse to hustle the opposite way. Many are coming out of the pavilion now, but few make it far before doubling over in agony.

I make it a few steps more before an armed guard stops me. A needle enters near my shoulder, and I jerk away, the syringe still sticking from my arm. I yank it painfully free. The needle is bent and the plunger is depressed. I throw it at the woman who deployed it, but it bounces harmlessly off her leg. A searing pain seizes hold, and I collapse. I land on a toddler who spasms under my weight. I manage to roll off him, but I know he'll die anyway. We all will.

More people scramble from the pavilion. They scream and tumble, one piling onto the next. Like the rest of them, I cough up mouthfuls of blood. Desperate for air, my burning chest heaves up and down, but I can't breathe. God, it hurts so much more than I could've imagined.

I reach for the toddler's hand and hold it tight until my vision mercifully goes dark.

I wake. I crawl out from under the reeking bodies of two women. Forcing myself to sit up, I see the once-proud residents of Jonestown strewn across the ground like trash in a landfill.

The toddler I fell upon stares emptily into the dawning sun, his young features stripped of life. I remember the pictures from TV so many decades ago, the shocking spill of hundreds and hundreds of bodies that flowed from the pavilion. Now I sit right in the middle of it. There's no impenetrable TV screen to shield me from the deathly stench of this place. Nothing to protect me from the close-up view of unfathomable tragedy.

Ten feet away, Barb's sisters are covered by a sheet. It's the only ounce of respect afforded any of the deceased. In the pavilion, I find Jim Jones dead of a gunshot wound. Barb comes up to me and rests a hand on my shoulder.

"Why did he do it?" I ask. "Why?"

"He was just a spoiled child. If he couldn't get what he wanted, he was going to kick over his sandcastle."

The weight of it all is too much, and I slump to the floor. I find myself seized by long, wracking sobs. I cry until my cheeks are wet and my ribs ache.

Barb tells me it's time to go. She lifts a bucket and asks me to hold the lid of the cooler open. "We only need a little," she says. "Too much would make the rum dangerous to drink." She pours in some of the cyanide-laced grape Flavor-Aid. It smells like almonds but not almonds.

"The taste of sorrow," she says.

Barb and I share a drink. We're celebrating the successful distillation of three barrels of rum. "It will be September soon," says Barb. "Think you'll stay around long enough to try the ten-year?"

I sip my rum. Though I haven't told her, I'm celebrating something else tonight. I've spent the last two hours in town talking to my lawyer on a satellite phone, instructing her to sell every last bottle in my collection except for the Depression-era cases of rum in the basement that need to be destroyed.

Take the money, I told her, and pay off the lawsuit as well as your fees. If any money is left over, donate it to a charity that serves the blind.

Oh, and the only condition for rum sales is this: buyers need to promise they'll drink the rum within one year of purchase.

When my lawyer asked me why the change of heart, I told her I wasn't going to knock down sandcastles. Now, I'm a builder. A producer.

"Hey, I'm talking to you, old man," says Barb with a teasing smile. "Think you'll live long enough to see September?"

I smile. "I'm not going anywhere. Not until I taste the twenty-year."

30 March 2001

"I smile. 'I'm not going anywhere.
Not until I taste the twenty-year.'"

As it doesn't take much cyanide for a fatal dose in humans, it is worth an inquiry to test the tainted Flavor-Aid for transmutation during the transportation of the liquid through time. However, the acquisition of this obscure Demerara rum has so far proven to be difficult to acquire. Other variations of the smoky, high-roller rum have proven to provide a pleasant repast, but the Caribbean distillates sampled so far have not been accompanied by the described visions. Investigation continues.

UMBRA ARCA
CASE NOTE

AGENT No. _____

MASSACOORAMAAN

Large, hairy monster
with white fur and
yeti-like features.

Dwells in rivers, stalking boats
and eating their passengers.

THE MASSACOORAMAAN

Christina Sng

Guyana

We drifted down the rivers of Guyana,
Ever mindful of the massacooramaan.

It was the only way to escape the plague
Engulfing the entire country,

Dead creatures rising to eat the living
Without remorse or regret.

We feared the plague
More than a myth haunting the river.

That was our first mistake.
It would not be the last we made.

We rode the Essequibo River
Heading to the Atlantic Ocean.

As the widest river in Guyana,
We were safe from both banks

But the massacooramaan
Was everywhere—over and under.

There was no place to go
But faster.

It knocked our boat at Linden
Before we swatted it with our paddles,

Chasing it away for a brief time
Before it followed us again.

Please, I begged the universe,
We were almost at Georgetown

Where we could board a larger boat,
Sail across the Atlantic,

Far from the plague
And the massacooramaan.

But the gods did not listen.
It pulled itself into our boat,

The white-haired Yeti-like creature,
Standing over all of us

Grabbing my husband
And biting him in half.

No loss, I thought,
Gingerly touching the black eye

He gave me last night.
I kicked them both into the river

And let the tides take them away.
Let the monsters have each other.

We reached Georgetown by morning.
It was empty

But for the dead bodies
Crisp under our Guyanan sun.

We took the largest boat,
Scampered and searched for supplies,

Memorized the map to the highlands
And let the sea take us.

No more plague, no more undead,
Only freedom from all the monsters.

ESSEX

19th Century
whaling ship

Sperm Whale

FOR THE FIRES OF FLOREANA

Cameron E. Quinn

Galápagos Islands, Ecuador

Before this land had the name scrawled on yesterday's maps,
between this volcanic island's first and last great fires,
when this place had more to lose—thus more to fear—she came.

What is a ship if not a seed?
Blown to grow fat on nutrients somewhere far from its mother's roots.

Its belly full of barrels, oil skimmed from the bloody death of whales,
Essex made landfall to fix and to feast.

What is a ship if not kindling?
Poised to set the world on fire.

The Englishman swapped tiller for tinder, thought a bush ablaze a lark
(ha), and—though it was all he'd ever sought—he lost
control. The incendiary cries of flycatchers and finches fell like

tears to jaws of leviathans buoyed by spermaceti, suspended tombstones
wearing the scars of kin who burned in lamps above the waves. The largest
rose like steam, echoing concern at the crackle of tortoises boiled to extinction.

What is a ship if not a seed?
Begging to be split open under the broad, Pacific sky.

The whale gained directions from dolphins who tripped over the *Essex*'s wake.
At night, the beast flossed with the tentacles of giant squid and hummed
the death-moans of geckos and iguanas like lullabies. By day it stalked the ship,
a bright shadow calling on ancient knowledge to recognize
waters too remote for rescue.

What is a ship if not kindling?
Waiting to be splintered.

Hull gave way to skull, scattering hands like seeds left to drift or drown,
but the arsonist escaped. The whale paced the ocean in contemplation, traced
a path like a spider's web, felt the sea tremble when the man alighted.
Whalesong tugged a thread like a current; called for justice.

What is a man if not a ship?
Carrying pathogens like passengers, queasy incubation between the planks,
eager to disembark.

The cautionary tale was tossed ashore like a breaker and carried further,
disguised in the carapacal crack of the crab-eating macaque,
the coos of koel and boobook,
the flight of dragons between timorous trees,
and buzz of mosquito assassins bearing vengeance.

The memory found the man and bit him, her proboscis
forged in brushfire intentionally set, lifted on wings of ash. The man burned.
His fever, a flame lit by his own body (ha)
to frighten his conscience as it gathered fuel.

22 September 1966

"Thought a bush ablaze a lark"

I was told that spectral flames could still be seen on the blackest nights, although I was unable to confirm this upon my visit. An old man, a self-described poet and a descendant of one of the first European families to call the island home, called me to his house one night and told me the following tale:

"When I was ten summers, I grew to know the hills and rocks of this island like my own skin. I spent days outdoors, combing through the grasses, digging in the sand, clambering over the stones. One evening, I was late returning home and somehow got turned about when coming down from a crest of a hill. I found myself in a spot of blackness and ash. The stones were scorched. The sand had melted and fused into sheets of glass. Not a living thing anywhere to be seen. I wandered around, confused and with increasing fear, for I had no idea where I was on all the island which I knew so well. I began to run in my panic, screaming for someone to hear me. Everything was dead and black. After a time, I stumbled and fell over a stone. When I pushed myself up on my hands and knees, I was shocked to see the lush greenery around me once more. I have never been able to relocate that spot in all my years. I only tell you this as a caution to be mindful of your surrounds as you ramble about this island. It has a fierce memory."

Mt.
Kunturiri

UMBRA ARCA CASE FILE

Acalica

Andes Mountains, Bolivia

Specimen #SW980-338:003

Coordinates: 18°2′30″S 69°4′28″W

Location: Kunturiri, Andes Mountains, Bolivia

Location Description: Kunturiri is a volcanic mountain peak
on the border of Bolivia and Chile. Although active, it is
covered in ice and snowfields. Caves, no bigger than pockets,
are strung about the upper reaches of the mountains like
pearls on a neck. Hydrothermal activity and periodic tremors
present.

Specimen Description: One pair of Acalica wings. Extremely
fragile. Full specimen was an individual Acalica, appearance resembling a miniature wizened man with moth wings.
Specimen was caught in one of the Kunturiri caves, although
soon perished upon removal to a lower altitude. Body quickly
became rotten and unsalvageable; only the wings were
preserved. Wings are composed of a proteinaceous membrane
covered with tiny hairs and platelike setae, or protein
scales. Wings are primarily blue in color with a sinuous black
pattern visible on both sides. They are 40 cm in length and 24
cm in width at their widest point.

Acalica are said to control the weather near their envi-
rons. Locals believe that if these tricksters can be appeased
through gifts of sweets, they will grant pleasant weather and
fewer earth tremors.

UMBRA  ARCA
C A S E   N O T E

THE SCARLET TANAGER

Starlene Justice

Andes Mountains, Peru

"**T**HEY GO AT NIGHT," my little sister told me. "The birds."

She was lying on her back in the pale grass that grew sparsely at high elevations, and her tone held a brevity reserved for the most serious situations. I looked over at her with interest. Her arms were stretched out at right angles to her body, mimicking the birds she was thinking about.

"Go? Go where?" I asked. "What birds?"

A rare warm day had pushed the temperature to just over 16 degrees Celsius. I was lying next to her, thinking of everything I needed to do, and wondering why my little sister, Windy, had the luxury to daydream and philosophize. She seemed so tranquil, sprawled out in her ten-year-old body that transferred almost no weight into the ground beneath her.

"Migratory birds," she said, not looking at me.

Here we go again with the birds. I was staring at the violet-blue sky that was so clear it could hold your gaze forever. I almost thought that if I stared into those vibrant depths for long enough, I would float into the heavens and simply become a part of the atmosphere. I thought that might be what it meant to "become one" with nature, and that seemed a better fate than the one that probably awaited me here.

"Can you imagine it?" Windy asked, her tone growing both wistful and frightened. "A billion birds crossing the night sky and, meanwhile, people sleep, completely clueless."

For her sake, I did try to imagine it. I pictured an inky black sky full of stars that kept getting blotted out by clouds of birds. Starlight flickering in and out as great waves of winged beings passed through, silent and eerie.

"Sounds creepy," I said.

I stood up from my seat on the dried-out grass of the Andean plateau we had climbed. She, in her black woven shoes and dress that looked like faded yellow burlap. Me, in my heavy sweater of multi-colored yarn—too warm for this day—and woolen boots. We were opposites, she and I. Born five years apart, but it may as well have been a generation. "Maybe you're just making it up," I added.

"I'm not!" Windy cried out so plaintively I felt a stab in my heart. She climbed to her feet and glared at me. I hadn't meant to be hurtful. And I knew she wasn't making it up.

I guess I was jealous. She was so smart, and she had a passion that emanated from her like an aura. I didn't understand why she loved birds so much, or how it could possibly matter. But if I could have had one-quarter of her love for—anything—I'd have had a better life. Or maybe if I had just been strong enough to hold onto the things I loved.

She grew quiet, shoving her hurt down into the cavity of her chest, as she had learned to do from growing up with an unhappy mother and a manipulative, now-deceased father. She was so transparent. "I am a scarlet tanager," she said to me suddenly, spreading her arms and twirling so that I could observe her clever disguise. When she lifted her arms, I saw the black on her sleeves that mimicked wings on a pale, yellow body.

"You're not scarlet at all," I said to her, forgetting that Windy would take to heart every word I said to her.

Her eyes met mine—dark orbs that held within their depths all the hope and bitterness she had never been able to reconcile. She was like a trusting dog that still sought love even when it expected only to be kicked. "I am a female," she said, quietly. "The females are not so bright."

"But you are," I said to her, meeting her sad gaze.

She smiled. A little crease in her round, childish face.

I walked to the edge of the plateau. Looking down, I could see the village where we live. It is Ritticapa, Peru. A city spilling down a mountainside in the wake of a glacier that hovers, eternally, just above it. In the background, the soaring, ice-covered peaks of Chopicalqui, like whitewashed castles catching the glistening light. Within my field of vision, I can just make out a sliver of blue, held captive in a basin I can't quite see. It is a lake, formed from a melted glacier. Legends tell a different tale; they tell of a lost boy who died and then became the lake. This is why the lake is named Rafael. Rafael of Ritticapa. But

unless you live here, you do not know of this city. It does not exist.

There is a city that *does* exist. It is called La Rinconada. It is far south of Ritticapa. You can actually find it on a map. I have been there with my father, this city in the sky. La Rinconada is the highest inhabited city in the world. A city in the clouds. Sounds so romantic, doesn't it?

It took many days of travel to get there, winding our way through glaciated valleys and along the edges of ice-shorn cliffs, climbing so high the world became a different color and the air didn't know how to fill our lungs. I have been acclimated all my life to high elevations, but this was different. I begged my father to turn back but begging from a child was like prodding to him. When I told him there was a fog in my head, and I was too cold to sleep, he told me to pretend I was in a dream. In a dream, you don't have to feel anything; you only have to observe.

I was told that La Rinconada was a city of gold, but, really, it was a city of gold *mines*. That's quite different, isn't it? What stunned my young mind, though, was all the trash. Not because it was there, or because there was so much of it, but because its presence stole some of the wildness from this inhospitable place and made it faintly comforting—as if you *could* survive, after all, if people had lived long enough to make all that trash. I drew strength from the idea, even though my head still felt like it was floating above my body in the thin, frozen air.

It was in this city of gold mines and garbage—that flowed down every hillside like an abomination—that my father stole his next wife, who became the mother of my little sister, Windy.

One day, my sister said this to me: "I was told that our father named me 'Windy' because he wanted a daughter who would not be held back by anything. A daughter who could not be silenced, who could not be stopped by man-made walls or God-made stands of trees."

I thought of this uncouth man who never cared for anyone but himself, and who once counseled me that I should let my brains rot because only men ever become scientists, and women were only made for being wives. I responded bitterly to my sister: "In death, it seems, people are made to be more eloquent than they were in life."

"Still," she said, narrowing her dark eyes at me, "I will not be held back."

Her determination was both a song in my soul and a thorn in my side.

In my country, the Incan kings lived in the lowlands, in the jungles to the east of us. From those jungles, our history and stories arose. All Peruvians know these stories. But those were not the only ones, were they? Peru is not a country that can be defined only by the rainforests. There are deserts, too, and mountains of such staggering elevation they defy inhabitation. And yet people live there. If there are legends and ghosts in the jungles, surely there are stories about the mountains, too. Who else lives here, with Windy and me, in these craggy heights, among these gaping, screaming canyons?

I think I know. Enormous, long-legged creatures like spiders. Spiders whose limbs could reach over every peak with a simple lifting. But that is not what frightened me the most. What frightened me was that these spiders had "herders," those who orchestrated their moves.

I imagined these individuals as tree-like creatures with wild hair and stern expressions, like old, stony men with bark for skin and long, empty branches sprouting from their heads. But I was only partially right. I discovered the truth when I saw them in La Rinconada. They were not like trees; they were like tattered cloth blowing in the wind with a mouth that gaped until a great will drew the ragged lips together and then a sharp whistling sound would emanate. I have heard that whistle once or twice and good things never came of it. When my father told me to pretend I was in a dream while I climbed to an unsurvivable place, these are the images I saw and the sounds I heard.

But in that moment on the plateau above Ritticapa, none of it mattered because Windy wanted to talk about the birds.

She had forgotten that I seemed impervious to her desires and her pain. She had forgotten that being sisters means being best friends *and* favorite enemies. She only remembered the "friends" part.

"Sometimes the scarlet tanagers overwinter in the coffee plantations," she told me, excitedly, following me to the edge of the plateau where I had retreated from her. "That is why they come this far south. The coffee growers help them. Isn't it amazing?"

"It's interesting," I said. "But I'm sure they don't help them on purpose."

Windy followed me in faithful devotion, as I left the plateau and skipped down the narrow trail that led us back to our village. I shed my woolen muffler and held it out behind me like a flag. I hoped she would want to play games instead of engaging in conversations.

What could I say to her anyway? I knew she would never go away to school. She would never be an ornithologist. She would never study flight patterns of endangered birds that filled the Peruvian jungle in December and rendered it a ghost town in July. She would never drink coffee specifically selected because the farmers made sure birds had a migratory home. She would, instead, grow disenchanted as every opportunity faded and turned to poison. She would likely get married in a Catholic church with a baby already in her belly. Her husband would find other wives, and she would grow angry at her own children because she could not save them. I did not want to know these things in advance and ruin my little sister's dreams. But all the same, I knew them.

My thoughts were interrupted by a whistle. It was shrill, and long, and it seemed to carry from the jagged peaks that sheltered Ritticapa. It ruffled my woolen muffler and lifted my hair away from my face. Windy stopped before I did. "Sissy!" she screamed, and I dug my feet into the ground just as a gash opened up in the trail in front of me.

If a snake had reared its head right in my path, I could not have stopped more suddenly. But I found that I could not hold my feet still, and my body swayed as if blown by a great wind. I crouched down on my heels. "Earthquake!" I screamed to Windy. But she was gone, running down the hillside in a straight line, her arms flapping like a bird, the dust billowing behind her as her heels dug up pillowed tufts of packed earth. I could not tell if she propelled herself down the mountain, or if the mountain heaved her along against her will, but I knew what she was doing: she was running to her mother. Running to safety.

I did not see the boulders flowing like a river in my little sister's wake. I did not see them because I could not look. Instead, I followed a whistling sound to the peak of Chopicalqui, and there, like in my nightmares, the spiders flowed over the top. Ghost-thin spiders with legs that tore into web-like strands as they struggled to come over the mountain and into the valley of Ritticapa. My heart seized with pity for them. It was as if they were dying in their moment of birth. Behind them, the tattered-cloth herder, whistling and screaming with a dark malignancy in its cry.

I watched the glacier give way. I watched it shudder horribly and slip along its path only a tiny bit faster than a person could walk. But that is so fast for a glacier.

The earth heaved beneath me again, like it harbored a great sickness, and I buried my head between my knees and held as still as possible while the mountain rolled, and buckled, and groaned, and cracked.

When it was over—when there was only the tiniest tremor, like the beat of a hummingbird's heart, over and over—I stood up and looked down.

Half the mountain had given way to my right. I stood on a narrow ledge somehow spared from the collapse. Below me, the glacier I had lived in the shadow of my whole life had consumed my village. Ritticapa had never been, according to the maps, and now it would never be. Seeing its demise should have wrung the deepest sorrow from me—for it was also the demise of my mother, and my sister's mother. But when I saw that place, like a grave of ice, my heart was only a stone.

None of it had ever meant anything to me. My whole life had been simple survival—and I had succeeded at that, hadn't I?—until my little sister came along. In her, I had discovered things I'd never known: affection, companionship, even love. And something else, too. Something like hope, but that is not an emotion I am familiar with, so I am not sure. What I think, though, is that people forego hope because they cannot bear the pain on the other side of it. I learned all of this in a matter of seconds, as my eyes frantically scanned the obliterated landscape, no longer holding anything familiar. That didn't matter to me, though; I knew what I was looking for.

I was looking for movement—like flapping wings—and a flitting songbird-of-a-girl in her yellow-colored dress. Windy, the female scarlet tanager with a straw-colored body and black wings. Windy, the one who could not be stopped. But I saw no movement. Nothing except another boulder dislodging and rolling slowly on a newly-formed path. White mountains, gray rocks, brown land, pale and anemic grass. The whitewashed sky, robbed of its blue-violet

color by the savage shaking of the earth that pitched dust, and snow, and other particles airborne.

And then—because I could not stop looking—I finally saw it: a splash of color. A blotch of red, down amongst the boulders. A bird? I strained my eyes. A male scarlet tanager.

I scrambled to my feet and leaned forward. Windy would be so happy! And then I learned anew of hope turning bitter, of a screaming pain rising from my legs into my chest, and I wondered if the spider-herders had once been children like me, and they had to give their pain and their screams into the sky because nothing else could ever hold it.

A mountain catches the wind and flings it upward. The rising air, seeking passage over this barrier grows cold as it slips higher into the atmosphere. Water vapor, evaporated from a distant rainforest, saturates the chilled air until it must, once again, condense into liquid water. Thus, the clouds form over the mountain and eventually release their payload of fresh water to soak the ground and give life to the flourishing vegetation.

And yet, it is also this wind and rain that batter the mountain; shaping it and, inevitably, shrinking it. In this way, the two are locked in a mortal dance: the landscape shaping the climate, and the climate, in turn, shaping the landscape.

I know of these things. I know because the library at my school had books that explained where the wind came from, and how clouds formed, and how water vapor could be held inside the air. How mountains and valleys were transformed by water—or the lack of water.

But what raised the mountain in the first place? Why a sea in one place, a basin of rivers and forests in another, and this mountain here, like the jagged teeth in the mouth of a predator? There were so few books in the library, and none that explained these things. Windy, of course, found all the books on birds.

What I knew—without any books to tell me—were the steps of another dance, the dance between this place and its people. They batter and bruise and build and transform each other. It is even said that they trade places with each other, from time to time. A boy becomes a lake. A tree becomes a man-like spider-herder. If this is so, then can a girl become a bird?

Please, let little girls become birds.

UMBRA ARCA
CASE   NOTE

AGENT No. _____

YA·TE·VEO

Anastasia Garcia

Amazon River, Peru

FOLLOW THE RIVER AS THE SUN RISES, paddle past the pod of boto dolphins twisting under the dark water like floating ghosts, and past the roving band of red fur monkeys who hang upside down from the trees. Soon in the dense canopy of foliage, the call of the white-throated toucan cuts through: *eo-wan-wan*. There beyond the shade of trees is where we live, in huts of dried shapaja palms like giant, shaggy bush dogs lying in rest on the jungle floor.

When I was younger, after gathering the fruit and nuts was done, I used to sit here with my sisters along an outstretched cashapona tree hanging over the river. We took turns stretching one leg low, to graze our toes in the warm water. We slurped passion fruit from the rind and giggled at the clumsy monkeys in the trees.

But I am now nearing eleven summers of life and can no longer revel in the things I loved as a child. We have no more passion fruit vines and the banana trees yield less and less each year. Our planted crops rot in their roots, fruit drops from the trees riddled with worms, and the river that used to flow strong and free, thick with fish, now barely trickles as if choked further upstream. Walking around the village, there is an unease settling in, taut like the string of a bow. Roving parties have trekked through the jungle in search of a more suitable land for our people, but when they return, the whole village fights amongst each other. To move or to stay, everyone has something to say.

Sitting around the fire, there is not much to be thankful for. The older ones pass a carved cup from palm to palm, sharing the cashew liquor and speaking to the sacred ones through hums and chants. I long for the time I will be allowed to share the drink in the cup carved with spiny vines and send my wishes up to the sky. I would ask the gods: *why are you so cruel?* Perhaps then they will hear me, because now I fear no one listens.

My people visit a sacred place in the jungle down a well-trod path carrying torches and meat to spare. They used to visit once during the planting season when my grandparents were children, but in my lifetime it seems they visit more often, every six rises of the sun. It is said they do this to ask favor, but I do not know if it ever works.

As night falls, it is time for the village to make their visit. The path there is treacherous and children are not allowed past the twin carved trees. But today I want to pay my respects, to let the sacred ones know that I am old enough to participate. So, I follow the sounds of the beating drums as the path begins to narrow further from the village until I reach the twin trees. Pausing at the trailhead, I wonder what would await me at the end of the path. *What does the sacred place look like? How difficult is the climb? Will there be any frightening relics or carvings or creatures?* And for a moment, fingers of fear creep up my back—as a hand grabs my shoulder.

"No, little one." Mama stops me from stepping onto the path. Mama is heavy with child, too burdened to walk with the others. My face is aflame with shame to be caught somewhere I am not supposed to be, so I let her lean on me as we return to our hut.

She is overtired, as seen in the sweat dotting her knitted brow and the pallor of her skin. I help her put my sisters to sleep and curl into the sleeping mat with them. Mama moans in the night when she thinks we're all asleep.

Father returns with the rest of the village late at night smelling of torch smoke.

The village's unease, like a bowstring, is now one notch closer to release.

———

With Mama so close to birth, the women of the village gather with us in Old Woman's hut bringing nut oils and roots to chew while we wait for the baby to come. When my sisters were born, I was too young to help, but here I stand at mother's side as she squats low and begins to scream.

The hours of birth are long and painful, and only after a full rise of the sun does the baby finally arrive—dead. Unmoving, cold, and impossibly small in Old Woman's arms. She wraps the baby carefully, using only one banana

leaf, weaving the ends closed, as Mama sleeps on a mat, spent, empty, and sick.

I hold Mama's hand, hot to the touch, and stare into the corner with wide, unblinking eyes that perhaps now have seen too much. In the corner of Old Woman's hut is one of my favorite old carvings, a great tree etched into a slab of pona wood. The branches of this great carved tree are less rigid and more like tendrils of smoke curling towards the sky, and the roots run deep, just as grand beneath the soil as above. I trace this carving with my fingers in the grooves worn smooth. My mind wanders to familiar questions: *who carved it, how long has it been passed down, and what kind of tree has no leaves?*

Exhaustion overtakes me on those nights, as I huddle near Mama on her sleeping mat, refusing to leave her side to eat or bathe. One night, fighting the fog of sleep, I awake to Mama's whispering voice, "Te-veo." *I see you.* Her eyes are wide, staring into the corner, speaking to someone in the dark.

"Mama?" I try to shake her from her stare.

"Te-veo. Te-veo. Ya-te-veo!" *I see you. I see you. I already see you!*

Old Woman rises at the sound of Mama's voice, pushing me away and trying to calm her.

"No! Don't feed us to it!" Mama screams. Old Woman fights to keep Mama prone on the mat. "No! Don't feed it!" Mama continues to scream.

"Why does she keep saying that? What does it mean?" I ask, the panic rising in my chest as the darkness of the hut begins to suffocate me. Mama slips away, her eyes roll back in her head as the fever steals her senses.

Old Woman deflates as if her body lost the air to breathe. She too was awake with us most days and nights, this illness taking its toll. "You are still too young, child. You will know soon."

"No! I want to know now!" I thrash at her with my fists, fighting her hands pinning me down. Too many times I've been called too young, unable to stop these things happening to my family, my people, my home. I know it is childish to flail and kick, but the fury burst out of me in an animal-like scream. I cry hot angry tears, as Old Woman wraps her arms around me until I slide onto the ground and sleep near Mama, now deathly still.

She dies in the night. In air thick with sweat and fear, her spirit passes like a cool breeze, as if she walks away from our hut into the thicket of trees, down the familiar path.

As night falls, the villagers gather at our dwelling. They carry torches and wear ceremonial jewelry that rattles on their wrists and ankles. Their skin is painted in thick black lines, each pattern unique. Tonight, they give Mama back to the earth at the sacred place. I don't allow myself to cry as they carry her body, now stiff, wrapped carefully in banana leaves with her baby. Long into the night they chant over her body, raising their hands high above their heads. Eventually forming a long line like a slithering snake, they begin the trek into the jungle.

Expected to wait for their return, we children watch their receding backs. My sisters tug at my hands, they cry now not because they understand Mama's death, but because they are hungry and confused. They want to be held, but I can't bring myself to care for them.

As the sound of their drums fade into the lush thicket, the jungle seems quieter that night than any other, no howling monkeys, no tittering of birds. Too tired to sleep like the other children, I wander aimlessly like a lost soul myself through the paths between our huts. In the dark, my tears can flow freely, and my feet find the way, and soon I stand before the markings etched into the twin trees on either side of the path. A warning sign that this path is forbidden.

The last time I stood here, Mama warned me away, but now I have no mother, and I will heed no more warnings.

As I step onto the path, it quickly narrows to only one person wide; the foliage on either side snags at my skin, but the thrill of the unknown pushes me forward. I did not bring a torch and find my way only by feeling for an opening in the brush. I am guided more by an inherited memory than by skill, following a path walked by all my ancestors. The path slopes upward and soon I'm climbing over rocks worn smooth by hundreds of feet. One step off the path and I would fall through the trees. But just over the ridge I hear the sound of drums and continue my climb. Soon I am near enough to see the ring

of fire as the villagers stand around a bright clearing lit by the moon and lined around the edge with torches.

Like a snuffed flame, the drumming stops and another sound emerges in the silence. Not a chant, but more of a whisper, as if the wind itself spoke through the leaves.

Te-veo. Te-veo. Ya-te-veo. I see you. I see you. I already see you.

The phrase is familiar, Mama's final words; but hearing them among the sacred place chills me to my core. Beneath the whispering is a clacking like a thousand beetles snapping their jaws, an almost eager sound.

Te-veo. Te-veo. Ya-te-veo.

My skin itches with the urge to run, run back down the path away from whatever makes these sounds. But I catch the movement of something large and black between the trees, positioned in the middle of the clearing, rising to an impossible height, setting all the jungle alive with the noise. The sacred place is not just a ceremonial site, but the home of something living that my people revere. *What is it?* Curiosity overcomes the instinct to run, but before I can inch closer, six men emerge carrying Mama's body towards the clearing. A sickening realization sets in. I never questioned why we always wrap our dead in banana leaves and carry them here. But now Mama appears less ceremonial and more like a sack of smoked meat. They carry her closer to the thing than the others are willing to go and swing her body once, twice, before throwing her towards the darkness at the center.

At the sound of crunching bones, I clap my hands over my ears, and turn to flee.

██████████

I awake feeling the tickling of a thousand pinpricks all over my skin. Leaping from my sleeping mat, I overturn a bowl of water left by my father and furiously rub my skin—but there is nothing there. My heartbeat quickens, and my eyes are wild, as I look around at an empty hut. Today the village is determined to gather more food. It was a small mercy from my father allowing me to sleep late into the day.

With the village quiet, I take my old perch in the cashapona tree hanging over the river, staring across the dark water and the sky reflected therein. I contemplate the horror of last night. Something alive, feeding on our people. Our village worships it as a merciful thing, but it is not a benevolent being. What I saw was a greedy, hungry thing. It has done more than accept our offerings, it is killing us so that its thirst for human flesh may be sated. The tree will only grow stronger as we die, and it will not stop poisoning our crops, choking our river, or eating our dead.

My people are too scared to leave it behind, believing it sacred and angry. They are willing to die in a never-ending circle of appeasement; they would doom us to death.

I can see only one way to free us from this torment.

Just a few steps down the winding path and my arms are already tired of carrying the torch high overhead. The flame glistens on the wet leaves, it lights my way back to the sacred place—a cursed place. The bag of throwing rocks on my back grows heavier with each step. In the distance, a monkey screeches a warning. Even the birds pound a panicked staccato on the trunks of trees, but I do not stop.

Until a sound rises that sets my teeth on edge: *ta-veo, ta-veo, ya-te-veo.*

My breath catches. In a brief moment of panic I think I could run again, all the way back to the village to my people. I could convince them, ask for their help, and then I would not have to do this alone. After a few moments, I steel my resolve, now stomping through the underbrush with a single-minded determination until I reach the clearing.

Ta-veo, ta-veo, ya-te-veo.

For the first time I see it clearly. The true horror of the monstrous tree is almost maddening.

The thick branches rise into the air wriggling like worms reaching for the sky, limbs rustle against each other making a sound like a whispering voice. *Ta-veo, ta-veo, ya-te-veo.* Each of the long tendrils unravel like licking tongues,

lined with countless pointed barbs clacking together, as they pulsate making a sound like chattering teeth. I take one careful step into the clearing, just as a hundred black eyes open wide staring from all the knots in the trunk of the tree, affixed to me and the flame in my hand. *Ta-veo, ta-veo, ya-te-veo.*

I throw one rock towards the tree, and one of the branches flicks out, surprisingly deft, knocking it from the air. Standing squarely in the clearing now, the soil slip-slides under my feet, as if something large slithered beneath the earth. I throw my bag of rocks high in the air to the left and dart to the right, avoiding the long tendrils as they whip at the rocks, the sound of the barbs whistling overhead. It takes all of my dexterity to leap from root to tangled root, a misstep means death. The black eyes buried in the tree trunk roll in their sockets following my path, and the tree limbs rattle their barbs in a cacophony of fury.

There is an opening, just large enough for me to slip the torch between the exposed roots to the heart of the tree. In a moment of wild surprise, it catches like a bundle of dried leaves. The heat singes my eyelashes, and I scurry to free myself from the roots now thrashing in the soil like roiling snakes. I turn to run just as a tendril swipes at my back, the pointed barbs snag skin and flesh, opening wounds like a flurry of whiplashes. Howling in pain, I throw myself from the clearing out of its reach.

It squeals like a wounded beast, the tendrils writhing in pain as the fire climbs from the bursting eyes on its trunk to the seething limbs of the tree. The death rattle hiss of its thousand barbs carries through the jungle. I clamp my hands over my ears against the sound. Unable to free itself from the rooted soil, it reaches higher to the heavens for salvation from the flame.

Soon there is the pattering sound of a hundred feet rushing, the villagers who must have heard its shrieking all the way back to the river. They surround the clearing, watching in awe. The tree alight reaches for the sky as glittering flames dance in our dark eyes. No one makes an attempt to save it, and no one makes a sound of sadness.

We watch in silence for hours as it burns, until all that is left are the smoking holes of its burned roots deep in the earth, and we can no longer feel slithering beneath our bare feet. Only then are we satisfied in its destruction and can return to our village with something akin to hope lighting our way.

It has been a generation since the burning of the monstrous tree, and our village on the river near the boto dolphins is once again prosperous; we no longer hide in isolation. Strangers paddle down the river on boats, and we greet them readily, exchanging goods such as nuts, fruits, carvings, and stories.

But from the opposite side of the mountain ridge, a small cohort of explorers cuts their way through the jungle, swinging sharpened machetes and dabbing their moist necks with water-dipped handkerchiefs. The party stops their slog through the dense underbrush, pointing to a sun-filled clearing ahead. Taking careful steps around the clearing, they see something that resembles a path now overgrown, and in the center of the clearing is a solitary mound rising as tall as a man.

As the group approaches, the only warning of danger is a soft rumbling beneath their boots of a sentient root system awakening to the smell of human flesh.

UMBRA  ARCA
C A S E   N O T E

AGENT No. _____

YACUMAMA
(Mother of the Water)

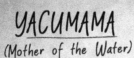

Enormous snake known
as the "Serpent of the River."

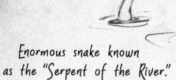

Mother to all
creatures of the water.

Will swallow anything
within 100 feet.

Locals blow into a conch
before entering the river to
reveal Yacumama's location.

YACUMAMA

Christina Sng

Ucayali River, Peru

I swam with Yacumama
When I was a child,
When I fell into the lake,
No one noticing I was gone.

Yacumama found me
And brought me back to shore,
The water mother herself,
100 feet long.

No one knew
Why she didn't eat me.
Maybe I was too small.
Maybe she saw me as a child

And decent mothers
Did not eat their children,
Much less
The water mother herself.

I swam with Yacumama often
In her lake off river Ucayali.
She hunted in the confluence,
Where two rivers merge to one.

The Peruvian rainforest is filled
With hidden treasures,
Deep in waters long forgotten,
Secret underwater caves

Where we dined on fish
And I sang till she'd sleep
And I, beside her, dreaming
Of a life beneath the lake.

It was the only place
I ever felt free
From the strictures of life
In Pucallpa, from the city,

Away from my father
Who tried to beat me
And my weeping mother
Who blocked me with her body.

I told him of the treasure one night
And the very next morning,
He took our small dingy
Out to Yacumama's lake,

And was promptly eaten by her
Before he found anything.
The treasure was not to be removed.
Not for him. Not for me.

It contained the alchemy
Keeping Yacumama alive.
That was what I understood
From the old texts with it.

Life became better
Without my father around,
But as an adult now,
Work was hard to come by.

I took every job I could.
Mama could not see anymore
And her medicine costs, sky high.
I held her on the day she died.

She clutched my hand
As if she knew it was time
And whispered to me,
"Follow your heart, follow your joy."

I returned to Yacumama,
Carrying Mama to her cave
Where I sang the songs
My mother once sang to me

And soon,
We all became part of the sea.

Villa Epecuén

UMBRA ARCA CASE FILE

Villa Epecuén

Argentina

Eyewitness Statements, Various (translated)
#SE12:137-42:00719
Re: Incident at Villa Epecuén, Argentina on 6 November 1985
Coordinates: 37°7'51"S 62°48'27"W

Adelmo Benitez, 52
"She was crying, her tears were spilling over the pampas,
which caused the dam to overflow like her sadness."

Cristina Fuentes, 19
"I woke to my mother screaming. She told me to get my brother
and climb onto the roof. I did this, and she came after, with
some food. The rain soaked us in seconds, and it was hours
before a neighbor with a boat came by and took us down."

Xavier Santos, 79
"When I was a boy, I lived in a town not far from here.
Everyone knew the story of Epecuén, a small boy and the only
survivor of a great fire that burned the forest to ash. The
levuche gave him the name of Epecuén, which meant 'almost
burnt' and raised him as one of their own. The daughter of
the chief fell in love with him, but he did not return her
love, and for that she cried and cried, filling the valley

with her salt tears. That is how the lake came to be. It is said that when a man is dishonest, she cries again, and the lake rises higher."

Agata Gomez, 20

"I cannot find my papa. I cannot find my grandmother. I cannot see through my tears."

Alejandro Molina, 34

"My wife and children are back in the city, thank god. A group of us came here on a company retreat. The air is pleasant, the waters said to be healing. I never expected this."

Lucia Perez, 49

"I always told my sons this was a sinner's town. Now look at it! We are being punished for moving here. Our business is drowned and so is our future."

Yaco Silva, 9

"I saw the lady crying. She was high up above my head, floating like. I told her to stop but she could not hear me."

UMBRA ARCA
CASE   NOTE

AGENT No. _____

THE LOST CITY
(The Nameless City)

Hidden deep within an expansive jungle.

Golden waterfalls feed a giant lake below.

Artifacts made entirely of gold.

NO MORE PRYING EYES
Maxwell I. Gold
Lake Parime, Brazil

Beneath viridescent nethers of dreamless jungles where the eyes of murky gods meandered through golden lakes, soon, their secrets, never meant to be spoken, were placated by the fleshy odors and funk of one thousand untouched human hands. Their mouths closed and lips sealed as deep trenches lined with waterfalls and golden secrets, protecting a truth that would never be.

Tenebrific oaths never meant to be broken, sealed by blood and shadow beyond high, cloudy walls, through infinitely expanding jungles littered with terrible beasts, an ancient lake swallowed a thousand souls who walked the streets of a nameless city.

Faster and faster, clearing the brush as the daytime star began to fade, the stars swarming the horizon with darkness, Parime and Takutu embraced, mouths closed, and lips sealed breathing billowing plumes of water and clouds towards the heavens,

    hidden.

      No

        more

          prying

            eyes.

Persisting on the pages of Someday, ink and memories died under a hot, unforgiving Brazilian sun as crinkled parchments withered into empty legends on forgotten atlases like words never spoken;

Mouths closed
and lips sealed.

Treasure ships from the borders of unknown maps hearing myths of the two great rivers where cities drowned in gold, skeletons swallowed by iron, and barbaric gods, sought their fortunes. Too late, they were met with oceans of silvery-tongued demons, carrion flowers, and hungry things stalking the night. Ruins of stone, rust, and whispers reached verdant canopies, cutting through towards vast, endless skies. The eyes of foreign invaders forever blinded by the dread of something they'd never understand;

Mouths closed
and lips sealed.
Only whispers and footsteps, utterances beyond Cyclopean trenches where Cariban chants wailed, echoing the sacrifices of flesh and fantasy into watery voids beneath craggy, fungi-covered shoals where Parime and Takutu bathed in stardust and death,
hidden.
No
more
prying
eyes.

UMBRA   ARCA
CASE   NOTE

_____

_____

_____

_____

_____

_____

_____

_____

_____

_____

_____

_____

_____

_____

_____

_____

_____

AGENT No. _____

MOON UNDER MANGROVES

Juliana Spink Mills

Santos, São Paulo, Brazil

THE MANGUEZAL AT NIGHT was a constant call and chatter of frogs and birds and insects, the humidity thick as syrup. Evie slapped at a mosquito; in the pale moonlight that filtered through the mangroves of the coastal swamp, the splat of disgorged blood was dark against her skin.

"João," she said, her gringa mouth unable to get the sound quite right. "Are you sure this is the right place?"

Her Brazilian guide grinned. "Yeah, it's the place, Dona Evie. This is what the police say: go up the river and past the bridge." His English was good, the vowels and consonants softened by his accent. "You wait. The night, it's young. And look!" He gestured at the growing pile of fish in the cooler at the bottom of the motorboat and continued baiting his line.

Evie shifted on the hard metal bench in search of a better position, her back protesting. João was right; the night was young, even if she wasn't. She pulled out her great-grandfather's compass and rubbed a thumb across the engraving on the case. São Paulo Railway Company, it spelled, in letters as soft and worn as the wrinkles on her face. For decades the compass had lain in a velvet-lined box, ever twitching, ever spinning, never settling. Until now.

There was a faint splash as João cast his line. A fishing rod would have been useless in the tangle of vegetation they had inched their way beneath. Instead, he had an old soda can with the extra line around it. A stray moonbeam caught the nylon thread and it gleamed like a knife slash, dividing the space in two. To one side, Evie and João, bobbing in a clear patch of water under the bowed branches of the mangroves. To the other, the dark water that swallowed the line, broken by roots and the gnarled trunks of short and stubby trees. Beyond, the swamp stretched out in an infinite checkerboard of light and shadows, black and silver where the full moon broke through the leaf canopy.

"Why don't you use a float?" she asked, brushing back sweat-damp hair.

"A what?"

"You know, a plastic thing that sits on your fishing line. It floats on the water, so you know when you catch a fish."

"No need." He raised his hand slightly so she could see the line wrapped around a finger. "Like this, see, I can feel them." He gave the line a twitch and began hauling it in. "Like so." He deftly killed his bright-scaled catch, tossing it into the cooler with the rest. "This one, we call pescada. The others are garoupa and carapicú."

He took fresh bait from a bucket, spiking a tiny shrimp on the hook. "It is good tonight. The fish are biting a lot."

"So are the mosquitos," she sighed, scratching her arm.

João gave her a shrewd look. "Everything is biting. Maybe your ghost will bite, too."

She didn't bother to correct him. It wasn't a ghost she was after, even if the locals believed in one. Two months before, her great-grandfather's compass had stopped its incessant whirring to point steadily southeast. From her home in Ohio, that could have meant anywhere, anyplace. But she knew in her heart it was Santos.

A port city that traced its heyday to the nineteenth century coffee boom, Santos was where her great-grandfather had lived and worked the railways, his young American wife and small son at his side. He'd died in Santos, too, lost in the mangrove swamp after one too many shots of cachaça.

His body had never been recovered, and so his widow and child had made their way back to the USA with nothing but a company-gifted compass to show for his years working the tracks. According to family legend, the compass had begun to spin the day Great-Grandma Rose stepped foot in her homeland and hadn't settled since.

Evie breathed in deep, pushing away a dead man's memory. The swamp was heady with the brine of saltwater and mud, and the green scent of the sub-tropics. It prickled at her skin and seeped into bones made brittle with the passing of years. These days it seemed as if the clock was hurtling on too fast, too soon. The sand was running out for her future self, for the Evie-that-might-be. When the compass had stopped, she'd taken it as a sign. One last

great adventure. One final attempt to seek purpose.

There was a scuttling noise on the bank. João switched on his flashlight. A crab froze, unblinking, beady eyes watching them back. Another one joined it; their armored shells and spidery legs were mud-splattered, covering any markings. One raised a claw, pincers clicking, almost regal in its attitude. Evie was sharply reminded of the tale of the Crab Prince.

"The police report said the bodies were eaten by crabs," she said.

"Not this type, I think. This is caranguejo-uçá—swamp ghost crab in English." He chuckled. "Ha! Ghost crab...! But this one, not a real ghost. And good to eat." He pointed at the creatures. "You see the claws? For digging mud. But also, different size, see? The little one for cutting, the big one for—" He smashed a fist into his open palm.

"Crushing? Like shellfish?"

"Yes, that. And seeds, nuts. Not dead bodies." He stopped and thought about it. "I guess sometimes they feed on dead things, so maybe they did eat the men. No killing, though. Too small." He waved an arm and the crabs scurried away.

João switched off the flashlight beam and everything went black for an instant as Evie blinked the afterimage from her eyes. She could still hear the crabs as they fled through the riverbank debris. The sound was *too big* in the dark, like a much larger animal was stalking the shadows.

"Do you believe in this ghost?" she asked once her night vision returned, voice slightly tremulous. "The ghost that haunts the swamp?"

"I think," he answered carefully, "that not everything is simple. This place, it hungers. And sometimes, it takes. But this here, I think this is just a story. The people, they are superstitious. So maybe there was a dead man, two dead men, three... Me, I think it's the gangs. Not a ghost." He mimed a gun, pulling a finger-trigger against his head.

"This is Santos," he added with a shrug, as if it explained things, and perhaps it did. Despite the name, there was nothing heavenly about the city nestled against the São Paulo coastline, with its high-rises and violence.

She clutched the compass a little tighter. "I guess we'll see."

He laughed, the sound bright and sudden as the moon that danced in and out of view beyond the treetops. "I guess we will, Dona Evie. And if not, you come to my house tomorrow. I don't have caranguejo-uçá for you to eat, but look!" He waved at the evening's catch. "My wife, she makes a wonderful peixada, a fish stew." He kissed his fingertips toward the heavens.

"I'd like that," said Evie. "Thank you."

Evie had first heard of the Crab Prince in the Lençóis Maranhenses National Park, an achingly beautiful place of sand dunes and blue-green lagoons that she'd visited as she made her way down the coast of Brazil.

"Not far from here," said the young German guide, "lived the Tremembé people. Long ago, there was a handsome prince of the Tremembé called Lupã who lived a life of pleasure, always flitting from bed to bed. One day, he fell in love with the maiden Yaramey. But even for her, he would not give up his ways.

"Saddened by his infidelity, Yaramey threw herself into the mangrove swamp, sinking into the mud to never again emerge."

The guide paused to pass around the bottle of xiboquinha—fermented sugar cane sweetened with honey, cloves, and cinnamon. "Is that all?" Evie asked, the heady taste of liquor settling in her stomach like sunshine. "Is that the end?"

"No." The guide stared at the darkening ocean, where reds and pinks still colored the horizon. "Lupã regretted the suffering he had caused his beloved and begged the gods to help find her. He was transformed, becoming the first crab. His claws, ideal for digging, still comb the manguezal, searching tirelessly for Yaramey. And so do his descendants, the river crabs. But they can never find her, and so she is lost forever."

Evie glanced down at the compass. It pointed unwaveringly into the depths of the mangroves, in the direction the crabs had taken. She thought of her great-grandfather. The manguezal had eaten him, like Yaramey, and now he,

too, was lost forever.

She was jolted out of her thoughts when João swore, full-mouthed and colorful in Portuguese. The swearing became a shout, and then a scream. Evie grabbed the flashlight, swinging it wildly. As she turned it toward João, she caught the word mão—hand. The fishing line wound around his finger had dug in, slicing so deep she could see the white glint of bone under the blood that welled up, thick and bright. He was scrabbling for the line, but there was no give, no slack, the nylon taut against the water.

He leaned over the front of the boat, trying to grasp the line with his free hand, but instead it hauled him in farther, dragging the nose of the boat down with him. Evie lunged for him, but water poured over the bow, and she stumbled backward to balance it out.

"João!" she yelled, even as she tried to rationalize the fear. A tree root, maybe? With the fishing line wrapped around it?

The guide let go, fumbling blindly for the knife he'd been using to gut fish, and hacked at the line until it snapped. The boat rocked violently, almost knocking Evie down as a wave of water surged over the stern. She dropped the flashlight, and it bounced off the seat with a clang and landed on the cooler. The frantic keening cut out as João drew back, clutching his hand and sobbing.

"Shit, shit, *shit*, João!" The angled beam picked out the muddy bank and a sea of beady eyes. The crabs were back, and in number. They were on the bank; they were in the water. She could hear the click and clatter of tiny claws against the metal hull and knew there had been no tree root to tangle the line.

João, still giving those awful shuddering sobs, ripped off his blood-splattered t-shirt and did his best to bandage his hand. "Dona Evie, untie the—" he faltered as he realized the tree the rope was knotted around lay right in the middle of the crabs. "*Cut the rope*," he ordered, desperate.

Evie sawed at the blue braided nylon as João tried one-handed to start the engine. It coughed, spluttered, and went out. He tried again, and again, then swore one long stream of profanity. "Merdacaralhofilhoda*puta!*" He stared at her bleakly, tear tracks glimmering in the artificial light. "Water in the motor. We got to row."

On land, the crabs were still gathering. More and more slithered into the river to join the others until the brackish water churned. "They're not going to let us go." Evie felt strangely detached as she put down the knife and stood up, holding onto a branch for balance.

João was babbling, his terror almost tangible. "It's me; it's my fault. I didn't believe, and now the ghost will eat us. I'm sorry, Dona Evie. Ai meu Pai, ai Jesus..."

She raised a hand to stop him. She took out the brass compass; in the flashlight's fickle glare, the needle still pointed steadily into the trees. "It's not you. They're here for me. All those bodies, it was to bring me here."

Evie knew it was true even as the words spilled unbidden. The deaths were bait, like the tiny shrimp on João's hook. Her great-grandfather had stirred something, all those years ago, and left the story unfinished. The emptiness in her life; that nagging sense of more, just beyond reach... It all led here, to a swamp outside Santos. She took hold of the rope and hauled the boat in until it bumped the shore. She smiled, afraid but serene at the same time. "Don't worry about me. You were wonderful. I wish I could taste your wife's peixada."

Evie stepped onto the bank, the crabs parting for her. Silver moonbeams filled the manguezal, almost enough to see by, but not quite. She stumbled over roots and rocks, moving steadily away from the boat. She tripped and fell into a pool, landing shin-deep in stagnant water. She knew on some level that she'd cut herself, that she would bruise, as she did too easily these days, but it didn't matter. She heaved herself up and kept moving.

The birds and frogs and crickets had gone silent. The only sounds were the skittering of the ghost crabs and her own steps—dead wood cracking underfoot and the sucking of her sensible sneakers in the damp and muddy spots. To all sides, the ground boiled with small dark carapaces. She kept moving, unsure if the crabs were some strange honor guard, or if they were herding her along. It didn't matter; she knew where she was supposed to go.

The brass São Paulo Railway compass led Evie to the middle of the mangrove swamp. The ground erupted as thousands of ghost crabs began to dig. The earth was cleared away in an instant, a skeleton lying in the revealed hollow. Any clothing had long rotted away, but metal glinted on one boney hand. She plucked it up, holding it to the moonlight. Inside, she could just

make out a wedding date and a name: Rose. These were her great-grandfather's remains, picked clean by scavengers and time. She slipped the ring onto her middle finger.

Evie understood now what the cursed compass wanted. Her great-grandfather had awoken the beating core of this place the day he'd died, and it had hungered until she was ready to fulfill his bargain with the mud. Until the Evie-that-was had all but given up on finding meaning in her life; until the now-Evie was the very last of her line and had nothing left to lose. She was old and fragile as fine porcelain, but she was strong inside, where it mattered. She was willing. And the manguezal *wanted*.

She got into the hollow and lay down beside her great-grandfather's bones. They were both Lupā, digging for meaning, but they were also Yaramey, somehow, giving themselves freely to the dirt and mud and the moon above. Evie closed her eyes. The circle was complete.

It didn't take long for the first crab to approach. She tried to be brave as it dug in vicious pincers. The small ones, she remembered, were for cutting and the large ones for crushing. She held firm at first, but the pain grew as ghost crabs swarmed her body, and before long she was screaming. Evie lost herself to the cresting swell of agony as hundreds of pincers tore her skin, ripped at muscle and sinew, and smashed her bones to dust. She embraced it. Blood flowed and ruptured viscera tainted the night with foul smells, but she was already beyond that, riding the shimmering wave of pain through the trees to the moon beyond.

A heartbeat. A long and shuddering breath. A hand moved, back and forth. An old, tarnished wedding ring gleamed on a middle finger. Evie sat up. She was alone. The skeleton of her great-grandfather was gone, reduced to a fine white powder. The crabs had disappeared. Her clothing was torn to shreds, covered with fluids and blood. She brushed the fragments aside as she stood.

She was alive, and whole. No, better than whole. The different parts of her—the now-Evie, the Evie-that-was, and the Evie-that-might-be—had been taken by the swamp, dismantled, and forged again. Ancient, but unbreakable. Like iron and rock, or the relentless ocean tide. Eternal as myth, half Evie and half Yaramey.

Evie clambered out of the hollow and set off back to the boat. She knew the way, unerringly. The manguezal was in her blood now. When she arrived, João was dozing, exhausted from terror and blood loss. She shook his shoulder, as she took hold of the raincoat he kept under a seat and wrapped it around her naked body.

He stared at her, speechless, but started the engine at her request. It caught at first try, and before long they had worked their way out of the inlet and were chugging down the main river toward the city. She didn't turn to look for the crabs. She didn't need to. Under her skin, pincers and armored shells quivered and boiled.

In a hollow in the middle of the manguezal, an old brass compass engraved with the words *São Paulo Railway Company* lay discarded in the moonlight.

7 July 1978

The São Paulo Railway Company, known as the 'Inglesa,' was a privately-owned British corporation that operated the route from Santos, on the coast, to São Paulo, in the highlands, between 1867 and 1946, when the line was nationalized by the Brazilian government.

IARA
(Lady of the Lake)

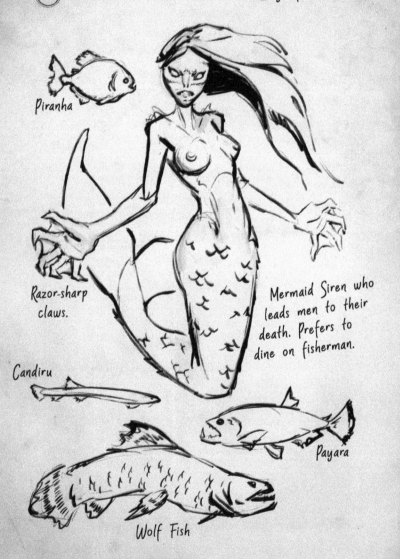

Piranha

Razor-sharp claws.

Candiru

Wolf Fish

Payara

Mermaid Siren who leads men to their death. Prefers to dine on fisherman.

IARA

Kathryn Reilly
Brazil

Patriarchy held my head beneath swirling silt-rich waters
demanding submission.

Never.

My brothers could kill me, but not me them;
my arm a golden lancehead, with reflexes my venom
I bested them in
Leadership   Strategy   Warfare
(everything except testosterone).

My py'a, my heart, grew into legend, and I sought a new taba, a new
village within the water.

The wrasses came, shimmering
coppery scales akin to my skin, blue magic glowing.
Change, they thought
so I did
not my sex as they could but my mortality.
Flung wide, my essence melds
skin and scales, hair and algae;
burning sempiternal purpose begins and
I emerge

Iara:

Strategic. Antagonistic. Vengeful. Cunning. Predatory. Protectoral.

Hunting now fast and far, sniffing out semen.
Rising from Amazonian waters, droplets decorate darkened areolas.
Scenting males, I sing, luring lust to the river's edge:
drown, drown, drown
on their knees,
obsecrate and expiate.
Drown, drown, drown.

Come candiru, piranha, payara, wrasse, little wolf fish.
Feast and eat your fill.

7 July, 1946

"Demanding submission"

First solo assignment. Four days out of Porto Velho, rainy season, Tupi guide leads us through swollen and wide tributaries that snake away from the main river and deep into the rainforest. Early rise and again all day on the barge, a shallow-riding pontoon-like vessel favored by the local peoples. My translator has been having some sort of argument with the guide all day. He won't divulge any particulars until he gets a straight answer from the guide.

8 July, 1946

Woken early morning by translator telling me guide has departed. Evidently he asked the polemen to pull up beside a low sandbar where he jumped off, disappearing down the finger of mud and silt and into the forest beyond. Over coffee, the translator at last told me what the guide imparted to him the evening before. Local legend calls her Iara, the mother of waters. According to the stories, this Iara, a beautiful woman beyond measure, was skilled also in the art of war. Overshadowing her brothers and winning the admiration of her father, in a patriarchal tribe, her brothers attacked her and she slew them. Later, she was hunted down in the depths of the jungle and drowned for her crimes. The waters welcomed her corpse and transformed her. When she or any of her kind are sighted, men die, their bodies found bloated and chewed up by the local fishes. The guide, upon learning of our purpose, refused to go further.

11 July 1946

"Scenting males, I sing, luring lust to the river's edge"

We are headed back to civilization, hearts heavy with our loss. The translator is dead so I have no way to speak to the polemen, those left of the crew, which number only three and myself. The past day is a blur, so fogged is my mind with her song. They dragged me from the water, pulled me up on the deck. I vomited mud in violent spatters on the planks. Although I am sure I must have seen her, her form is illusive to my mind, and all I can remember is the green glint of her eyes. Whatever horror I feel, however, is tempered by the certain fact that she allowed me to live. For surely, had she wished me dead, I would be so. Level 6 classification, highly dangerous but possible to avoid, does not inhabit highly populated area.

UMBRA ARCA
CASE   NOTE

AGENT No. _____

DOOR TO DOOR

Josh Malerman

São Paulo, Brazil

P AULO SAYS THE WORST THING a child can say to a parent, storms out of the room, heads upstairs, cursing with glee. His mother Maria attempts to make sense of what was said.

Someone knocks on the front door.

In this family neighborhood of São Paulo, Brazil, this is not unusual. Still, the knock is so sudden, it acts as an exclamation point for Paulo's cruel words, and Maria feels slapped across the heart a second time.

"Don't answer it," Bruna says. Bruna, Paulo's sister, peeks out of the kitchen, eying the front doorknob like she would if she feared a home invasion.

But Maria isn't thinking about anything but what her son just said. And how things have been building to this moment for years.

Maria crosses the room.

"Don't," Bruna repeats. Then, something that brings Maria to pause before rolling her eyes. "O homem do saco."

Maria opens the door.

"Senhora Costa?" the man says.

He wears a fine suit, a fine hat, and looks so clean, he reminds Maria what she was doing when Paulo erupted: cleaning up after the kids.

"Yes?"

"You are Senhora Costa, right?"

The man carries a suitcase in one hand. If Maria had met him on the street, she'd think he was going on vacation. As it stands, she knows he must be a salesman.

"I am."

"And you have..." he looks farther into the home. "Children?"

Bruna repeats, "O homem do saco," before slinking deeper into the kitchen. Only the very top of her head would be visible to her mother if Maria turned around now. And even then it would take some searching.

"Who are you?" Maria asks the man.

The man nods, having expected this question.

"Senhor Homem," the man says. "I've been on your street all day. I think your daughter saw me out her bedroom window."

"What are you selling?"

The man lifts the case with one hand and lightly slaps it with the other.

"Peace of mind," he says.

Maria eyes the case and shakes her head no.

"I'm sorry," she says. "Not the best time."

"Is it ever?"

Maria silently agrees with the man, but doesn't like that he said it.

"Thank you, but no."

She begins to close the door but Senhor Homem says:

"It's for troublesome children. Problematic ones. The ones who behave so poorly it's like you, as the parent, can't comprehend from where they came. It's for the kind of kid who makes you, the parent, wonder if some nefarious strategy wasn't employed at the hospital after you gave birth; it's as if someone switched children on you, for how little you recognize what you see in the one you brought home."

Maria doesn't close the door. She looks to the case.

"What is it?"

"May I enter?"

"No," Bruna says from the kitchen, her voice small but firm.

"Yes," Maria says. "Come in."

She steps aside, and Senhor Homem removes his hat as he enters. Maria opens a palm toward the couch, and the man sits as she takes the chair facing.

Homem sets the suitcase on the table between them.

"That's nice music," he says. "What is it?"

"Nepomuceno."

"Ah."

"Well?"

"Yes, let's get to it." Homem looks to the stairs, up the stairs, but there is no sign of Paulo. "Some children aren't really... *ours*," he says. "Just because we

have them, doesn't mean they are *us*. Have you ever felt this way before?"

"No."

Homem nods.

"It's certainly an odd concept. I mean, forgive me for being crass, but the child literally exited your body, and therefore he or she must be part of you, am I correct?"

"What are you selling again?"

"An idea, perhaps. A philosophy, I suppose. But at its root is the physical. When you sneeze, do you mourn the loss of snot?"

Maria looks to the door like this might be the end of this conversation after all.

"When you laugh, do you long for that air to come back? And when you speak... do you cry over the words? How many times a day does something leave your body that is best expelled, and left to fend for itself? Urine, feces, tears, snot, a failed organ, semen for men, and, even blood, yes, sometimes even losing blood can be for the best. How about flaking skin? Clipped nails? A shaved bunion? Vomit? Your hair when it's cut? Aren't all of these things, at some point, also elements of you? Yet, you let them go. Without a thought, you never think of them again. And yet... a child. This one thing, in all the world, in all our physical makeup, this *one thing* we're supposed to devote our entire lives to, to sacrifice our dreams, to make time for the child and the child alone, to lose ourselves in the life of the child, to focus on his or her betterment long before we consider our own. Is this fair? And were we warned of this? Were we given options?"

Homem taps the case.

"I saw your daughter in the window, but you have two children, Senhora Costa?"

"Yes. A daughter and a son. Paulo."

"Yes. Named after the city?"

"Yes."

"And just as complex, no?"

"Yes."

Both eye the case.

"Another thing that was never discussed, a thing we were never warned of, is how truly *awful* children can be. Far beyond the daily chores of changing diapers and helping with homework, there are actual children who are *bad people*. And bad adults once started as children. What do you say to those who blame the parents for bad people?"

Maria doesn't respond. Then realizes he was asking her opinion.

"Uh... well... I don't blame the parents."

Homem smiles and snaps.

"Neither... do... I. And why should we? And how could we? Do we put such little stock in free will? Are we all, each of us, purely products of our parents? And if so, who are any of us anyway? If we're not individuals, who are we loving when we say we must love our kids? Are we actually attempting to love ourselves? Is it all so selfish? Well, it's more complex than that. There is such a thing as evil, born that way, where no nurture can penetrate. There is *nature*, after all. There is darkness in some children that only appears innocuous because they *are* still children. But all the monsters of the world were once children, too. And wouldn't you, Senhora Costa, nip a child in the bud if you had the chance, the opportunity to go back in time, to kill a child you now know will one day grow into a terrible, *terrible* man?"

"O homem do saco," Bruna whispers from the kitchen.

Maria looks to the case.

"I would," Homem says. "I absolutely would. Because one thing most people overlook when they talk about parenting is... *the parent.* Do you have personal dreams, Senhora Costa? Do you have goals that do not include your children?"

"Yes."

"Do you see yourself in any future, a fantasy future, without children?"

"I see myself doing things alone, yes."

"Do you ever feel like you are being eclipsed by your children?"

"Of course."

"And do you ever feel like that exchange is... unfair? On the days when one or more of your children are behaving so badly... do you ever think to yourself, *What have I traded my freedom for?*"

"Yes."

"*Hell* yes."

"What are you selling?"

"I never really admitted to being a salesman, but I'm here for a specific purpose indeed. What I have for you is no physical object, no device, but rather, a worldview, a perspective. Consider me a seller of perspective."

"I don't-"

"How bad does he get, Maria?"

"Excuse me?"

"So bad that you fantasize about leaving him far from here, a place so remote he will never find his way home? A place so far... nobody will know what you did?"

Maria looks to the case.

Homem unlatches the clasps.

"I'm not asking you to be a poor mother," Homem says. "I'm saying bad kids grow into bad people, and they should get what they deserve."

He opens the case.

From where Maria sits, she can't see inside it quite yet. But darkness rises from it like mist.

"What is it?" she asks.

Homem looks into the case with pride.

"It's a place far enough away that he won't be able to find his way home."

Maria looks to the foot of the stairs.

"What did he do this time?" Homem asks.

Maria looks at him like she might end the moment now. The darkness from inside the case obscures his features, makes it look, momentarily, like she's facing a faceless man.

"O homem do saco," Bruna whispers from the kitchen.

"He's what you're describing, yes," she says. "There isn't a kind bone in his body. His father was only a little better. But Paulo... pure evil. No matter how much love and attention I show him. Gifts mean nothing. He has no friends because he believes everybody else inferior. He's mean to all living things. I've found things in his bedroom that would get us all arrested."

Homem nods knowingly.

"A *bad* child," he says. Then, "Come... look."

"Mamãe," Bruna says from the kitchen.

But Maria scoots the chair forward and peers over and into the suitcase. Then she leans back to look below the table, to make sure what she's seeing is possible: the bottom of the suitcase must be lower than the table, the floor, the house, the world.

She looks into the case again. The darkness curls about her neck and face, reaches up into her hair, so that she, too, looks momentarily faceless.

"What's way down there?" she says. "Are those..."

"Yes," Homem says. "Paulo is not the world's only bad child."

Maria sits back, inhales deeply with a hand to her chest.

"Just because the child is yours," Homem says, "does not mean he is *you*. No more than ear wax is, no more than a shit."

Senhor Homem turns quick to see Paulo is standing at the bottom of the stairs.

"Who the hell are you?" the boy asks.

Homem looks to Maria. And Maria looks to the case.

"Come here, Paulo," she says.

"No."

Maria breathes deep and rises. She steps to the stairs and, without warning, grabs Paulo, snakelike, by the wrist.

"*Come here.*"

She drags him across the room, a hand to the back of his neck.

"Mamãe," Bruna says from the kitchen.

"There is no nature versus nurture," Homem says. "It's only something we've invented to rationalize the bad ones."

Maria, sweating, shoves Paulo's head above the case. Then, with a strength she did not know she has, she shoves him entirely into it.

Once partially inside, Paulo slides easily the rest of the way, howling as he falls into the darkness.

Senhor Homem quickly closes the case and latches it.

Silence then, as Maria stares at the case. As Homem watches her. And as

Bruna says from the kitchen:

"O homem do saco."

Homem nods and rises. Grips the handle of the suitcase, puts his hat back on his head.

"Senhora Costa," he says. "You will never regret today. Tell me... doesn't it already feel lighter in here?'

Still staring at the case, she considers this. She looks to the ceiling, looks to the floor, *feels* the space.

She smiles.

"Yes," she says. "A little lighter already."

Homem makes for the door.

"I can see myself out. Thank you for hosting. It was truly wonderful making your acquaintance." Then, to Bruna peering from the kitchen: "And you. Don't change."

He winks. He opens the door. And, with suitcase in hand, he exits the home.

Bruna leaves the kitchen and meets Maria at the door. They watch Senhor Homem as he crosses the street, walks four houses, then climbs the steps to the Matos's front door.

"Ah," Maria says. "Adriana Matos."

"She's even worse than Paulo," Bruna says.

They see the front door open. See Senhor Homem remove his hat and step inside.

Maria places an arm around her daughter's shoulders.

"You heard the man, Bruna," she says. "Don't ever change."

15 May 1989

Stories of the Sack Man have been documented throughout
Latin countries with special emphasis in Brazil, Spain, and
Portugal. In Brazil, reports of o homem do saco consistently
include the description of the renowned kidnapper as a tall
man who prefers to target the most cruel and disobedient
children. In Chile and Argentina, the Sack Man usually
makes his appearance during the dinner hour. Parents who
willingly deliver misbehaving children to the Sack Man
cannot be prosecuted by the law. Needless to say, his
appearance is often greeted with delight, and he's been
known to stay for a repast when offered an especially
appealing digestif or dessert.

It was during a fateful encounter with the Sack Man on
assignment that I began to find myself at odds with the
Umbra Arca. The long-standing policy of no interference tore
at me the night I watched a family turn their nine-year
old son over to the beast. I'll admit the coward I was
then, for it has haunted me ever since. The child kicked
and screamed at first, and then seemed to lose all hope.
The other children covered their eyes, crying silently into
their hands. It was horrible to behold. I had nightmares for
months, years after that assignment, which colored each and
every assignment I've since been given. How can I continue
to stand by and do nothing?

UMBRA ARCA
C A S E   N O T E

AGENT №. _____

Invunche

UMBRA ARCA CASE FILE

El Invunche of Chiloé

Chile

MEMO - CONFIDENTIAL

TO: Agent B. Sokolov
FROM: West Director
CC: Discipline & Control; Membership Chair West Region
DATE: 15 August 1988
RE: Incident at Quicaví

Agent B. Sokolov is hereby ordered to report to Discipline
& Control, no later than midnight on the 20 of August 1988,
to be remanded into the custody of the Regulators for due
process for transgressions made on 10 August 1988 on the
Island of Chiloé, in the Archipelago of Chiloé, Region X Los
Lagos, Chile.

The following transgressions are listed for the record:

1 - Interruption of a ritual of transformation
Agents of the Umbra Arca are charged with documentation and,
in highly regulated situations, to serve as emissaries of
parley. On 10 August 1988, Agent Sokolov interrupted a Ceremonia de Romper Hueso (Ceremony of the Breaking of Bones)
in a sacred cavern outside the small town of Quicaví. The
ceremonia is a highly secretive event, wherein a local child,
given to the island's brujos (warlocks) to be made into

their servant, is physically transformed through a ritual
breaking and twisting of bones. The resultant Invunche is a
bent being, unable to speak. Its torso is twisted, its leg
broken and bent over one shoulder, and its neck torqued and
tongue split so as to allow it to speak the language of the
serpents. Agent Sokolov caused a disruption which dispersed
the brujos temporarily and removed the child from the scene.
Umbra Arca agents have been unable to recover the child to
return to the brujos for completion of the ceremony. Interference or interruption of local custom or manner is to
result in severe class 4 penalties.

2 - Revelation of the Umbra Arca to non-members
All members of the Umbra Arca are charged with secrecy in all
matters relating to the society. In causing the disruption at
Quicaví on 10 August 1988, Agent Sokolov caused the brujos
to scatter and hide by falsely declaring that the society had
members present to take them into custody. In truth, Sokolov
was acting independently, and no other agents were present
at the time. Sokolov, however, had revealed enough for the
brujos and those well-connected in local Chilean government
to begin asking questions about the Umbra Arca and its business in Chile. Revelation of the Umbra Arca to non-members in
a manner unrelated to society business or recruitment is to
result in ultimate class 9 penalties.

Agent Sokolov is encouraged to settle all personal affairs
prior to appearance.

UMBRA   ARCA
C A S E   N O T E

AGENT No. _____

EL CULEBRÓN

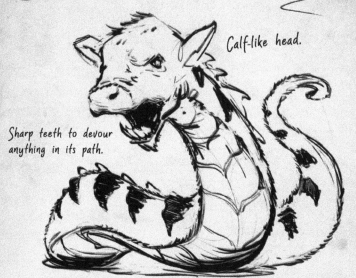

Calf-like head.

Sharp teeth to devour
anything in its path.

Large, hairy snake-like body.

Subterranean. Prefers
deep, dark caves.

To summon one of these creatures, pluck three of its longest hairs, put
them in a bowl of milk, and three Culebrón infants will emerge. The
strongest will devour its siblings, and the victor will be yours if—and
only if—sacrifices are made to the beast. The blood of those sacrifices
must be left in a secret location known only to you and El Culebrón.

EL CULEBRÓN

Christina Sng

Chile

I saw it one night—El Culebrón,
The legendary hairy snake
With an enormous calf's head.

I was running in the dark
Through the flat grassy plains
When it loomed in my path,

Opening its mouth
To swallow the three men
Chasing me, after my blood.

Afterward, it watched me
With its sad black eyes, guileless
And unaware it saved my life.

Would it eat me now? I wondered
As I slowly backed away,
Past its line of sight.

Or did it see me as an acolyte,
Bringing it tribute every night,
Watched by the council of stars

Through the cloudless sky,
So I did, each day,
Luring evil men to its cave,

Letting them chase me
As I ran into El Culebrón's home,
Watching as it gladly fed,

My heart calm, my purpose sated,
The world rid of yet
Another terrible human.

Soon, the countryside of Chile
No longer faced crime
And I won the Olympics

For the 1500m—
A new record.
The fastest time.

UMBRA ARCA
C A S E   N O T E

THE NGURUVILU

River-dweller.

Serpent-like tongue,
covered in moss.

Long tail with nails
it uses like a claw.

Looks like a fox
with a long body
similar to a snake.

PUERTO COLÍCO

David Davies

Araucanía, Chile

When they come, they come from the lake,
moss-tongued and creeping through the ripples of the quiet surface,
lurking out from the stagnant mud of their mirror world
up to the warm lamplight and rough doors cracked open,
the rich smell of new hearths filled
with the gathered wood; nearby the overfed dogs sleep.

No one heeds the movement, the underexplored forest,
the night a slick thing that offers no obstacle,
inside eyes away from the empty windows.

Their icy limbs pad quiet through old growth,
while the swamp air drops its sticky moisture to needle frost
from a foreign season, and rotting leaves
come crisp to the bite of cold among the felled logs.

The customs and tongues that have no place here
draw them; fresh clearings and trails and pens and borders
that mark a push for domain cannot hold them, not enclose them
like the pack animals whinnying and fretting with senses sharper
than those of their masters.

In through unlatched entrances they stalk in stuttering parody
of human movement,

the sanded boards shrinking to their touch, wood frames twisting on rusted nails,
the stink of spoiled provisions, scraping gaunt claws over hand-forged tools,
pausing at the tepid skin that tightens on the bones of those who sleep.

Visitors who rested in comfort shiver from a suffocated fire,
fuel that will only smoke in the pale ash of burned-out embers,
wicks that no longer hold a flame.
Settlers surrender the wish to move, only shift in blackening dreams
and let thin blankets fall unnoticed,
now offerings before hungry miscreations
in territories men believed unclaimed.

Clouds have lowered the sky to nothing.
The iron stoves give no more heat.
As the listless daylight builds
it shows only mist rolling on water
and a cold settlement of silence.

UMBRA ARCA
CASE NOTE

EDITORIAL EMAIL

From: Alvaro Zinos-Amaro
Sent: Sunday, August 15, 2021 4:15 PM
To: Josh Viola; Hillary Dodge; Carina Bissett
Subject: A Geography of Unknown Maps

When I was nine years old, I met a boy who could breathe underwater.

I was vacationing with my family in the small town of Almuñécar in the south of Spain. Within a few days of arriving at our apartment complex, newly constructed and one of the first of its kind, time became tanned by a sense of endless possibility. Each morning, before my parents woke up, I'd creep out onto the ocean-facing balcony. There I would sit in silken silence and let my gaze wander to the far right, where I could see an outcropping of land that ended in a place called Punta de La Mona. I pictured this outcropping extending all the way to the horizon, a peninsular needle growing from the larger peninsula that is Iberia, rendered infinitely long by my imagination. This construct I christened Punta del Horizonte. In those breezy, serene moments before the noise of the toaster and the clinking of coffee cups from the kitchen told me my parents were up, before the hubbub of excited tourists visiting Spain for the first time, the potential of the future was as far-reaching as Punta del Horizonte. I didn't realize at the time that I was performing a double act of alchemy, transforming geography into imagination and abstraction into fictive geography.

What's more, during our first week in Almuñécar, I glimpsed several flashes of uncanny illumination that kept me tethered to those nearly holy moments of pre-dawn possibility. The first of these experiences occurred on the beach on a Tuesday, a little after 3 p.m., when my parents were dozing in their fold-out chairs under the shade of our green-and-white-striped parasol. I was goofing around with my brand-new water goggles, studying various conches and seashells with great assiduousness, observing refracted sunbeams bouncing off their caramel-banded carapaces.

About ten feet in, where the waterline reached my armpits, I spotted a little circular formation of sand on the sea floor that seemed inexplicably exempt from the ordinary effects of light and shadow. I tried holding my hand over it, but it remained as well illuminated as when I removed it. Further, I noticed that no shadows fell on the circle either. No matter how I positioned myself and interposed my body between the sun above the water and the circular formation, it remained undimmed, its brightness forever unaltered. In frustration, I scooped up the lips of the circle and let the sand fall off to the sides, in essence erasing the structure from existence. Guilt washed over me almost as quickly as the water that seeped in through my suddenly faulty right goggle. I stood up to rub the salt out of my eye and then submerged my head again, this time with only my left eye open. The circle was gone, and there was nothing special about the place where I thought it had been. With one clumsy move, I had eclipsed a fraction of the world's wonder.

A few days later, I decided to wander around the apartment building during my parents' siesta. They had told me I wasn't to venture outside the apartment alone, but they'd let me get ice cream from the vending machine on our floor, so I figured as long as I stayed inside the complex I was fine. I worked my way towards the back of the building, which faced a sheer wall of mountain, about twenty feet back, that cast the edges of the apartments on that side of the building in perpetual shade. A small balcony off the side of a service elevator offered a tantalizing view of the mountainside. I lost myself in its study for several minutes. The more closely I studied the fine formations in the limestone surface, the more they seemed to come alive, subtly shifting and swirling. I was roused from my reverie by a hand on my shoulder.

"Está viva," the boy said, grinning. He was thickset, had a Nordic accent, sparkling blue eyes, and about two inches on me. "Es un mar de caliza."

I asked him his name, and he shrugged, as though it were unimportant.

"Soy Juan," I lied.

"No te creo," he said, and smiled again.

He asked me if I knew a boy by the name of Pedro, another named Esteban, and so on. By my third shake of the head, he must have gathered that I was new to the building.

"Mañana a las cuatro en la piscina," he declared, and marched away.

When I studied the mountainside anew, the subtle rippling had ceased.

I told my parents I'd made a friend, which was true to an extent, and told them there'd be a supervising adult at the pool tomorrow with the other boys, which was true if misleading, because I had the lifeguard in mind. It was enough to obtain permission for the outing.

The Andalusian sun was especially relentless on the appointed afternoon, and when I got to the pool, I wasn't surprised to find it deserted, save for the lifeguard. Even he seemed only partially there, a ghostly presence tucked away under shades and a hat. I looked around, saw no one, and thought I'd been set up. A bunch of bratty teens were probably pointing down at me from some balcony, jeering. I decided I might as well cool off in the water before traipsing back upstairs. I climbed down one of the little side-ladders and saw two shapes beneath the water. They seemed to open up from some compact configuration, blossoming into bright red and blue swim trunks. Two bodies emerged, that of the stocky kid I'd met the previous day and that of an older, svelte adolescent.

"Mi hermano," said my friend-in-the-making. No name was provided.

I noticed a curious silver ring on the brother's index finger. I made out the image of a finely-carved figure with its hands holding open the mouth of a lion, and the word "Fortitudo" engraved above it.

The boy my age noticed my fascination and said his brother's ring showed the four cardinal virtues: Prudentia, Iustitia, Fortitudo, Temperantia. One for each of the four corners of the Earth to which they would be traveling, he said. "El anillo viene de muy lejos," he added. I was unsurprised to learn the striking object's provenance wasn't local.

We proceeded to exchange looks and a half-dozen inanities, during which I noticed that the older brother had the same vaguely Nordic accent as the boy my age. Then the true purpose of our little congregation was revealed.

In unceremonious terms, the younger brother told me we needed to submerge ourselves and stay underwater for as long as possible. I explained that my dad had explicitly forbidden me from breath-holding contests, because two summers prior a seven-year-old had passed out in one such exercise and proceeded to drown.

"Vamos a aprender a respirar bajo el agua," the boy said, as though I had been a dullard for thinking otherwise.

The older brother, who hadn't opened his mouth the entire time, locked eyes on me. The world receded like a mirage.

While he continued to stare at me with this singular effect, his younger partner in crime, in a firm voice that sounded at least a decade older than the body from which it emerged, spoke with eerie plausibility of an ancient technique whereby one could retrain the blood vessels in the mouth to process oxygen directly. "Como branquias," he said. "Mira."

The taller boy lowered his head underwater. All was still on the surface. His brother studied me with what seemed a combination of mild disdain and honest pity, then went under too.

After about a minute, I followed suit. The chlorine in the water stung my open eyes, but I pushed through the pain.

The older brother, sitting on the pool tile in the lotus position, was pinching his nose shut. His mouth was open just a smidgeon. Impossibly, I could see water circulating around his thin, sun-chapped lips. The movement of fluid was apparent because the water coming out wasn't exactly the same color as that going in. What emerged from the almost imperceptible parting of his lips had a faint reddish hue to it.

He remained like this until both his brother and I had to come up for air. After we did, he waited another minute or so, and then placidly stood up to join us.

"Abre la boca," I said, figuring he must have some secret contraption inside.

I regretted my words at once. He opened his mouth wide to reveal deep, bloody wounds on his tongue, the skin itself split open in dozens of eruptions that followed teeth-like patterns. Not teeth-*like*, I realized, but actual teeth indentations. He'd bitten into his tongue so hard he'd pierced it dozens of times. Bloody spittle oozed out, as he smiled at me. In that moment, his blue eyes seemed to turn so dark they resembled those of a shark.

Woozy, I stammered an awkward apology and fled. Back inside our apartment, I took a long, cold shower, trying to cleanse myself of what I'd seen.

But a fascination persisted, a curiosity that the humdrum quality of the next few days could not assuage. During the following siestas I returned to the balcony where I'd first met the boy, then tried the pool at various times of day. Nothing. About a week later, as I was staring out at my imaginary Punta del Horizonte a little before dawn, I saw the brothers exit the building, look up at me with a smirk, and continue on towards the beach. I wanted nothing more than to run downstairs and join them, but I knew this was a step too far with my parents. I tiptoed into their bedroom and shook my mom's arms gently.

"¿Pero qué pasa, Álvaro?"

"Mis amigos me están llamando," I said. I told her they were going for a morning jog on the beach esplanade and had invited me to join them.

Mom squinted. "No swimming," she said. It wasn't a question.

"Claro," I agreed.

She told me to make sure I was back by breakfast, which was about an hour from now. I nodded with unfeigned enthusiasm.

A short sprint later, I found the duo on the sand, in a spot not too far from where my parents and I had set up our stuff the previous week. The sea was utterly calm, and the beach was empty save for an old man sweeping back and forth with a cheap-looking metal detector.

"Ya era hora," said the kid.

His adolescent sibling grunted.

They turned and waded out into the sea.

Silencing my mom's voice inside my head, I curled my toes in the cool morning sand, shivered, and followed.

About ten feet in, roughly at the same depth where I'd found that strange circular formation, they submerged, adopted the lotus position on the sea floor, and closed their eyes.

I held my breath for a minute-and-a-half or so, went up for a gulp of air, and came back down to continue observing them. Rinse and repeat for the next ten minutes. At last, they resurfaced.

"Se ha movido," the older boy said, pointing to the right.

I asked him what he was talking about, but he ignored me.

The younger replied, "El agujero azul."

A few droplets of blood ran down the sides of their lips. I clenched my mouth and ignored them.

I'd never heard of a blue hole before, but it didn't take long to understand what they were talking about. After wading for a while, with me in tow, they stopped and pointed up ahead. The water seemed to be a different color there, a much deeper and richer blue than the clear Mediterranean I was used to. This startling area of cobalt blue was roughly the size of a soccer ball.

The older brother reached his hand down into it, all the way to his elbow.

"Pronto," he said, emitting a satisfied sigh.

Without any further utterances, they walked back to the shore, practically ignoring me on the way.

"Vuelve en dos días," the boy my age said, and they shuffled off.

Two days later, our rendezvous began in the same stony silence as our previous parting. Our escapade proceeded in a similar fashion too: underwater meditation followed by the tracking down of the blue hole, which had not only shifted position but grown considerably. Its radius in the sea floor was now at least as wide as me.

Seeing this, the older brother intoned some words in a language I couldn't understand, and before I could ask what he was intending to do next, he dove headfirst into the hole. I'll never forget the underwater look of consummate pride on his younger brother's face as he watched his sibling disappear in one graceful vault.

Above the water, he told me we should wait for his brother to return.

I couldn't hide the trepidation and disbelief in my voice when I asked him where the hell exactly his brother had gone.

"Muy lejos de aquí," he said, words that reminded me of his description of his brother's ring.

Time passed in silence. We stood, the waterline at our armpits, and waited. Folks started arriving on the beach, first in small droves, then in a steady drizzle. My mind, stunned into a kind of torpor, settled into a cadence of droningly repeating questions without answers. In the midst of this daze, we both felt a strong undercurrent, followed by a splash.

"Se va a cerrar pronto," said the older brother, pointing to the blue hole. His skin seemed sallow and oddly varicose. He trembled with excitement. "Un día más."

His younger brother pointed to his ring and whispered a question I couldn't make out.

"Don't worry," the older brother replied. "I'll get you something before it closes."

That night I dreamt I fell through a portal that sucked me into my own past, where I cruelly taunted infant me in a crib before being discovered and chided by the dream version of my rejuvenated parents.

The following morning was hotter than any other day, and I woke up with a headache. By the time I joined the brothers on the beach at sunrise, I had serious reservations about this whole endeavor. Though they did their best to hide it, the oppressive quality in the air, a sort of stultifying humidity, seemed to be making them anxious as well. Nevertheless, they pushed on through the meditation and eventually we found the blue sinkhole, farther out than before, and twice as large.

Once again, the older brother dove in without a backward glance, and we idled at the surface. A long time passed, too long perhaps, and the features of the boy's face began to harden, as though kilned by concern. More worryingly, we noticed an eddy beneath our feet, and observed that the blue hole began to close in on itself before our very eyes.

What happened next happened very fast. The boy, upon realizing the hole might be completely gone within minutes, dove down towards the opening, which was already barely large enough for him to enter. A cataclysmic knot in my stomach made me reach out and grab his ankles. He kicked, trying to free himself from my grasp, as the hole continued to shrink. I held on to him with everything I had. Intuiting he wouldn't be able to release himself from my clasping hands in time, he changed his strategy and swam down with furious vigor, taking me down with him.

An instant later I thought I heard a muffled cry beneath the water, and I could swear I saw the older brother's hands reaching out of the hole, toward us, as it continued to collapse. The kid locked his fingers around his sibling's hands, but it was too late. A hammer-like force, like a pressure wave, shot up and sent the two of us tumbling upward. It was followed by a huge compression bubble that formed and collapsed right beneath us, sealing in his brother and evaporating any trace of the blue hole.

Floating upright, I blinked several times. A severe ringing in my ears slowly passed, and my vision, blurred by the violent upthrust, returned to normal. That's when I realized the boy floating beside me was unconscious, presumably concussed from the blow of the pressure wave, which had struck him head on.

I grabbed his arms and got us to the shore. Exhausted and breathless, I pulled him out and called for help.

The day was July 26th, 1958, the day before my tenth birthday.

The name of the boy whose life I saved, I learned soon after the event, was Dane Essa.

The concussion had wiped out all his memories of the last week. He didn't have a clue what had happened or who I was.

His older brother, Frederik, was never seen or heard from again.

We were interviewed by police and parents over and over. Nobody believed my story. The boy's lack of memories, at least, were medically justified. My account must have come across, I can see with the benefit of hindsight, like the delusional narrative of a possibly unstable mind.

I'm sure that the adults in our world must have assumed we swam out too far and the older boy drowned in some kind of accident. But the sea had been perfectly calm, and despite a week of searching, no corpse was ever retrieved, and no evidence was found to implicate either of us in any wrongdoing.

Eventually, the matter was dropped from the public eye, and that was when the acuteness of the tragedy truly took root in the Essa family. My parents, desperate to put the whole sordid business behind them, forbade me from speaking to him again, and until Dane's name came across my desk decades later, their wish held true.

I've never shared my story before, but I decided, in light of Dane's recent letter attempting to discredit Professor Sorensen, that it was at last time to come clean. Thank you for showing me Dane's letter before it's published in your volume, so I can set the record straight.

You see, Frederik Essa was a pioneer. A complete natural. His remarkable intuition and abilities had led him to be initiated into the Umbra Arca by the age of thirteen. He'd tapped into forces that Sorensen would later classify as Level 5 before Sorensen had ever even heard the words "Shadow Atlas." Dane himself shared, to a lesser extent, some of his brother's gifts, but the trauma of loss he endured, combined with his inability to reconstruct what had happened, closed off his conscious mind and body to such liminal phenomena.

Dane, then, is a man containing within himself two contradictory beings. On the one hand, as an apprentice to Sorensen, his subconscious guided his actions in a way that did more to further Sorensen's cause than any other student before or after. This is his true, submerged, nature. On the other hand, his calm, rational mind, feeling betrayed by the former's doings, has become entrenched in outspoken denial and skepticism. It knows only that the last time he ventured into these waters, as a boy, he ended up losing his brother—his best friend and role model. In the sea floor of Dane's mind, a blue hole opens up to the true possibilities of the world. Above the surface, all is stifled and motionless.

Context is not only king, but ultimately law, and this is the context I thought necessary to share before tackling a few specific comments from Dane's letter. I am deeply sorry for what Dane went through. I am. But I can't let that be justification for his attempts to sully the reputation of a brilliant mind and to discredit its greatest accomplishments. As another one of Sorensen's former students, and one with the sole distinction of having known Dane as a boy during a pivotal moment of his life, it's my responsibility to, let's say, expand upon Dane's account.

In his letter, Dane writes that "if one cannot participate in history, then one must reinvent it, with one's own life rough-hewn into the preferred narrative." Dane himself, having understandably repressed the vital qualities within him needed to be an active participant in history, must surely regret his impotence in this regard, his role purely as an observer. The absence of any official record of his work speaks for itself. Dane Essa has, throughout his life, contributed no original ideas to his so-called chosen profession, and yet freely attaches his commentary to the deeds of those who have. Later, when he writes "I'll not demonstrate all the ways Donald could be cruel in his jests [...]. Doing so might make this entire letter seem nothing more than justification for a non-existent personal grudge." He doth protest too much.

"And once he had them all won over," Dane continues, "once he had them all professing Atlantis must be true, Donald pivoted to laugh in their face." Alas, this is a willful misreading of what actually happened. Sorensen, as any of his subsequent interviews will show, was trying to call attention to weaknesses in the academic process, so that it could be made more robust and impermeable to precisely these kinds of hoaxes. His goal was always to teach and ennoble, never to mock.

Dane goes on: "Though he claimed to be visiting for the first time, it soon became clear my cherished friend was lying. He navigated the labyrinth of rooms with too much certainty." This is precisely the kind of response one might expect from someone with Dane's complicated past. He himself might have navigated that labyrinth of rooms with equal ease, had he but allowed himself to. Yet his conscious mind could not help but judge Sorensen's actions unfavorably, leaping to the wrong conclusion in the process. It is also worth noting that Dane's comment "you may remember his last rambling lecture at Naropa University" is another value judgment, bordering on character assassination, and easily disproven by anyone who cares to check out the actual lecture recording. Sorensen's scope was wide-ranging, yes, but only as befitted his subject. To an impatient mind, one rebelling against its own talents and shackling itself with rigid linearity, Sorensen's approach may have come across as fanciful, or even rambling. That is not a reflection on the content of the lecture itself, but rather on its recipient.

Dane also writes that "even very intelligent people can be swayed by charisma. Innumerable cults demonstrate this fact." It might be obvious, but should still be pointed out, that just because charisma can engender cults, not everyone who is charismatic is perpetrating falsehoods with the goal of starting a cult.

Sensing dangerous territory as he proceeds, Dane at least has the good sense to avoid any material that would undo his own thesis. "I'll not detail how our relationship soured in the ensuing years," he says off-handedly. Of course not. Having his misguided pettiness and self-inflicted rancor on public display would not abet his cause. Nonetheless, the last few pages of Dane's letter may reveal more than he probably wanted to let on. "The first page was blank," he remarks upon finally accessing the cherished volume bestowed to him by his erstwhile mentor. Notice how, despite decades of research and work in the field, Dane fails to do the obvious thing in a situation like this and probe the pages for information through means other than simple visual inspection. Even paintings are routinely analyzed by X-rays these days, but Dane does no such thing. His way of handling that rare book offers a sorry and cautionary view into a mind that has turned against itself and jettisoned any shred of imagination.

"I shook my head," Dane confesses, at last getting to the heart of the matter, "angered that he'd withheld the information from me all these years." That is, in a nutshell, Dane's inadvertent confession of his emotional state when writing this letter. He felt let down and deceived. But the real culprit of this treachery isn't Sorensen. It's Dane's own history, which, in order to preserve his sanity, sundered his mind into two contradictory and competing spheres of operation.

Lest I commit the same type of folly as Dane, I'll stop myself from commenting on his denunciation here, and let you be the ultimate judge of events. You've had the opportunity to peruse, amongst others, the attested chronicles of the sighting, via a dimensional shift not unlike the blue hole I've reported, of Huitzilopochtli in Aztlán in 1752; of a snake-like creature using potent means to lure men to their doom in Brazil in 1946; of dogmen in Ohio in 1972; of a shape-shifting creature near the Volcano la Malinche in 1979; of mysterious spectral flames and inexplicable ash on the Galápagos Islands; of the Sack Man performing his despicable duties in São Paulo as recently as 1995; and so on. This is but a small sampling of the very real dangers at large that we are trying to expose. Focusing on Sorensen the man, whatever his eccentricities, is a calculated move by Dane and his ilk to distract us from these dangers. As Umberto Eco once wrote, "every conspiracy theory steers the public psyche toward imaginary perils, thereby distracting it from genuine threats." Calling history myth, and arguing that facts are fiction, is the ultimate conspiracy theory to distract us from the innate strangeness of the universe and, even more importantly, the untapped capabilities of our own psyches.

I implore you, don't make the mistake that Dane made when he thought the pages of his book were blank. Don't make the mistake of thinking that ink ever tells the full story and that a blank space is truly empty. The oath of the Umbra Arca entreats us to remember the power we hold within.

Our consciousness is both the cat in the box *and* the observer beyond it; second by second, we select realities by our chosen perceptions of them. Don't ever believe that your existence is subject to the whims of some external onlooker. You have agency enough to alter the cosmos itself through the power of your beliefs.

The stories you've encountered here, and all others across time, are the true *Shadow Atlas* of the world. As long as they are told, our imaginations will continue to refashion all of existence and us along with it. The spaces between the words are most valuable of all. Every place you go contains its own Punta del Horizonte. Your mind can stretch that peninsula of possibility as far as you want.

During that fateful summer of 1958, in the days immediately after Frederik disappeared, I swam out at least a dozen times to where the blue hole had ruptured our lives, looking for any possible trace of what we'd lived through. One overcast evening my zealous searching paid off. A faint glint of silver caught my eye, and I unearthed a ring. At first, I assumed it was Frederik's, but upon closer examination realized that was an error. It was made of the same type of silver as his, yes, but instead of the four cardinal virtues, it depicted four other figures initially unknown to me. With some effort, I discovered that these four figures represented the four chief Anemoi, or wind gods, of ancient Greece: Zephyrus, Boreas, Notus, and Eurus, winds of the west, north, south, and east respectively.

I knew that Dane should have the ring. Surely, Frederik had brought it back from whatever mysterious realm he'd visited for his younger brother, not for me. But I told myself that because my parents had forbidden any contact with Dane, I was justified in keeping the ring. I told myself it might make Dane upset to see it, that the past was best left undisturbed. Lies. I held on to the damned thing because it was the only shred of proof, even if circumstantial, that I hadn't hallucinated the entire ordeal. Breaking free from a nightmare on a blistering summer night, I'd fish it out of my night table and wish the winds engraved on it would blow me away.

The error of my ways now lies plain before me. Dane is lost. The letter he wrote is the testament of a fractured being. His words are an ode to the suffering of a soul unable to reconcile itself to its true nature.

But I can make things right. I can select one of those new realities for us. Dane cannot be easily located by most, but I'm confident that I'll be able to track him down. While it's true that we're both in our seventies, the ways of the Umbra Arca have conferred upon me the appearance and spryness of a man several decades younger. It's time to put that energy to use. I will get Frederik's ring to him, and he will be set free. I will restore meaning to Dane Essa's compass, and point him back towards true north, where the *Shadow Atlas* awaits us all.

Sincerely,
Alvaro Zinos-Amaro

TRANSLATIONS

WORDS

AGUARDIENTE -> fire water

BALLENA -> whale

BASTA -> enough

CACHAÇA -> liquor from Brazil

CAMPESINOS -> farmers

CHALE -> nah

CHAMUCO -> devil

CHICHARRON -> pork rind

CHIVO -> goat

CUCHILLO -> knife

DIABLO -> devil

FINCA -> estate

GAMBERROS -> hooligans

GÜERA -> blonde girl

HOLA -> hello

FRONTERA -> border

LAGO -> lake

MANGUEZAL -> mangrove

MIERDA -> shit

MIGRA -> border patrol

MOJADOS -> wet

MUNDO -> world

NOPALITO -> prickly pear

OSCUROS -> dark

PETATE -> duffel bag

PUNTEROS -> pointers

SEGUIN -> follow

TIO -> uncle

VATO -> guy, dude

PHRASES

BUENO, DALE. -> Well, go ahead.

ESTAMOS CERCA. -> We are close.

ERES EL JEFE. -> You are the boss.

ES TU TAREA. -> It is your task.

LLEGAMOS. -> We arrived.

LOS MAS CHICOS. -> The youngest.

LOS SENUELOS. -> The decoys.

NUEVE CAJITAS. -> Nine little boxes.

QUE CALOR. -> What heat.

VAMONOS. -> Let's go.

GLOSSARY

ALUX (ALUXOB):

These magical beings from the Mayan tradition are reputed to live in regions once inhabited by the Nahuatl people from the Yucatán Peninsula and Guatemala. They represent harmony in nature and tend to work as protectors of both wild and culti-vated spaces. Although they are usually invisible, they occa-sionally appear to humans in physical form. They are dwarfish in nature, no taller than three feet, and are depicted as wearing a loincloth and hat. In some stories, they are created rather than being born, which connects to the legend that they are the incarnations of pre-Columbian clay figurines.

AZTLÁN:

Located in Mesoamerica, this homeland of the Aztecs takes its name from the Nahuatl language. Derivations of the word have been translated as "The Place of Herons" or "The Place of Whiteness." Aztlán and the northern migration of the ancient Mexica culture can be found in multiple ethno-historical sources. Whether or not this Aztec homeland is a myth is still up for debate, but historical commentary tends to place it in the high desert region located in northwestern Mexico and the American Southwest.

DARK WATCHERS:

For more than three hundred years, people traveling along the range of California's Santa Lucia Mountains claim to have seen supernaturally large sentinels watching their progression from the hazy peaks. These twilight apparitions were first documented in the 1700s by Spanish explorers who called them "los Vigilantes Oscuros" (a term which literally means "the Dark Watchers"). These giant silhouettes wear capes and are diligent in their observations of humankind. When they are approached, they mysteriously disappear. In his 1938 short story "Flight," American author John Steinbeck wrote, "No one knew who the watchers were, nor where they lived, but it was better to ignore them and never to show interest in them."

LA MALINCHE (MALINTZIN):

Located in the Mexican states of Tlaxcala and Puebla, this active volcano is named after the Nahua interpreter who aided Hernán Cortés in the conquest of the Aztec Empire. There are several legends linked to the peak. The Tlaxcaltecs believed it to be the local equivalent of Chalchiuhtlicue, a goddess of rain and song, and named it Matlalcueitl ("Lady of the Blue Skirt"). In another tale, the Tlaxcaltecs describe a reptilian monster that once lived on the mountain and would slink down to the village to abduct and devour children during the rainy season. The monster was eventually killed, and its head can reputedly be found mounted over the entrance to a house still standing in the historical district of Puebla today.

LOST DUTCHMAN'S MINE:

Sometimes lost mines stay lost for a reason. This is the case with the incredibly rich lode discovered by German immigrant Jakob Waltz in the 19th century. Some historians believe Waltz may have actually stumbled across an old mine worked in the 1840s by the Peralta family of northern Mexico. Legend claims that all but one of the Peraltas were massacred by the Apache during an expedition to Mexico. Their mine was reputedly located in the Superstition Mountains, east of Phoenix, Arizona - the same mountains haunted by the ghost of Jakob Waltz. Other accounts refute the claim of the Peraltas as pure fiction. However, it is an agreed upon fact that Waltz would periodically disappear into the Superstition Mountains only to return with large amounts of gold. He kept the location a secret even in death, and to this day the Dutchman's famous gold mine remains hidden in the depths of this unforgiving desert wilderness.

LUTIN:

These hobgoblins are well-known in French folklore. In fact, Marie Catherine d'Aulnoy documented them in the French fairy tale "Le Prince Lutin." These house-spirits eventually immigrated with French settlers to the Canadian province of Quebec. They are known to be mischievous, but are generally helpful in maintaining a well-kept house. Lutins can take the form of animals and are especially known for their ability to shapeshift into horses saddled and ready to ride. A variant of the Lutin is the Nain Rouge, a creature found in Michigan, whose presence indicates coming misfortune.

MAYANTU:

This reptilian, frog-faced god inhabits the depths of Peru's Amazon rainforest. He straddles the physical and spiritual realms and is a master at camouflage. Mayantu lives in the canopy and has been known to aid humans in peril with his vast knowledge of medicinal plants. However, native remedies and toxins can also be used to kill, and Mayantu is not afraid to punish those intent on destroying the rainforest or causing harm to the jungle's inhabitants.

MICTLÁN:

According to the *Codex Borgia*, this Aztec underworld mythology consists of nine levels and takes four years for the dead to travel. Some of the obstacles along the way include a dangerous river crossing, blood-thirsty jaguars, crashing mountains, and scouring winds. Mictlantecuhtli and his wife Mictlancihuatl preside as Lord and Lady over this ancient underworld, which is also linked to the origin of Aztec creation.

PLAYLAND AT THE BEACH:

This seaside amusement park near Ocean Beach, located on

the western edge of San Francisco, was originally the site
of a 19th-century temporary settlement inhabited by squat-
ters. This all changed in the 1880s when the beach gained a
roller coaster and San Francisco's trolly lines ventured out
of town. Amusements and concessions quickly filled up the old
settlement, and by 1924 brothers George and Leo Whitey had
purchased most of the attractions and changed the name of the
complex to Playland at the Beach. Ten years later, Playland
had expanded to cover three city blocks; the Midway featured
fourteen rides. It closed Labor Day weekend in 1972.

QUETZALCÓATL:

The name of this Aztec deity means "Plumed Serpent," which
comes from the Nahuatl words quetzal (the emerald-plumed
bird) and coatl (serpent). He is one of the most important
gods in the mythology of ancient Mesoamerica. Not only is
he a god of the winds and rains, but he is also a creator
god responsible for the formation of both the world and
humankind. Other important connections to this god include
the creation of the calendar, the cardinal directions, the
morning star, opossums, and corn (maize). Documentation of
Quetzalcóatl exists in Teotihuacan dating from the third
century; however, he is rarely depicted in human form before
the Late Post-classical period.

TAMOANCHÁN:

Descriptions of this Mesoamerican paradise can be found in
the *Codex Telleriano-Remensis* and the *Codex Borgia*. Although
this place was known to the Nahuatl, the word actually comes
from the Mayan language and can be loosely translated as
meaning "Place of the Misty Sky" or "Place Where the Gods
are Born." After the Spanish Conquest of Mexico, the clergy
attempted to use parallels between Tamoanchán and the Garden
of Eden to persuade the indigenous peoples to accept Chris-
tianity. Modern archeologists have proposed Tamoanchán as
having a presence in the physical world, and it has been

tentatively linked to the Mexican southern state of Morelos.

TLAHUELPUCHI (TLAHUIHPOCHTLI):

These blood-sucking, shape-shifting witches are known as
living vampires and can be found in the Mexican state of
Tlaxcala. They are known to the Nahuatl and are associated
with the god Tezcatlipoca ("Smoking Mirror"), a major deity
in the Aztec pantheon and the brother of Quetzalcóatl. The
Tlahuelpuchi crave human blood. When they are hunting, they
can be traced by the glowing haze that surrounds them. Unlike
their Western counterparts these vampires are not created
by others of their kind. Instead, they are the products of
a curse that manifests when they reach puberty, with the
females being more powerful and dominant than the males.

INDEX

SCRIBES OF THE UMBRA ARCA

MARIO ACEVEDO is the author of the national bestselling Felix Gomez detective-vampire series, most recently *Steampunk Banditos: Sex Slaves of Shark Island*, the YA humor thriller, *University of Doom*, and co-authored the Western novel, *Luther, Wyoming*. His work has won an International Latino Book Award, a Colorado Book Award, and has appeared in numerous anthologies to include *A Fistful of Dinosaurs, Straight Outta Deadwood, Psi-Wars*, and *It Came From The Multiplex*. Mario serves on the faculty of the Regis University Mile-High MFA program and Lighthouse Writers Workshops.

COLLEEN ANDERSON lives in Vancouver, BC, where she searches for mermaids. She is a Pushcart, Aurora, Rhysling and Dwarf Stars Award nominee, and has received Canada Council and BC Arts Council grants for writing. Her works have appeared in numerous venues such as *Polu Texni, Silver Blade,* and HWA Poetry Showcases. *A Body of Work*, Black Shuck Books, UK (short fiction) is available online and her poetry collection, *I Dreamed a World*, is forthcoming in 2021 from LVP Publications. *www.colleenanderson.wordpress.com.*

KAY CHRONISTER is a Shirley Jackson and World Fantasy Award-nominated writer from Tucson, Arizona. Her fiction has appeared in *Clarkesworld, Beneath Ceaseless Skies, Strange Horizons, The Dark*, and elsewhere; her first collection, *Thin Places*, was published by Undertow Publications in 2020.

DR. SARA CLETO and **DR. BRITTANY WARMAN** are award-winning folklorists, teachers, and writers. Together, they founded The Carterhaugh School of Folklore and the Fantastic, teaching creative souls how to re-enchant their lives through folklore and fairy tales. Their fiction and poetry can be found in *Enchanted Living, Uncanny Magazine, Apex Magazine, Liminality*, and others.

The poems of **DAVID DAVIES** explore the traditional-made-new, something he has lived as a first-generation immigrant to the USA. His writing has been published in *Typishly Literary Journal, The Underwood Press, Rise Up Review*, and

Green Lantern Press, among others. He is a two-time winner of the King Edward Prize for youth poetry, and an active member of the Science Fiction Poetry Association of America.

SEAN EADS is a librarian in Denver, Colorado. He's been a finalist for the Shirley Jackson Award, Lambda Literary Award, and the Colorado Book Award. He is originally from Kentucky.

ANASTASIA GARCIA is a Mexican-American writer of horror and speculative fiction. Anastasia's writing is featured in the Lunatics Radio Hour Podcast, an anthology from Ghost Orchid Press, the *Nottingham Horror Collective* magazine, and *Corvid Queen*. In 2020, Anastasia was named a recipient of the Ladies of Horror Fiction writer's grant. Originally from Texas, Anastasia now works at Instagram and lives in New York City with her partner and her cats. Follow her writing journey on Instagram *@anastasiawrites* or at *www.anastasiawrites.com*.

OWL GOINGBACK is the author of numerous novels, children's book, screenplays, magazine articles, short stories, and comics. He is a three-time Bram Stoker Award Winner, receiving the award for Lifetime Achievement, Novel, and First Novel. He is also a Nebula Award Nominee, and a Storytelling World Awards Honor Recipient. His books include *Crota*, *Darker Than Night*, *Evil Whispers*, *Breed*, *Shaman Moon*, *Coyote Rage*, *Tribal Screams*, *Eagle Feathers*, and *The Gift*. In addition to writing under his own name, Owl has ghostwritten several books for Hollywood celebrities.

MAXWELL I. GOLD is a Rhysling Award-nominated prose poet whose work has been featured in numerous publications and anthologies including *Spectral Realms*, *Space and Time Magazine*, *Weirdbook Magazine*, *Startling Stories*, and many others. Maxwell has published over 100 prose poems and short stories since 2017 focusing mostly on weird and cosmic fiction. His debut prose poetry collection, *Oblivion in Flux*, was recently released from Crystal Lake Publishing.

WARREN HAMMOND has authored several science fiction novels, quite a few short stories, and a graphic novel. His novel *Kop Killer* won the 2012 Colorado Book Award for best mystery. His latest series, *Denver Moon*, is co-written with

Joshua Viola.

ANGIE HODAPP is the Director of Literary Development at Nelson Literary Agency. She holds a BA in English and secondary education and an MA in English and communication development, and she is a graduate of the Denver Publishing Institute at the University of Denver. She has worked in publishing and professional writing for the better part of the last two decades, and in addition to writing, she loves helping authors hone their craft and learn about the ever-changing business of publishing.

JIMENA JURADO was born in Cuernavaca, Morelos, in 1991. She is the author of the poetry books *Confín de Nadie* (FEDEM, 2018) and *Fungifuturismo* (which will be published in 2022 by Ediciones El Transbordador, in Spain). She was also a participant in *Desde el contorno, antología de poesía morelense* (Ediciones Simiente, 2019), a fellow in the Under the Volcano 2019 program and, currently, a beneficiary of the PECDA Morelos 2020-2021 program, in the poetry category. Her virtual skylight is The PoemTube, a channel where she reviews literature and disseminates poetry, and she is part of Librosb4tipos, a group that makes intellectual work by women more visible.

STARLENE JUSTICE been teaching geography for over 10 years—most recently, as a tenured faculty member at Norco College in southern California. As a geographer, it could be said that place is her area of expertise! In addition to her degrees in geography and social science, she also holds an MFA in creative writing. Her published works include pieces of fiction, creative nonfiction, and one article on historical geopolitics. She lives with her husband, two sons, and a plethora of cats, dogs, and other pets. Writing, traveling, hiking, and horses are a few of her great loves.

GWENDOLYN KISTE is the Bram Stoker Award-winning author of *The Rust Maidens, Boneset & Feathers, And Her Smile Will Untether the Universe, Pretty Marys All in a Row,* and *The Invention of Ghosts.* Her short fiction and nonfiction have appeared in *Nightmare Magazine, Best American Science Fiction and Fantasy, Vastarien, Tor's Nightfire, Black Static, The Dark, Daily Science Fiction, Interzone,* and *LampLight,* among others. Originally from Ohio, she now resides on an abandoned horse farm outside of Pittsburgh with her husband, two cats, and not nearly enough ghosts. Find her online at *www.gwendolynkiste.com*.

GERRI LEEN is a Pushcart- and Rhysling-nominated poet from Northern Virginia who's into horse racing, tea, collecting encaustic art and raku pottery, and making weird one-pan meals. She has poetry published in *Strange Horizons*, *Dreams & Nightmares*, *Polu Texni*, *Liquid Imagination*, NewMyths.com, and others. She also writes fiction in many genres (as Gerri Leen for speculative and mainstream, and Kim Strattford for romance) and is a member of HWA and SFWA. Visit *www.gerrileen.com* to see what she's been up to.

JOSH MALERMAN is the New York Times best-selling author of *Bird Box* and *Goblin*. He's also one of two singer/songwriters for the rock band The High Strung, whose song "The Luck You Got" can be heard as the theme song to the Showtime show "Shameless." He lives in Michigan with artist/musician Allison Laakko.

JULIANA SPINK MILLS was born in England but spent most of her life in Brazil. Now she lives in Connecticut, where she writes science fiction and fantasy and has a soft spot for making her characters suffer. She is the author of the *Blade Hunt Chronicles* YA series, and has short stories published in several anthologies. Besides writing, Juliana works as a Portuguese/English translator and as a library assistant. You can find her online at *www.jspinkmills.com*.

TIFFANY MORRIS is a Mi'kmaw editor and writer of speculative poetry and fiction. She is the author of the chapbook *Havoc in Silence* (Molten Molecular Minutiae, 2019). Her work has been featured in *Room Magazine*, *Prairie Fire*, and *Eye to the Telescope*, among others. A member of the Indigenous Editors Association, she writes, edits, reads tarot and hunts UFOs in K'jipuktuk (Halifax), Nova Scotia.

LEE MURRAY is a multi-award-winning writer from Aotearoa-New Zealand (Sir Julius Vogel, Australian Shadows). A double Bram Stoker Award®-winner, her work includes the *Taine McKenna Adventures*, *The Path of Ra* series (with Dan Rabarts), and fiction collection, *Grotesque: Monster Stories*. The editor of eighteen anthologies, including Shirley Jackson Award-winner *Black Cranes* (with Geneve Flynn), she is co-founder of Young NZ Writers and of the Wright-

Murray Residency for Speculative Fiction Writers, HWA Mentor of the Year 2019, NZSA Honorary Literary Fellow, and Grimshaw Sargeson Fellow for 2021. Lee's debut poetry collection, *Tortured Willows*, is forthcoming from Yuriko Publishing. Read more at *www.leemurray.info*.

ANNIE NEUGEBAUER is a novelist, blogger, nationally award-winning poet, and two-time Bram Stoker Award-nominated short story author with work appearing in more than a hundred publications, including *Cemetery Dance, Apex, Black Static*, and *Year's Best Hardcore Horror* volumes 3, 4, and 5. She's a columnist and writing instructor for LitReactor. She's represented by Alec Shane of Writers House. You can visit her at *www.AnnieNeugebauer.com*.

GERARDO HORACIO PORCAYO (1966, Cuernavaca, Mexico). He has a Master's degree in Iberoamerican Literature from the Universidad Ibero Puebla. Winner of many short story awards in Spanish, national and international. He is considered the introducer of Cyberpunk to Hispanic-American literature with the publication of his first novel *La primera calle de la soledad* (1993). He is also considered a fundamental figure inside Mexican Neogothic for his literary works in this genre. He has published twelve novels, three short story compilations and three sf anthologies. In 2018, he attended Worldcon 76 as a panelist and a member of The Mexicanx Initiative.

CAMERON E. QUINN is an eccentric story spinster, whether as captain on the blustery deck of a ship or costumed in a school library. Cameron is at home in the varied landscapes of the Pacific Northwest and passionate about protecting wilderness the world over. To explore more of their creative projects, visit *www.TheCameronQuinn.com*.

SARAH READ's stories can be found in various places, including Ellen Datlow's *Best Horror of the Year* vols 10 and 12. Her collection *Out of Water* is available from Trepidatio Publishing, as is her debut novel *The Bone Weaver's Orchard*, both nominated for the Bram Stoker, This is Horror, and Ladies of Horror Fiction Awards. *Orchard* won the Stoker and the This Is Horror Award, and is available in Spanish as *El Jardin del Tallador de Huesos*, published by Dilatando Mentes, where it has been nominated for the Guillermo de Baskerville Award. You can find her *@inkwellmonster* or at *www.inkwellmonster.wordpress.com*.

By day, **KATHRYN REILLY** investigates the power of words and helps her students master grammar's awesomeness. As a mythology nerd, she loves introducing classes to simply everything, and begins with Gaiman's *American Gods*. In the evenings, she's reading retold myths and fairy tales when she isn't breathing life into new ones herself. Her poems and stories appear in several anthologies; you can find her on Instagram *@katecanwrite* to see what's coming next.

JULIA RIOS (they/them) is a queer, Latinx writer, editor, podcaster, and narrator whose fiction, non-fiction, and poetry have appeared in *Latin American Literature Today*, *Lightspeed*, and *Goblin Fruit*, among other places. Their editing work has won multiple awards including the Hugo Award. Julia is a co-host of *This is Why We're Like This*, a podcast about the movies we watch in childhood that shape our lives, for better or for worse. They've narrated stories for *Escape Pod*, *Podcastle*, *Pseudopod*, and *Cast of Wonders*. They're *@omgjulia* on Twitter.

BETTY ROCKSTEADY's cosmic sex horror novella *The Writhing Skies* is the winner of the 2018 This Is Horror Novella of the Year award, as well as being nominated for the Splatterpunk Award. Her latest work is the surrealist extreme horror collection *In Dreams We Rot*. She also draws spooky cartoon illustrations and wanders strange trails in Nova Scotia. Visit *www.BettyRocksteady.com* for more.

MARGE SIMON lives in Ocala, FL, City of Trees with her husband, poet/writer Bruce Boston and the ghosts of two cats. She edits a column for the HWA Newsletter, *Blood & Spades: Poets of the Dark Side*. Marge's works have appeared in *Pedestal Magazine*, *Asimov's*, *Crannog*, *Silver Blade*, *New Myths*, *Daily Science Fiction*. She attends the ICFA annually as a guest poet/writer and is on the board of the Speculative Literary Foundation. A multiple Bram Stoker award-winner, Marge is the second woman to be acknowledged by the SF &F Poetry Association with a Grand Master Award. *www.margesimon.com*.

ANGELA YURIKO SMITH is an award-winning American poet, author, and publisher with over 20 years of experience in newspaper journalism. Publisher of *Space & Time* magazine (est. 1966), a Bram Stoker Awards® Finalist and HWA

Mentor of the Year for 2020. To find out more visit *www.angelayurikosmith.com.*

CHRISTINA SNG is the two-time Bram Stoker Award-winning author of *A Collection of Dreamscapes* and *A Collection of Nightmares.* Her poetry, fiction, essays, and art appear in numerous venues worldwide and have garnered many accolades, including the Jane Reichhold International Prize, nominations for the Rhysling Awards, the Dwarf Stars, the Pushcart Prize, as well as honorable mentions in the Year's Best Fantasy and Horror, and the Best Horror of the Year. Visit her at christinasng.com and connect @christinasng.

JEANNE C. STEIN is the award-winning, national-bestselling author of the Urban Fantasy series, *The Anna Strong Vampire Chronicles,* and with Samantha Sommersby, *The Fallen Siren* series. She has stories in over three dozen anthologies including Hex's *Nightmare's Unhinged.* Recently, she completed the third book in a Sci-Fi, action, adventure series called *180 Degrees Magnetic: Suicide Sail* with co-author Jim Schoendaller which will be available in November.

Critically acclaimed author **TIM WAGGONER** has published over fifty novels and seven collections of short stories. He's a three-time winner of the Bram Stoker Award and has been a multiple finalist for the Shirley Jackson Award and the Scribe Award. He's also a full-time tenured professor who teaches creative writing and composition at Sinclair College in Dayton, Ohio.

CHRISTA WOJCIECHOWSKI is an American dark fiction writer who lives in Panama. She is the author of the *Sick* series and the founder of the Writers' Mastermind. Christa's stories have been featured in multiple publications and anthologies. She is crafting her first long fiction projects for release in 2022. Christa Wojciechowski is a member of the Horror Writers Association. She loves to play Chopin and sip Hendrick's gin. When she is not reading or writing, she can be found rambling through the wilds of Panama with her two dogs or traveling with her dashing husband, Marco.

STEPHANIE M. WYTOVICH is an American poet, novelist, and essayist. Her work has been showcased in numerous venues such as *Weird Tales, Nightmare Magazine, Year's Best Hardcore Horror: Volume 2, The Best Horror of the Year: Volume 8,* as well as many others. Her Bram Stoker award-winning poetry collection, *Brothel,* earned a home with Raw Dog Screaming Press alongside *Hysteria: A Collection of Madness, Mourning Jewelry, An Exorcism of Angels, Sheet Music to My Acoustic Nightmare,* and most recently, *The Apocalyptic Mannequin.* Her debut novel, *The Eighth,* is published with Dark Regions Press. Follow Wytovich on her blog at *www.stephaniewytovich.blogspot.com* and on Twitter @SWytovich.

MERCEDES M. YARDLEY is a dark fantasist who wears red lipstick and poisonous flowers in her hair. She is the author of *Beautiful Sorrows,* the Stabby Award-winning *Apocalyptic Montessa* and *Nuclear Lulu: A Tale of Atomic Love, Pretty Little Dead Girls,* and *Nameless.* She won the Bram Stoker Award for her story "Little Dead Red" and was a Bram Stoker Award nominee for her short story "Loving You Darkly" and the *Arterial Bloom* anthology. Mercedes lives and works in Las Vegas with her family and strange menagerie. You can find her at *www.mercedesmyardley.com.*

JANE YOLEN's 400th book came out in March 2021, and almost ten more will be published by year's end. She writes in almost all genres, but is best known for her poetry, children's books, short stories, and novels. Her three children and so far two of her grandchildren are published writers as well. She has won many awards, from Nebulas to Massachusetts State Awards for her work. The statuettes and certificates fill her house. She teaches writing and mentors writers. Six New England colleges and universities have given her honorary doctorates. She lives in Western Massachusetts, Connecticut, and St. Andrews, Scotland, with her second husband, a poet and educator. They are working on a book of poetry together.

E. LILY YU is the author of *On Fragile Waves,* published in 2021, and the librettist of *Between Stars,* with composer Steven K. Tran, for the Seattle Opera's 2021 Jane Lang Creation Lab. She received the Artist Trust LaSalle Storyteller Award in 2017 and the Astounding Award for Best New Writer in 2012. More than thirty of her stories have appeared in venues from McSweeney's to Tor. com, as well as twelve best-of-the-year anthologies, and have been finalists for the Hugo, Nebula, Locus, Sturgeon, and World Fantasy Awards.

ALVARO ZINOS-AMARO is a Hugo- and Locus-award finalist who has published some fifty stories, as well as over a hundred essays, reviews, and interviews, in a variety of professional magazines and anthologies.

ARCHIVISTS
OF THE UMBRA ARCA

CARINA BISSETT is a writer, poet, and educator working primarily in the fields of dark fiction and fabulism. Her short fiction and poetry have been published in multiple journals and anthologies including *Upon a Twice Time*, *Bitter Distillations: An Anthology of Poisonous Tales*, *Arterial Bloom*, *Gorgon: Stories of Emergence*, *Weird Dream Society*, *Hath No Fury*, and the *HWA Poetry Showcase Vol. V, VI*, and *VIII*. She has also written stories set in shared worlds for RPGs at Green Ronin Publishing and Onyx Path Publishing. Bissett also teaches generative writing workshops at The Storied Imaginarium and works as a volunteer for the Horror Writers Association (HWA). In 2021, she was acknowledged for her volunteer efforts at HWA with the prestigious Silver Hammer Award. Her work has been nominated for several awards including the Pushcart Prize and the Sundress Publications Best of the Net. She can be found online at *www.carinabissett.com*.

HILLARY DODGE is the author of several speculative short fictions as well as three nonfiction books, including *Gather Round the Table: Food Literacy Programs, Resources, and Ideas for Libraries* (ALA 2020). She spends a good deal of time traveling, going places that are forbidden, and eating. She once had tea with a Roma in a cave in the mountains of Spain. Another time found her eight hours from civilization in the heart of the Atacama with a mad desert hermit. She has been published in online magazines, podcasts, and print anthologies, including Pseudopod, Space Squid, Hellbound Books, and Hex Publishers. You can find her at *www.hillarydodge.com*.

ALEC FERRELL is a graphic, motion, and audio designer based out of Durham, NC. Check out his work at *www.clearlymedia.net* and *www.clearlyrecords.com*. Follow his audio/visual work @clearlyalec, his independent original music label @clearlyrecords, and his long-game meta-rock band The All Things @allthingsthe.

AARON LOVETT is a mixed-heritage Asian American artist and has been published by AfterShock Comics, *Tor.com*, *The Denver Post*, and *Spectrum Fantastic Art 22 & 24*. His *Nightmares Unhinged* (Hex Publishers) cover art was licensed by AMC for their hit TV show *Fear the Walking Dead*. He was the artist for the HWA's *StokerCon™ 2021 Souvenir Anthology*. You can see his most recent work in *Monster Train* (Shiny Shoe and Good Shepherd Entertainment), which was a number one Global Top Seller on Steam and named Best Card Game of 2020 by *PC Gamer*. His art can be found in various other video games, books and comics. You can view his portfolio at *www.artstation.com/adlovett*. He paints from a dark corner in Denver, Colorado.

BRET SMITH retired from IBM after thirty-four years as a program manager. He's a lifelong *Star Trek* fan and loves all things pop culture. He met his wife **JEANNI SMITH** on a blind date while she was attending the University of Arizona for her BFA. They've been happily married for over thirty-five years, attending conventions together since the 1980s—their most beloved decade— including over fourteen San Diego Comic-Cons. They raised two artistic sons, Xander—a successful Hollywood artist, and Cameron—a multi-talented musician. Today, when Jeanni isn't busy working as an antiques dealer, she and Bret are focused on their responsibilities as co-founders of the Colorado Festival of Horror. To tie into that convention, they collaborated with Joshua Viola of Hex Publishers on the anthology *It Came From the Multiplex: 80s Midnight Chillers*. They live in Longmont, Colorado, with five cats and a lot of books.

JOSHUA VIOLA is a 2021 Splatterpunk Award nominee, four-time Colorado Book Award finalist, and editor of the *StokerCon™ 2021 Souvenir Anthology* (Horror Writers Association). He is the co-author of the Denver Moon series (Hex Publishers) with Warren Hammond. Their graphic novel, *Denver Moon: Metamorphosis*, was included on the 2018 Bram Stoker Award® Preliminary Ballot. Viola edited the *Denver Post* bestselling horror anthology *Nightmares Unhinged* (Hex Publishers), and co-edited *Cyber World* (Hex Publishers)—named one of the best science fiction anthologies of 2016 by Barnes & Noble. His short fiction has appeared in numerous anthologies, including *One of Us: A Tribute to Frank Michaels Errington* (Bloodshot Books), *DOA III: Extreme Horror Anthology* (Blood Bound Books), *Doorbells at Dusk* (Corpus Press), and the forthcoming *Classic Monsters Unleashed* (Crystal Lake Publishing/Black Spot

Books). He is also a regular contributor to Denver's popular art and culture magazine, *Birdy*, and has reprints available on *Tor.com*. He is the owner and chief editor of Hex Publishers in Denver, Colorado, where he lives with his husband, Aaron Lovett, and their dogs, patiently awaiting the birth of their first child and daughter, Nova. You can learn more about Joshua Viola online at *www.joshuaviola.com*.

EMILY WISMER is the owner/printer/writer at Lady Pilot Letterpress. At the age of 19, she found some letterpress type in an old barn in Michigan, and like any magical object in a children's book, it led predictably to a fascination with and dedication to arcane machinery. Emily is the board president of Liberty Arts, a multi-disciplinary arts studio where she focuses on community outreach making things. Find her *@ladypilotletterpress* & *www.ladypilotletterpress.com*.

DEAN WYANT is a forty-five-year resident of Colorado. He is a bookseller, book collector and avid reader. His previous co-authored short stories have appeared in *Nightmares Unhinged* and *Blood Business* by Hex Publishers and *Found* by RMFW Press.

SHADOW ATLAS
DARK LANDSCAPES OF THE AMERICAS

Edited by Carina Bissett, Hillary Dodge, and Joshua Viola

Copyedits by Bret Smith and Jeanni Smith

Proofreading by Emily Wismer and Dean Wyant

Cover illustrations by Aaron Lovett

Cover layout by Damonza.com and Joshua Viola

Interior illustrations by Aaron Lovett
Interior graphics by Aaron Lovett and Joshua Viola

Flipbook art by Aaron Lovett

Art direction by Joshua Viola

Typesets, layout, and formatting by Alec Ferrell

A Hex Publishers Book
Published & Distributed by Hex Publishers, LLC
PO BOX 298
Erie, CO 80516

www.HexPublishers.com

Joshua Viola, Publisher

Paperback ISBN: 978-1-7365964-1-8
e-Book ISBN: 978-1-7365964-2-5
Hardcover ISBN: 978-1-7365964-3-2

First Edition: November 2021

10 9 8 7 6 5 4 3 2 1
Printed in the U.S.A.

ACKNOWLEDGMENTS

EDITORIAL CONTENT, POETRY, AND STORIES

"FBI Directive" copyright © 2021 by Sean Eads and Joshua Viola

"Letter from Dane Essa" copyright © 2021 by Sean Eads and Joshua Viola

"Editorial Email, Subject: Letter from Dane Essa" copyright © 2021 by Carina Bissett, Hillary Dodge, and Joshua Viola

"Oath of the Umbra Arca" copyright © 2021 by Sean Eads and Joshua Viola

"New Growth" copyright © 2021 by Sara Cleto and Brittany Warman

"The Shadow Atlas I" copyright © 2021 by Jane Yolen

"Daughters of the Bear" copyright © 2021 by Lee Murray

"Moon-Eyed Women" copyright © 2021 by Kay Chronister

"The Keeper" copyright © 2021 by Angie Hodapp

"Will-O'-the-Wisp" copyright © 2021 by Tiffany Morris

"The Man Who Wasn't There" copyright © 2021 by Betty Rocksteady

"God Spelled Backward" copyright © 2021 by Tim Waggoner

"The Time That Is Left" copyright © 2021 by Sarah Read

"Cinnabar" copyright © 2021 by Colleen Anderson

"Things to Do in Playland When You're Dead" copyright © 2021 by Gwendolyn Kiste

"Los Vigilantes Oscuros" copyright © 2021 by Angela Yuriko Smith

PHOTOGRAPHS

CPSIA information can be obtained
at www.ICGtesting.com
Printed in the USA
LVHW031545081221
705638LV00018B/756/J